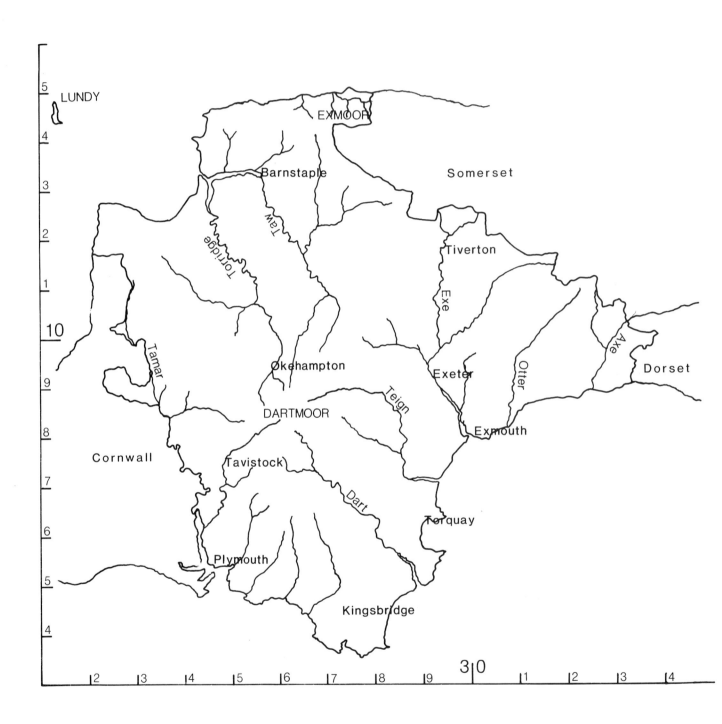

LUNDY

EXMOOR

Somerset

Barnstaple

Tiverton

Torridge

Taw

Exe

Tamar

Okehampton

Exeter

Otter

Axe

Dorset

DARTMOOR

Teign

Cornwall

Tavistock

Dart

Exmouth

Torquay

Plymouth

Kingsbridge

ATLAS OF THE DEVON FLORA

ATLAS
OF THE
DEVON FLORA

Flowering Plants and Ferns

by

R. B. IVIMEY-COOK

Department of Biological Sciences
The University of Exeter

The Devonshire Association for the Advancement of
Science, Literature and Art,
Exeter

1984

ISBN 0–85214–047–9

Printed by the Devonshire Press
Torquay

CONTENTS

Throughout the atlas the distribution maps apply to the species described immediately above the map.

Outline maps of the County of Devon showing the main rivers and some of the towns are printed inside the front and back covers.

Hon. Editor for the Devonshire Association

G. T. BOALCH
c/o The Devonshire Association,
7 The Close,
Exeter

INTRODUCTION

The decision to prepare this Atlas of the County flora was taken at a meeting of the Botanical Section of the Devonshire Association in October 1969. The Devonshire Association had been responsible for the publication of the existing County Flora, compiled by G. T. Fraser and the Rev. W. Keble Martin with help from several contributors. Although this flora had been published in 1939, and was thus quite recent in comparison with many similar publications, it was already out-of-print and not readily obtainable, as only 500 copies had been printed. It was also, by modern standards, very out-of-date. It discussed the distribution of each species on the basis of its occurrence in the various parishes in the county, which made it difficult to use by anyone not fairly familiar with these. Under most of the species were included records or sightings from each of the several botanical districts into which the county had been divided; this meant that moderately common plants were often dealt with in a very cursory fashion, with little or no information on their distribution patterns. Also, although published in 1939, much of the information on distribution and occurrences had been collected considerably earlier. One of the objects of preparing the new Atlas was to provide some evidence on recent changes in the distribution of species, and what effects modern agricultural practices might be having on their occurrence.

The advent of the Botanical Society of the British Isles Distribution Maps Scheme in the 1950s, and with it the concept of recording species distributions on the basis of some subset of the National Grid, revolutionised the way in which County Floras could be prepared, and has resulted in a great deal more information becoming available on the distribution and distribution patterns of many species both locally and nationally. The more recent availability of computing facilities, and later still, of efficient graph plotting facilities, has made the preparation of distribution maps a relatively simple task. The maps which appear in this Atlas have been prepared with the minimum of direct human intervention.

A work of this magnitude cannot be accomplished without assistance from many people; assistance which has often had to be given over a long period of time. Basic to the whole project was the help given by many members of the Botanical Section of the Devonshire Association, several of whom had been involved in the original decision to prepare the new Atlas, in collecting the enormous amount of data on the occurrences of species in tetrads; the magnitude of this task will become apparent later. The project owes much to the facilities provided by the Department of Biological Sciences in the University of Exeter, and to the Director and staff of the University Computer Unit who have, from time to time, been faced with particular problems both of data storage and, more recently, in the preparation of the distribution maps. A list of those who have contributed records is given at the end of this Introduction.

A great deal is also due to the County Recorder, Miss Maureen Turner, who has not only checked much of the data and incorporated some of her own, but was also responsible for organising the completed recording sheets. This greatly facilitated the checking of questionable records when these turned up.

Finally, one must thank five members of the Botanical Section in particular—Dr. M. C. F. Proctor, Mrs. M. Spooner, Mr. W. H. Tucker, Mrs. M. Tulloh and Mr. T. J. Wallace, who have read through the manuscript and added, or deleted, comments on many individual species.

GEOLOGY

A proper appreciation of the underlying reasons for the distribution patterns of species is only possible if one understands the environmental conditions under which they are growing, and of these conditions, one of the most fundamental is the soil. All soils are derived ultimately from rocks and although not all soils are formed directly from the rocks underneath them, a knowledge of the underlying rocks and the type of soil they are likely to produce is important in our understanding of plant distribution. Information on the soils of Devon is scanty; there are accounts of the soils of Dartmoor and of the Exeter district but other parts of the county do not appear to have been treated in a similar fashion.

The following account of the geology is based on those given in Edmonds, McKeown & Williams (1969) and Durrance & Laming (1981); the reader is referred particularly to the latter for fuller information. Fig. 1 is a diagram setting out the principal geological eras which are mentioned in the following paragraphs. Fig. 2 shows the distribution of the main geological strata in the county.

GEOLOGICAL HISTORY

In Ordovician times, about 500 million years ago, the south-west peninsula of England lay beneath a fairly shallow and warm sea which deepened northwards and which, in the Silurian, became more extensive. In the late Silurian and early Devonian, a period of mountain building (orogeny) raised land to the north, in what is now Wales and Scotland, and perhaps as far north as Norway. Under a tropical climate, and at a time when few land plants had evolved to provide a vegetation cover, weathering and erosion were extensive. Drainage was southwards and westwards through this Devonian sea, and in it there accumulated what now form the Lower Devonian rocks. They accumulated in fairly deep water and comprise slates and sandstones, with some beds of fish bones and detrital limestones.

The oldest rocks in Devon are probably the green schists and mica-schists of Start Point, but other Lower Devonian rocks are well represented. They are found over a large part of the South Hams, from Dartmouth to south of Plymouth. In the north of the county are the Lynton Beds, which were formed in fairly shallow water and consist of sandstones and mudstones, with thin bands of shells. Subsequent

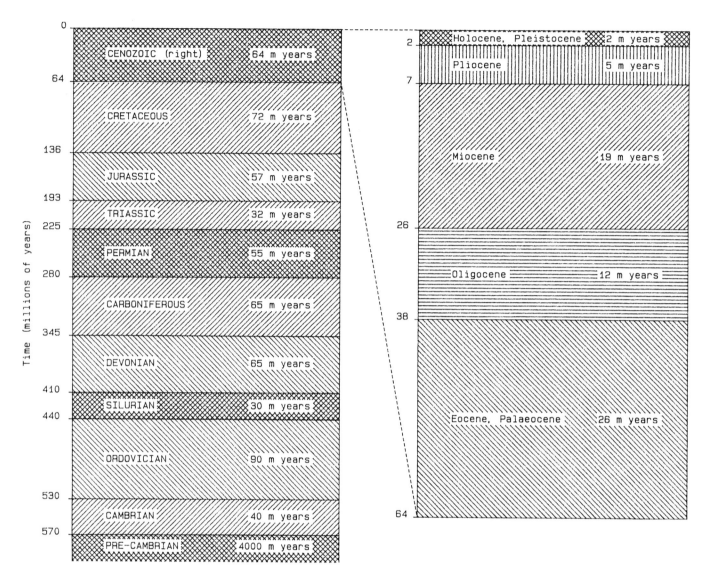

CENOZOIC (right)	64 m years
CRETACEOUS	72 m years
JURASSIC	57 m years
TRIASSIC	32 m years
PERMIAN	55 m years
CARBONIFEROUS	65 m years
DEVONIAN	65 m years
SILURIAN	30 m years
ORDOVICIAN	90 m years
CAMBRIAN	40 m years
PRE-CAMBRIAN	4000 m years

Time (millions of years)

0
64
136
193
225
280
345
410
440
530
570

Holocene, Pleistocene	2 m years
Pliocene	5 m years
Miocene	19 m years
Oligocene	12 m years
Eocene, Palaeocene	26 m years

2
7
26
38
64

FIG. 1. The principal geological eras. The Coenozoic, covering the last 64 million years, is shown expanded on the right.

deposits of slates and mudstones represent still more erosion as this northern land was gradually worn down to a rolling plain.

The Middle and Upper Devonian rocks take the form of complex sequences of slates which alternate from time to time with quite thick limestones. There are some thin limestone beds, which seem to be derived from calcareous muds or fragmented limestone. It has been suggested that considerable volcanic activity during this time may have assisted in the formation of limestone by providing the shallow seas necessary for the growth of corals, subsequently killing the polyps with poisonous fumes. In North Devon, the extensive Ilfracombe Beds comprise marine slates with thin limestone bands. Under the prevailing hot climatic conditions, iron ores became oxidised to haematite and the deposits tend to be red in colour. The Old Red Sandstone is of Devonian age, and there are deposits of this in N. Devon.

The Upper Devonian saw the start of a marine transgression in which, in the south, the Middle Devonian limestones became overlaid by deep-water limestones and shales. In the north, the new

deposits were deltaic or fluviatile. There was still considerable volcanic activity, so that areas of lava occur, and also shallow-water limestones on sea floors built up by this activity. In the north, the Morte slates are sandstones with calcareous nodules, formed in shallow seas, but there followed a gradual subsidence in N. Devon and the Baggy Beds comprise a mixture of sediments probably deposited in a delta.

During the Lower Carboniferous, further and often calcareous silts and muds were deposited, and there was further volcanic activity. The sea covering the south-west peninsula became steadily shallower; the Upper Carboniferous sandstones and shales seem to be derived to a considerable extent from river-borne sands and muds. Local earth movements led to considerable variations in the level and pattern of sedimentation.

The Carboniferous rocks are termed the Culm Measures; the derivation of this word is uncertain. They are very prominent in the north, from Barnstaple to Tiverton, extending as far south as the northern edges of Dartmoor. The Lower Carboniferous forms only narrow belts on the northern

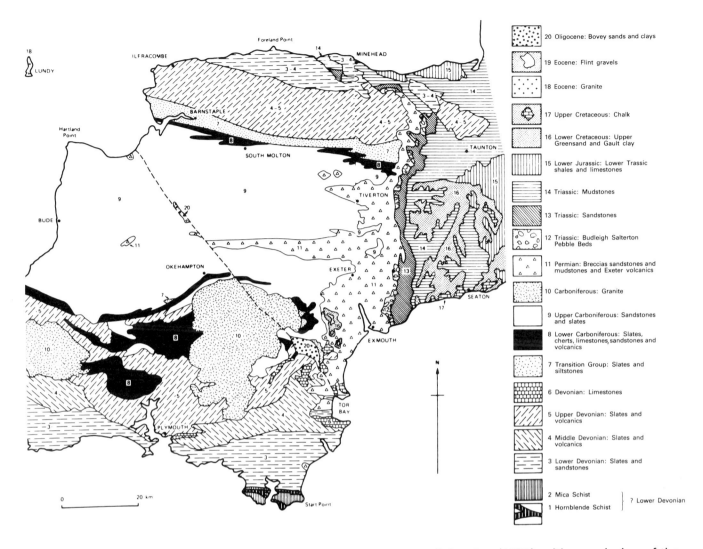

FIG. 2. The main features of the geology of Devon (from Durrance & Laming (1981), with permission of the authors).

The legend of the map reads:

20 Oligocene: Bovey sands and clays
19 Eocene: Flint gravels
18 Eocene: Granite
17 Upper Cretaceous: Chalk
16 Lower Cretaceous: Upper Greensand and Gault clay
15 Lower Jurassic: Lower Triassic shales and limestones
14 Triassic: Mudstones
13 Triassic: Sandstones
12 Triassic: Budleigh Salterton Pebble Beds
11 Permian: Breccias sandstones and mudstones and Exeter volcanics
10 Carboniferous: Granite
9 Upper Carboniferous: Sandstones and slates
8 Lower Carboniferous: Slates, cherts, limestones, sandstones and volcanics
7 Transition Group: Slates and siltstones
6 Devonian: Limestones
5 Upper Devonian: Slates and volcanics
4 Middle Devonian: Slates and volcanics
3 Lower Devonian: Slates and sandstones
2 Mica Schist
1 Hornblende Schist   ? Lower Devonian

and southern edges, and comprises a mixture of shales and slates, with some limestone and chert. The major component of these deposits are of Upper Carboniferous age and comprise submarine shales covering an extensive area. These deposits have weathered to produce the agricultural soils so characteristic of this part of Devon at the present time.

At the end of the Carboniferous, the very thick Devonian and Carboniferous deposits became folded by the Variscan (Armorican, Hercynian) orogeny. The forces involved were sufficient to allow the intrusion of granite from a single large batholith which is now exposed at various points along the south-west peninsula, and forms the uplands of Dartmoor (as well as Bodmin Moor and the Isles of Scilly). The granite is sometimes exposed as rugged tors which probably represent residual rocks after fragmented and rotted rock and other material have been washed or eroded away. It was probably intruded as a liquid or semi-solid mush, and during the later stages of its cooling at depth, gave off a variety of solutions and gases, leading to the processes of tourmalinization (by boric acid), greisening (by fluorine) and kaolinization (by acid solutions). This last has resulted in the production of china clay, most characteristic of the Cornish granite, but which is also found in S. W. Devon.

Subsequently, south-west England became part of an extensive land surface. Britain was, at this time, still fairly close to the equator, as continental drift had not yet brought it to its present position in the Northern Hemisphere. Thus the Permian climate was arid and desert-like, although periodic torrents washed down quantities of rock debris and there were extensive scree slopes. The laying down of these non-marine Pebble beds, sandstones and marls continued into the still arid Triassic.

The generally red-coloured deposits laid down in the Permian form the New Red Sandstone and weather to give the very characteristic red soils of E. Devon. They form a band running from north of Bampton southwards and largely east of Exeter, to the coast, though there is a tongue-like projection to north of Okehampton; they form the colourful and often massive cliffs between Seaton and Paignton, but vary considerably in their detailed composition. There were also local lava flows, especially in the vicinity of Exeter. The Triassic beds are found to the east of the Permian deposits; between Budleigh Salterton and the Axe estuary they form cliffs of Bunter and Keuper sandstones and marls. Inland, the Budleigh Salterton Pebble

Beds form an escarpment whose easterly dip slope is marked by heathland, which contrast sharply with the rich grassland of the Permian marls.

During the Jurassic, a warm shallow sea spread over southern England, though much of the south-west probably remained as land. Limestones were again formed, the Lower Lias outcrop on the coast between Axmouth and Lyme Regis is one of the best Jurassic exposures in the country. The White Lias comprises almost pure calcite, but has a high strontium content; the Blue Lias comprises alternating bands of limestone with clay and shale and locally lignite. In the vicinity of Lyme Regis, these rocks are noted for the number of fossils, especially of ammonites, which they contain.

The Jurassic sea was followed in the Cretaceous by delta swamps from rivers flowing in from the west. This sea eventually advanced as far as the eastern margin of Dartmoor. Sands deposited in the shallow waters formed the Greensand; in deeper and less disturbed water, finer deposits formed the Gault, which thins rapidly westwards from Lyme Regis. The Upper Greensand comprises two main groups. The first is a series of glauconitic and variably calcareous sands, which are exposed at cliffs near Seaton. Above these lie variably calcareous sands, with bands of chert which can be quite thick. The chert has been used for palaeolithic implements and also as road-stone. The rocks are overlain unconformably by Gault and Upper Greensand, and are so susceptible to landslipping as to be locally dangerous. The Dowlands Landslip is a substantial landslip which took place rather over a century ago and is now forms a very fine example of chalk scrub and woodland within the Axmouth-Lyme Regis Undercliffs NNR. Inland, the Greensand tends to be relatively siliceous, especially in the vicinity of the Blackdown Hills, and carries considerable amounts of heathland, especially on the summits of the hills.

Later, further subsidence allowed the development of a considerable sea into which few rivers appeared to have flowed, and within which there accumulated vast amounts of calcareous material which later became consolidated into the Chalk. Chalk is poorly represented in Devon, but there are several exposures, of rather variable thickness, at several points along the coast from Salcombe Regis eastwards, e.g. at Beer Head.

In the early Tertiary, an uplift caused this sea to retreat; The granite mass of Lundy was probably intruded during the Eocene and the land became drained both southwards and eastwards. Sands and gravels of possible Tertiary age and marine origin can be found on Haldon Hills and are possibly outliers of the Bagshot Sands. Much of the material appears to consist of Chalk flints, and although the nearest Chalk outlier is some 15 miles east, could imply that the Chalk was more extensive in the Eocene. In the late Oligocene there was further subsidence, and local deposits of clay, sand and gravel, with some lignite, can be found, e.g. at Bovey Tracey. These were deposited in a substantial lake fed by several mountain torrents from Dartmoor. Quantities of wood and peat which were washed in later formed lignite. The Alpine orogeny during the Miocene raised the whole of the British Isles above sea level, a process aided by the lowering of the sea when much water accumulated in the north polar ice cap. Subsequent sea level changes have been on a relatively small scale, but have led to the development of rivers with deep valleys, the mouths of which have subsequently become flooded as the sea level rose again.

CLIMATE

The temperature experienced by a land mass is largely determined by the amount of incoming solar and other radiation; this is largely a function of latitude, and over a county the size of Devon, does not vary to an appreciable extent. An often decisive factor is the nature, frequency and persistence of the air masses which commonly originate in the western Atlantic and then pass over the county from the south-west; the temperature of the surfaces over which these air masses have passed is of considerable significance in determining the weather pattern, as is the amount of water vapour they carry.

The mean annual temperature is approximately 10°C (at Tavistock); it decreases gradually north-eastwards. Winter temperatures also decrease gradually north-eastwards, but from April to September, the land mass of central England warms appreciably and the temperature gradient reverses, the south-west becoming cooler than the north-east. Dartmoor and Exmoor are often slightly warmer than the rest of the county.

Data on the distribution of maximum, minimum and daily mean temperatures are available from a number of stations in Devon, but most of these stations are situated on, or in the vicinity of, the coast; the only inland station was at Princetown, on Dartmoor, but this is no longer operational. There is thus a paucity of data from many areas which would be of much interest from the point of view of the distribution of flora.

February is the coldest month, with a mean minimum around 4.5°C dropping to 0.5°C at Princetown; the mean maximum is about 8.5°C. The temperature rises during spring and early summer to the highest mean monthly maximum and minimum, which are generally recorded in August; the August minimum ranges from 10.5°C at Princetown, with 14°C at Ilfracombe, on the N. Devon coast, while the maximum reaches 20°C in some of the S. Devon coastal resorts. After August, the temperature means drop gradually again.

An interesting concept is that of the 'summer day'—those days in which the maximum temperature rises above 25°C, which show an average of 1.5 (max. 6) in July for Plymouth, as compared with 5.4 (max. 16) for Kew (Revesz, 1969). Corresponding to the summer day is the number of 'frost days', which are substantially lower in number than occur in eastern parts of England, at equivalent altitudes.

Changes in relative humidity closely follows those in temperature; there is a small diurnal range in winter and a larger one in summer. In general, humidity is lowest in summer away from the coasts, while in winter, there is no appreciable difference over the entire county.

Sea fogs, formed when relatively moist air passes over cooler water, are a fairly common feature of the climate in summer and autumn, and often spoil otherwise fine, sunny days. Radiation fogs, formed by the cooling of air in valleys and hollows are also quite common at these times. Frequent low cloud on the moors, tend to be features of the climate of Dartmoor and Exmoor, especially in autumn and winter.

Pollution is not a major factor in the county, except locally and on a fairly small scale, though there is some evidence of pollution on the south-western slopes of Dartmoor from industries in Plymouth.

The topography of the county, with moorland uplands in the centre and most of the lowland around the coast, has a strong effect on the distribution of rainfall. Rainfall reaches 230 cm (90") on Dartmoor, with rather less on Exmoor (180 cm, 70"). Near both coasts, the rainfall is in the region of 100–110 cm (40–45") a year, but it is lower around Exeter (80 cm, 32") and along a narrow band extending north-westwards from Exeter to Barnstaple, where the ground is largely in the rain shadow of Dartmoor.

The seasonal distribution of rainfall generally shows a maximum in late autumn and winter; the drier half of the year is from March to September; June is usually the driest month. The monthly variation is rather less in the west than in the east of the county.

The distribution of rainfall is, by itself, insufficient to characterise this aspect of the climate. Also important is the extent and distribution of the evaporation pattern. Some rainwater percolates into the ground; some of this is stored but the rest feeds surface water streams. Much evaporates from the ground and plants, in the form of transpiration. Such data as are available suggest that around the Exe estuary there is a summer deficit of around 3", being the sum of the various losses over precipitation, a surplus of a similar size on Dartmoor and a small deficit over much of the rest of the county. This relates to the need for irrigation, especially of shallow-rooted crops and must clearly have its effect on the distribution of native species of plants.

FLORA AND VEGETATION

Devon has a rich flora which is interesting from many points of view and reflects the very varied topography as well as the generally mild climate. The flora of the British Isles is often separated into two aspects, a "montane" aspect to the north and west of a line drawn approximately from the Exe to the Tees, with vegetation growing mainly on acid, Palaeozoic rocks, and a "lowland" aspect on the softer and often calcareous rocks to the south and east. Devon lies astride this line, and elements of both aspects can be found in the county.

Many plants which are widespread in south-western Europe reach their northern limits in the British Isles. These are plants with an "oceanic-southern" type of distribution and include, for example, the common Wall Pennywort, *Umbilicus rupestris,* as well as the much less frequent Yellow Bartsia, *Parentucellia viscosa.* The precise factors limiting the distribution of such plants are often not known, but the relatively warm winter temperatures seem to be important and the distribution of the Madder, *Rubia peregrina,* seems to correspond with the 4.5°C January isotherm.

Moderately high summer temperatures coupled with a relatively dry spring will allow species with a "southern-continental" distribution to be represented as well. Some of these species are calcicole, such as *Asperula cynanchica* and the Horse-shoe Vetch, *Hippocrepis comosa,* and are especially characteristic of the chalk or of the limestones around Torquay; others, such as *Lathyrus nissolia,* or *Melittis melissophyllum* seem to have no particular habitat preferences, though all the species are rare or local. Some, such as *Quercus ilex* which can regenerate from seed in some localities, *Helianthemum apenninum* and *Senecio cineraria* contribute to botanical vistas which are not too far removed from those of the Mediterranean coast of France.

A characteristic and important element of the flora comprises plants with an Atlantic type of distribution; these are species which tend to be limited to the western coasts of Europe. Quite a number of common British plants fall within this category, such as the bluebell, *Hyacinthoides non-scriptus,* the heather, *Erica cinerea,* the gorse, *Ulex europaeus* and the foxglove, *Digitalis purpurea,* but perhaps especially the Western Furze, *Ulex gallii.*

Another common Atlantic species is *Agrostis curtisii,* a common grass on the south-western moorlands and a characteristic species of dry heath, with *Erica cinerea, Calluna* and *Ulex gallii.* In valley bogs and wet heaths, *Hypericum elodes, Anagallis tenella* and *Pinguicula lusitanica* are quite frequent, while *Wahlenbergia hederacea* is locally frequent in damp grassy moorland. *Oenanthe crocata* is conspicuous along lowland streams and ditches, and often presents a major problem to farmers, as it is highly poisonous to cattle. *Sedum anglicum* is frequent on thin dry soils on acid rock outcrops and inland is sometimes associated with one of our local rarities, *Hypericum linarifolium,* while along the coast, it may occur with the locally abundant *Scilla verna.* The filmy-ferns, *Hymenophyllum tunbridgense* and *H. wilsonii* occur locally on the higher but sheltered parts of Dartmoor.

The factors which limit the spread of these Atlantic species are frequently far from obvious. It seems to be some combination of mild winters, a relatively small annual temperature range and high humidity, but the details remain to be worked out for many species, and there is no reason to suppose that they are the same for all. It is, perhaps, these same conditions which enable us to see typical woodland plants, such as bluebells and primroses, flowering freely in Devonian hedgebanks and pastures.

Dartmoor, rising to a maximum height of 620 m (2039 ft), is the most southern of the major uplands in Britain; Exmoor reaches 520 m (1706 ft), but its highest point is in Somerset. A few northern and montane species have outposts in south-west England, a good example being the club-moss, *Huperzia selago*. This is quite common on mountains in parts of Britain, but very local on the higher Dartmoor tors and sporadic in heath and moorland elsewhere. Other northern species include *Empetrum nigrum* and *Listera cordata*; the former is now very rare in Devon, the latter occurs only in a single locality on Exmoor. The south-west has no real montane plants, and several species from northern Britain, such as *Myrica gale*, *Drosera anglica* and *Hammarbya paludosa*, which do occur in Devon, are more frequent in other parts of the south, such as the New Forest.

Notable absentees from the county flora, or species which are found surprisingly rarely, include *Rhamnus catharticus*, *Ononis spinosa* and *Campanula rotundifolia*; the general absence of lakes and large rivers, and a general paucity of fresh-water eutrophic habitats, accounts for the virtual absence of many common aquatics, such as *Hippuris vulgaris*, and the water-lilies, *Nymphaea alba* and *Nuphar lutea*. Many calcicole plants also have a very local distribution, due to a shortage of suitable habitats, though the variably calcareous nature of many of the Devonian rocks means that the less demanding calcicoles often appear in rather surprising localities.

REGIONAL FEATURES

a. *East Devon*

East Devon has a very characteristic landscape, which comprises a dissected plateau rising from about 160 m (500 ft) near the coast to nearly 350 m (1000 ft) on the Blackdown Hills. The underlying rocks are Permian and Triassic New Red Sandstones which are relatively soft and weather to give good quality agricultural land. In contrast, the flat tops of the hills often carry rather poor quality pasture, heathland or conifer plantations. These New Red rocks vary considerably in composition and may even be somewhat calcareous. The Budleigh Salterton Pebble Beds, of Triassic age, which form a prominent escarpment running from Exmouth northwards to Ottery St. Mary and beyond, are also covered with heathland which comprises varying proportions of six species, *Calluna vulgaris*, *Erica cinerea*, *E. tetralix*, *Ulex gallii*, *Agrostis curtisii* and *Molinia caerulea*. The grasses are favoured relative to the other species by burning and conspicuous 'fire-lines' can be seen in many heaths as a result of not-infrequent fires. Some areas are dominated by bracken, *Pteridium aquilinum*, while *Ulex europaeus* is abundant along roadsides and in disturbed places. *Carex binervis* is locally frequent especially along tracks, while in rather damper areas, *Trichophorum cespitosum* and *Dactylorhiza maculata* may be conspicuous.

The dip slope is cut into by numerous shallow valleys, where the vegetation changes to that of wet heath, generally lacking *Agrostis curtisii*, but with several species of the bog-moss *Sphagnum*, while *Erica tetralix* and *Molinia* become prominent. The sandstones immediately under the Pebble

Beds are quite rich in calcium carbonate and water emerging in springs is often calcareous, giving rise to calcareous flushes in which *Molinia* and *Schoenus nigricans* may be luxuriant, while *Carex hostiana*, *Cirsium dissectum* and *Succisa pratensis* are often frequent in a species-rich wet heath. Scattered scrub and woodland occur frequently; although the most abundant species is *Pinus sylvestris*, probably introduced about the end of the 18th century, other species of *Pinus* have been planted, while *Betula pubescens* and several species of *Salix* can be found.

Further east, where the overlying Cretaceous rocks include some chalk, heathland may still be found on the tops of the hills, but more of the plateau is cultivated and the slopes of the hills may bear ashwood, with calcareous and sometimes fenny vegetation on the valley sides. Fragmentary chalk grassland occurs along the coast, between Salcombe Regis and Seaton, and at Axmouth. Large parts of the coastal cliffs between Axmouth and Lyme Regis slipped in 1839/40 to form broken and tumbled slopes which have become overgrown with calcareous scrub and woodland, with some grassland.

b. *Torbay and S. Devon*

The two limestone headlands of Hope's Nose and Berry Head enclose the well known holiday resorts of Torquay and Paignton. Hope's Nose itself is probably less interesting floristically than Long Quarry Point and Daddyhole Plain on either side of it. There are a number of other limestone outcrops further inland. Usually the rock is covered by an appreciable depth of soil, resulting in good quality agricultural land, though many calcicolous species are present, such as the Traveller's Joy, *Clematis vitalba*, and *Cornus sanguinea*, while limestone woodlands of ash (*Fraxinus excelsior*), oak (*Quercus robur*), elm (*Ulmus glabra*) and sycamore (*Acer pseudoplatanus*), often with maple (*Acer campestre*) as an understorey, can be found and are locally fairly extensive. The field layer of these woods may be quite rich, and includes *Allium ursinum*, *Phyllitis scolopendrium* and *Lamiastrum galeobdolon*. Outcropping limestone cliffs can be seen especially at Chudleigh and Torbryan.

The flora of the limestone headlands is probably the most noteworthy, as it includes a number of species which are rare and local in Britain, such as *Helianthemum apenninum*, which also occurs in Somerset; *Aster linosyris*, which has scattered records elsewhere near the western coast of Britain, and is a member of the continental-southern element in our flora; *Trinia glauca* which is locally abundant on Berry Head, but elsewhere in Britain occurs only in Somerset and Gloucestershire. *Ononis reclinata* and *Bupleurum baldense* both occur sporadically in the calcareous grassland on Berry Head, and are rare elsewhere in Britain. The reasons for such a notable collection of plants in such a limited area has been much debated. The generally accepted view is that they represent a collection of late-Glacial relics which were able to survive in an area which was probably never covered by forest.

Between Bovey Tracey and Newton Abbot lies a basin filled with Oligocene clays and sands which has been much worked for lignite and still produces ball-clay. Substantial areas of acid heathland remain, though they are not in prime condition as the area is partly occupied by an industrial estate. The derelict pits left after the extraction of minerals have become filled with water and provide an interesting new habitat for both plants and animals. Attempts have been made to establish suitable vegetation around these pits which have met with some success. Nevertheless, species have also been lost and the only habitat for *Galium debile* was destroyed by mining a few years ago.

Further south and west, the South Hams are an area in which soils are relatively deep and base-rich, especially in comparison with those of the Culm in mid-Devon. Much of the area forms an undulating plateau at an altitude of around 150–180 m (500–600 ft) above sea-level and is relatively wind-swept. It is dissected by a number of small and a few large valleys, while the high hedgebanks are a characteristic feature. The principle underlying rocks are Devonian shales which are rather variable in composition. Noteworthy species are rather few, but *Scrophularia scorodonia* is relatively frequent; *Melittis melissophyllum* also occurs here, but is rather more common elsewhere. The best known and most spectacular feature of this region is the coastline. The shingle bar and lake of Slapton Ley are well known by tourists as well as by the students who have attended the Field Centre there. The margin of the Ley is the only remaining British station for *Corrigiola littoralis,* which occurs quite frequently on seasonally flooded gravel. The water in the lagoon is somewhat affected by the sea and carries a varied and interesting aquatic and marginal flora. The flora of the shingle bar is also interesting with the Yellow-horned Poppy, *Glaucium flavum.* Further south and west, the sea cliffs are extensive, with much bracken, and blue-bells in spring. The more exposed areas often carry heathland, with *Calluna vulgaris, Erica cinerea, Ulex europaeus, U. gallii* and *Agrostis capillaris,* but small herbs, such as *Scilla verna, Lotus corniculatus* and *Thymus praecox* ssp. *arcticus* occur frequently with the heath species, while *Geranium sanguineum, Moenchia erecta* and *Carlina vulgaris* are local. *Asplenium billotii* and *A. marinum* are also locally plentiful along this coast, in suitable crevices in the rocks.

There are several long and winding estuaries which breach this coastline and these frequently contain areas of brackish marsh. *Schoenoplectus triquetrus* can be found in such habitats in the R. Tamar, while *Eleocharis parvula* used to occur near Aveton Gifford in some quantity.

The Devonian limestone reappears near Plymouth, but in general carries a much less spectacular flora than around Torbay. Nevertheless, species such as *Pimpinella major* are especially frequent here, while a number of introduced species are noteworthy, such as *Eryngium campestre,* and *Carduus pycnocephalus* and *Silene vulgaris* ssp. *macrocarpa* on Plymouth Hoe.

c. *Dartmoor*

The vegetation of the granite outcrop of Dartmoor, which extends over some 770 km² (300 sq. miles) and rises to over 600 m, has much in common with similar upland areas in Wales and elsewhere in Britain. The highest and wettest parts, those in which the rainfall exceeds 180 cm (70″) per annum, are covered with blanket bog, forming a mantle of peat which covers all except the tors and steepest slopes. The blanket bog covers two separate tracts of the moor, a large area north of Princetown lying mostly above about 470 m (1500 ft), and a smaller and rather lower area to the south, the division being a shallow valley which is followed by the principal road across the Moor. In general, the peat is 2–3 m in depth, though this may be exceeded locally in hollows. The vegetation of the blanket bog is dominated by *Molinia caerulea, Calluna vulgaris, Eriophorum vaginatum,* with a range of other species including several of the bog-moss, *Sphagnum.* There has been considerable erosion of the blanket peat in many parts of the Moor, sometimes reaching down to the underlying granite, leaving haggs of bare peat. Partially eroded peat surfaces may be colonised by *Eriophorum angustifolium.* The flora of these regions is often poor in species, 20–30 in a tetrad often representing all those present.

Outside the area dominated by blanket bog, much of the Moor is covered by grassy heathland in which *Agrostis curtisii, A. capillaris, Festuca ovina* and *Pteridium aquilinum* are dominant in the better-drained areas, while *Nardus stricta* and *Molinia caerulea* become prominent in the wetter parts or where drainage is impeded. True heathland is local on the Moor and occurs mainly around its periphery. It has probably been reduced considerably in extent by grazing and also by agricultural "improvement". The characteristic heath communities of E. Devon occur only marginally on Dartmoor, mainly near Bovey Tracey. *Vaccinium myrtillus* may be prominent locally on hillsides, but the bottoms of valleys are frequently occupied by valley bogs, with *Juncus effusus, Sphagnum* carpets and sometimes quite abundant *Viola palustris.* Especially damp areas around streams may be marked by carpets of *Sphagnum auriculatum,* with *Montia fontana, Ranunculus omiophyllus* and sometimes the introduced species, *Epilobium brunnescens. Hypericum elodes* may be found in quaking peat in such situations, often with *Potamogeton polygonifolius.*

The extent of previous forest cover on Dartmoor has been extensively debated. There seems no doubt that trees could have grown above 600 m in the south-west, given the present temperature and weather regime, and thus the Moor could have been completely forested. However, exposure, and the likelihood that blanket bog has been a climatic climax vegetation there for many centuries militate against this. The ancient designation of Dartmoor as a Royal Forest does not, of course, imply coverage by trees. Pollen diagrams suggest that only between a quarter and a half of the total pollen count was from trees, thus reinforcing the view that much of the Moor has remained unforested, while few wood remains and residues have been found embedded in peat above about 400 m (1300 ft). It seems probable, therefore, that at least in the west, there were few trees above that level.

Today, woodland is confined to deep valleys cut into the margin of the Moor, and is seldom found above 300 m (1000 ft), though 3 small wooded areas at higher altitude may give an indication of former forest cover. These are Black Tor Copse in the W. Okement valley, Wistman's Wood in the W. Dart valley and Higher Piles Copse in the Erme valley. The ecological conditions in all three are very similar; they all occur on granite clitter, on the steep west- or south-west-facing slope of the valley. They may owe their survival in part to the free drainage and general protection from grazing afforded by the clitter, but they are also on the side of the valley which receives the greatest amount of insolation. It must remain a matter for conjecture whether they represent the remnants of a former forest; hut circles exist in the vicinity, but there is no reason to suppose that the trees were planted and they have suffered little human interference in the past few centuries. Wistman's Wood has been well known for the extraordinarily gnarled growth of its oaks and for the luxuriance of the bryophyte cover on the trees and rocks. There is considerable evidence to support the view that the trees have become less dense and the bryophytes less luxuriant over the past few decades, which suggests that the older oaks may have been pioneers in a much more open community, with a harsher environment.

All these Dartmoor woods are dominated by *Quercus robur,* as are most other woods on the granite, whereas those on the Culm Measures are dominated by *Q. petraea.* To some extent this pattern is followed quite faithfully, but there are areas where considerable hybridisation and introgression seem to have taken place. In general, valley bottoms, often with much granitic material, support *Q. robur,* while *Q. petraea* woods clothe the valley sides. Many of these woods have been coppiced in the past, to provide timber for smelting and bark for tanning, and on the steep valley sides, often the only trees to accompany the oak are birch (*Betula pendula*) and rowan (*Sorbus aucuparia*), though beech, (*Fagus sylvatica*), has been widely planted on parts of the Moor for hedges and windbreaks, and also in woods, where it readily naturalises. The herb layer of the valleyside woods is generally rather heathy, sometimes dominated by *Vaccinium myrtillus,* with *Luzula sylvatica, Holcus mollis* and other grasses, *Rubus fruticosus* and *Pteridium aquilinum* in those with deeper soils, and usually with a range of the larger mosses characteristic of acid woodland. The deeper and moister soils of the valley bottoms often carry a wide variety of trees, with an abundant herb layer which will usually include bluebells (*Hyacinthoides nonscriptus*) and wood anemone (*Anemone nemorosa*), while sallows (*Salix* spp.) and *Frangula alnus* are locally conspicuous.

d. *Exmoor and Mid-Devon*

Almost the whole of Devon north and west of Exeter have soils derived from shales and sandstones, the Carboniferous Culm Measures to the south, and Devonian Old Red Sandstone to the north. Over much of the area these rocks form a tract of undulating country, with a few summits 200–250 m (600–800 ft) above sea level, and dissected by numerous small and a few larger valleys, but otherwise with few noteworthy features. In general, the Culm Measures weather to give an acid and rather clayey soil, and the area is one of rather damp permanent pasture. There is a good deal of arable cultivation on the flatter summits, many of which have been brought into cultivation in the past few decades, having previous carried grassy moorland. The natural vegetation includes such species as *Succisa pratensis, Valeriana officinalis, Eupatorium cannabinum, Pulicaria dysenterica,* and several species of *Juncus;* patches of *Quercus petraea* woodland occur on the sides of the valleys, while in more heathy areas, *Molinia caerulea* may become prominent, with *Achillea ptarmica* rather frequent, especially in ditches, while *Dactylorhiza maculata* is not uncommon. There may be local indications of the influence of base-rich ground water, reflecting the calcareous nature of some of the underlying rocks, and here *Carex hostiana, Cirsium dissectum* and other mildly calcicole species may become quite common, as in the east of the county. The western parts of the Culm Measures carry some quite extensive areas of marshy moorland which are one of the chief habitats of the rare *Hypericum undulatum,* with *Carum verticillatum* rather frequently accompanying this.

The Old Red Sandstone forms the high ground of Exmoor, a large part of which lies within Somerset. The vegetation of Exmoor is predominantly moorland; substantial areas are heathy, with *Calluna vulgaris, Erica cinerea, Ulex gallii* and *Agrostis curtisii,* and *Deschampsia flexuosa* not uncommon in the higher parts, but there is a considerable amount of poor quality, damp grassland, especially over the Morte slates, and dominated by *Nardus stricta* and *Molinia caerulea.* Boggy areas are largely confined to the valleys, where *Erica tetralix, Nardus stricta, Molinia caerulea* and *Eriophorum angustifolium* become prominent, but there is little development of blanket bog on Exmoor. Much of the area has been reclaimed for agriculture and extensive areas are now enclosed and provide rather poor quality pasture for sheep and cattle.

To the north, the land drops steeply into the sea of the Bristol Channel, and the cliff slopes and deep valleys cutting back into the Moor are frequently heavily wooded. Within these woods are stations for a number of notable species, including *Stellaria nemorum* and *Euphorbia hyberna,* while several endemic species of *Sorbus,* such as *S. vexans* and *S. subcuneata* are known to occur. *Vicia sylvatica* is quite common along the northern coast, while further west, at Hartland, the Culm Measures form some spectacular cliffs remarkable for the occurrence of prostrate forms of *Cystisus scoparius* and *Genista tinctoria.*

One of the most celebrated features of the northern coast is the large dune system of Braunton Burrows, which covers about 10 km² (4 sq. miles) of coast to the north of the estuary of the rivers Taw and Torridge, and west of Barnstaple. Less well known, but also quite rich floristically, is the smaller dune system of Northam Burrows, to the south of this estuary.

The dune system of Braunton Burrows is built up from calcareous, shell-rich sand, of which wide expanses are exposed north of the river estuary at low tides. The watertable, of fresh water, under the dunes has a dome-shaped profile and drains both westwards into the sea and eastwards into Braunton Marsh. The strand-line is rather poor, though *Salsola kali* and *Cakile maritima* can be found in small quantities; there is a well-developed fore-dune ridge carrying *Elymus farctus,* but colonisation of the sand is soon taken over by *Ammophila arenaria.* The main yellow dunes are among the highest in the country; between the discrete clumps of Marram Grass are numerous weedy species, including the two spurges, *Euphorbia paralias* and *E. portlandica. Festuca rubra* often contributes to the stabilisation of the sand surface. Further inland, there are extensive areas of variably stabilised dune grassland, together with numerous and often quite large dune slacks. Near the sea, these tend to have relatively open communities which are frequently covered by moving sand; *Carex arenaria* is frequently prominent around the margin of these slacks. *Salix repens* is common in slacks flooded for 3–5 months of the year, as well as in extensive areas landward of the main dunes. Associated species include *Juncus maritimus, Carex nigra* and a number of orchids, including *Dactylorhiza praetermissa* and *Epipactis palustris.* The landward side of the dunes comprises a complex series of communities in which grasses and sedges are prominent in the turf, but including many other species, especially *Hydrocotyle vulgaris, Potentilla anserina* and *Anagallis tenella,* while *Teucrium scordium* has one of its few British stations in this habitat. The flora of the Burrows is very rich; among the more notable other species can be mentioned *Equisetum variegatum, Matthiola sinuata, Pyrola rotundifolia, Liparis loeselii, Holoschoenus vulgaris* and *Juncus acutus.*

e. *Lundy*

Lundy is interesting botanically for the occurrence of a number of rare plants. Most of the island is covered with heathery moorland, with rather large quantities of *Pteridium aquilinum* on the cliffs to the east, but giving way to communities dominated by *Armeria maritima* to the west. The endemic species *Rhynchosinapis wrightii* is confined to the island, while the prostrate form of *Cystisus scoparius,* which also occurs on Hartland, is also found there.

COLLECTION OF THE RECORDS

Devon is a large county, about 130 km from east to west and almost the same from north to south. It covers all or parts of 95 10×10 km squares of the National Grid. Squares of this size were the recording unit for the Botanical Society of the British Isles

Distribution Maps Scheme, but 100 sq. km is much too large to be used as a basis for a local flora, as it would obscure many details of local distribution patterns. On the other hand, to collect records on the basis of 1 square km units would be very informative but far too time-consuming. It was therefore decided that records should be based on 2 km×2 km squares (tetrads), a pattern which has been adopted by the writers of several other recent county floras. There are 1843 tetrads wholly or partly within Devon.

The definition of the county boundary itself presents some problems. Devon has suffered relatively little from the activities of various Boundary Commissions; the administrative county boundary is fairly coincident with that portrayed on maps, and there have only been minor recent variations in parts of the west in relation to Cornwall, and small areas to the east with respect to Dorset. The administrative county still approximates to the old Watsonian vice-counties of 3 (S. Devon) and 4 (N. Devon). The actual boundary used for the survey was that shown on the 1:50.000 1st Series Ordnance Survey maps. Tetrads which are only partially in Devon as so defined were recorded only from the part which actually fell within the county. In a few cases, the area involved was so small, or inaccessible, that it was ignored, or the data amalgamated with the most appropriate adjacent tetrad; similar principles were applied to a very few tetrads around the coast, where the area of land was exceedingly small.

The occurrence of species of angiosperms, gymnosperms and pteridophytes in the various tetrads was recorded. Many people assisted in the recording, and these are listed in the appendix. The use of recorders with a wide range of expertise inevitably results in rather uneven recording, but in the early stages it was felt desirable to try to involve as many people as possible in the project. Towards the end, gaps had to be filled in by a few of the more knowledgeable. A range of recording sheets were prepared, and recorders were invited to use those most appropriate to their experience, but this also results in uneven recording; species which are difficult to identify or relatively inconspicuous tending to be under-recorded.

The starting point for the collection of records was 1950. This meant that any suitable records made for the Distribution Maps Scheme could be included, though in practice, it was found that few of these were sufficiently precisely located. The vast majority of records are new, and date from 1970.

The entire process of storing and retrieving data was computerised from the outset. Every species was given a serial number, and information including the date, recorder number, list number and grid reference, together with species numbers, were put onto punched cards and stored initially in the form of card-images. This format was devised so that individual punched cards were self-contained and there would be no problems if card batches were dropped. Developments in data handling methods for computers meant that later in the project, cards became obsolete, but the card-image format was retained for data storage, for compatability reasons. From these stored card-images, it was possible to sort the data into distribution maps for each individual species. Thus from quite an early stage, it was possible to see distribution patterns over the county, while these maps were also used to prepare lists of the species which had been recorded from individual tetrads. In the later stages, these lists were exceedingly valuable as they enabled omissions to be pin-pointed and helped to avoid a lot of duplicate recording.

In addition to storing the lists of recorded species in a form very similar to that in which they were submitted, the individual recording sheets were also filed. Together, these made it relatively simple to check for the more obvious errors, as specific records could be related to a recorder and list number, and the actual list then checked. Such errors generally fell into one of two categories— clear misidentifications by the recorder, or mispunched numbers on the computer card. Both could be dealt with, though the former was difficult, as there must clearly be an area within which one could not say for certain whether a particular record was an error or not. Endeavours to refer such queries back to the recorder generally proved unsatisfactory.

Initially, it had been hoped to record data on the habitat preferences of species, and even to record from habitats within tetrads rather than tetrads themselves. Although this would have provided much useful information on distribution patterns, it proved difficult to define a suitable list of habitats, and even more difficult to persuade recorders to use such a list effectively. It also made the recording task too lengthy, and although some recorders used it for a period, it was eventually dropped.

In all, about 600,000 records of species occurrences in tetrads were made, of which about 365,000 represented original records and the remainder were duplicates. This represents an average of almost exactly 200 species/tetrad, but there is considerable variation over the county. Over 450 species/tetrad were recorded from Braunton Burrows, Slapton Ley and in scattered tetrads elsewhere, especially in the vicinity of limestone, whereas in several tetrads on Dartmoor only 20–30 species could be found. It is difficult to estimate the degree of completeness which this represents; there are undoubtedly omissions, especially in agricultural districts. Although farmers were, on the whole, co-operative, and some were actively involved in the project, in heavily farmed regions access to interesting areas was often difficult. In quite a number of agricultural tetrads, only about 180 species recorded; around 230 might well be more realistic. Overall, the total probably represents about 90% of the county flora.

Not the least of the problems was that of converting the data stored in the computer into maps suitable for publication. An outline map of the county was available and eventually, a technique was devised for superimposing the distribution pattern for a species onto this, in the form of suitably located solid octogons. The whole map was then photographically reduced.

ARRANGEMENT OF THE ACCOUNTS

In the preparation of an Atlas of the County Flora, which contains no means for the identification of the species discussed, it is important that the names used should relate easily to some readily available flora that includes keys. It was felt that the 3rd Edition of Clapham, Tutin & Warburg's "Excursion Flora of the British Isles" was the most suitable of those available. Not only are the scientific names reasonably up to date, but considerable care has been taken over the choice of vernacular names. However, it was also necessary that the species could be related to those discussed in the previous "Flora of Devon", so that distributions could be compared and the status of a number of these could be discussed. In the text of the present work, references to the previous Flora of Devon are given in a non-standard manner, using the abbreviation "Fl. Dev.".

The order of families and genera in the 3rd Edition of the Excursion Flora leaves a certain amount to be desired. The recently published "Flora Europaea" (Tutin et al., 1965–82) allowed taxonomists the opportunity to revise the arrangement of these, and the present Atlas follows the order of families, genera and species given in Flora Europaea.

The treatment of a number of the more complex genera has inevitably been rather cursory. In a number of genera, e.g. *Rosa,* the Flora of Devon had discussed the distribution of large numbers of infraspecific taxa, many of which are probably only ecotypic variants and are not now generally accepted. The relatively recently published treatments of *Hieracium, Taraxacum* and *Euphrasia* are scarcely compatible with the accounts presented by Fraser & Martin. *Rubus* presented a particular problem. Quite a lot of work has been done on this genus in the last few decades, but although the nomenclature is rather more settled, there is very little detailed information on distribution and no keys to enable accurate identifications to be made. Rather than try to correlate the sketchy information which was available, it was felt it would be preferable to await the publication of the forthcoming "Flora of Great Britain & Ireland", in which both keys and such distribution data will be included. It is clear that much more work needs to be done on the distribution in Devon of species of all these genera.

The accounts of the species have been set out in the following pattern:
a. Species names follow those given in the Excursion Flora;
b. English names similarly, except that some additional ones from the old Flora of Devon have been included;
c. Synonyms include equivalent names in the old Flora of Devon and also in Flora Europaea;
d. All native, introduced and adventive species have been mentioned, including a number reported in the old Flora of Devon, but now certainly no longer to be found.
e. All hybrids have been mentioned, together with their putative parents. With the exception of those which have been reported in Stace (1976),

many of the records of hybrids are old and the rarer probably need treating with considerable scepticism. Much work is needed on the distribution of hybrids in the county.

f. The number in brackets following the end of each account is the number of tetrads from which the species has been recorded in the present survey.

The words "recorded" and "reported" have been used with care in the text. "Recorded" means that there has been at least one definitive record of the plant—it has been seen by someone; "reported" means that it is said to have been seen, but the evidence is suspect or the information lost.

No attempt has been made to guess at the origin of species which are, or in all probability are, not native in the County. Wool and other aliens are quite frequent in parts of E. Devon and around Newton Abbot, and also in the vicinity of docks and harbours. Such plants are less frequent now along railways, but a few have been introduced along motorways. Many plants are introduced by gardeners and frequently get dumped in various parts of the county in rubbish and garden waste—a deplorable habit, but quite prevalent. With the relatively favorable climate, it is quite common for, e.g., potatoes and tomatoes to establish themselves for short periods. There are even well-meaning people who sow seeds of native or quasi-native species in local hedges to help ensure their survival! Only in a few cases is there documented evidence as to how or when a species was introduced and in many cases the information is not available and it is unlikely that it will ever be.

One of the objects in preparing this Atlas was to try to illustrate the current distribution of species. It is difficult to say with certainty how these relate to previous distribution patterns, such as those detailed by Martin & Fraser. It is clear that agricultural practices have caused the decline or extinction of many of the "cornfield weeds", especially annuals. "Agricultural improvement"—destroying hedgerows, and reclaiming parts of moorland—has probably not endangered many species, but it is difficult to be certain what is happening and it is a process which must be watched very closely. Some habitats, such as salt-marshes and estuaries, are frequently at risk through successive small reclamation schemes, while cliff-tops are under increasing pressure from recreation. These, and other anthropogenic activities have untoward effects on the flora, generally resulting in the eradication of the more sensitive or more demanding species, which are usually also the more rare or interesting.

It is hoped that the existence of distribution maps will help pin-point problems in these areas, but as can be seen, maps of species with records in fewer than 10 tetrads have not been included. One reason was to save space—the occurrence of these species can often be described better in words. More importantly, they could help locate the rarer species; within the area of a tetrad, particularly given the rather specific habitat requirements of a rare species, it is often easy to find it. Knowing the propensities of some people for searching out rare plants for whatever purpose, it was felt better to keep this information well guarded.

NATURE CONSERVATION IN DEVON

The Devon Trust for Nature Conservation was established in 1961 with the object of conserving wildlife, plants and habitats. It currently manages 35 nature reserves totalling approximately 1000 ha (2200 acres); the majority of these are open to the public. They include 14 Sites of Special Scientific Interest and embrace a wide variety of the more noteworthy habitats in the county. A detailed list of the reserves and details of the conditions under which they can be visited can be obtained from the Trust Secretary.

There are also 5 National Nature Reserves—the Axmouth—Lyme Regis Undercliffs, Bovey Valley woodlands, Braunton Burrows, Dendles Wood and Yarner Wood, together with the Forest Nature Reserves of Black Tor Copse and Wistman's Wood, both of these on Dartmoor. Local Nature Reserves include Berry Head, Dawlish Warren and Sugar Loaf Hill and Saltern Cove; these are largely the responsibility of Local Authorities.

The Royal Society for the Protection of Birds has two reserves, at Chapple Woods in N. Devon and on Aylesbeare Common, east of Exeter.

A number of local farmers and other landowners are very conscious of the need for conservation and have set aside areas of their land where wildlife can be relatively undisturbed; some of these have been recognised as Approved Wildlife Conservation areas. Local industries are also concerned that conservation principles should be observed, either in laying out their grounds, or in remedying the consequences of their operations.

The Devon Trust also actively fosters interest in conservation in schools, and a number of Educational Reserves have been set up. The County Council also cooperates in various ways, especially in endeavouring to minimise the disturbance to certain lengths of hedgerow where there are rare species.

REFERENCES

Baker, H. G. (1955) *Geranium purpureum* Vill. and *Geranium robertianum* L. in the British Flora. *Watsonia* 3(3): 160–167.

Barling, D. M. (1962) Studies in the Biology of *Poa subcaerulea* Sm. *Watsonia* 5(3): 163–173.

Barlow, F. (ed.) (1969) *Exeter and its Region.* University of Exeter.

Clapham, A. R., Tutin, T. G. & Warburg, E. F. (1962) *Flora of the British Isles* 2nd Edition. C.U.P.

Clapham, A. R., Tutin, T. G. & Warburg, E. F. (1981) *Excursion Flora of the British Isles* 3rd Edition. C.U.P.

Cope, T. A. & Stace, C. A. (1978) The *Juncus bufonius* L. aggregate in Western Europe. *Watsonia* 12(2): 113–128.

David, R. W. (1977) The Distribution of *Carex montana* L. in Britain. *Watsonia* 11(4): 377–378.

David, R. W. (1981) The Distribution of *Carex punctata* Gaud. in Britain. *Watsonia* 13(4): 318–320.

Durrance, E. M. & Laming, D. J. C. (1982) *The Geology of Devon.* University of Exeter.

Edmonds, E. A., McKeown, M. C. & Williams, M. (1969) *British Regional Geology: South-west England.* 3rd Ed. H.M.S.O. London.

Graham, R. A. (1958) Mint Notes VII. *Mentha* × *maximillianea* F. Schultz. *Watsonia* **4**(2): 72–76.

Jermy, A. C., Arnold, H. R., Farrell, L., & Perring, F. H. (1978) *Atlas of the Ferns of the British Isles* Botanical Society of the British Isles and the British Pteridological Society, London.

Jones, E. M. (1975) Taxonomic studies of the genus *Atriplex* in Britain. *Watsonia* **10**(3): 233–251.

Lousley, J. E. (1953) *Rumex cuneifolius* and a new hybrid. *Watsonia* **2**(4): 394–397.

Lovis, J. D. (1963) The taxonomy of *Asplenium trichomanes* in Europe. *British Fern Gazette* **9**: 147–160.

Martin, W. K. & Fraser, G. T. (1939) *Flora of Devon* T. Buncle & Co., Arbroath.

McClintock, D. (1972) *Gaudinia fragilis* (L.) Beauv. *Watsonia* **9**(2): 143–146.

McClintock, D. (1978) Oenotheras in Britain. *Watsonia* **12**(2): 164–165.

Perring, F. H. & Sell, P. D. (eds.) (1968) *Critical Supplement to the Atlas of the British Flora.* Nelson.

Perring, F. H. & Walters, S. M. (eds.) (1962) *Atlas of the British Flora.* Nelson.

Pritchard, N. M. (1959) *Gentianella* in Britain. *Watsonia* **4**(4): 169–193.

Roberts, R. H. (1964) *Mimulus* hybrids in Britain. *Watsonia* **6**(1): 70–75.

Smith, P. M. (1973) Observations on some critical Brome-grasses. *Watsonia* **9**(4): 319–332.

Stace, C. A. (ed.) (1975) *Hybridization and the Flora of the British Isles* Academic Press, London & New York.

Stace, C. A. & Cotton, R. (1974) Hybrids between *Festuca rubra* L. s.l. and *Vulpia membranacea* (L.) Dum. *Watsonia* **10**(2): 119–138.

Tutin, T. G. *et al.* (1964–80) *Flora Europaea* Volumes **1–5**. C.U.P.

Walters, S. M. (1953) *Montia fontana* L. *Watsonia* **3**(1): 1–6.

Wigston, D. L. (1977) The distribution of *Quercus robur, Quercus petraea* and their hybrids in south-western England. *Watsonia* **10**(4): 345–369.

Wigston, D. L. (1979a) *Lycopodiella inundata* (L.) Holub at Fox Tor Mires, South Devon. *Watsonia* **12**(4): 343.

Wigston, D. L. (1979b) *Nothofagus* Blume in Britain. *Watsonia* **12**(4): 344–345.

Wigston, D. L., Pickering, D. & Jones, S. (1981) *Lycopodiella inundata* (L.) Holub at Smallhanger, S. Devon. *Watsonia* **13**(4): 326–327.

Yeo, P. F. (1956) Hybridization between diploid and tetraploid species of *Euphrasia*. *Watsonia* **3**(5): 253–269.

Young, D. P. (1958) *Oxalis* in the British Isles. *Watsonia* **4**(2): 51–69.

Young, D. P. (1962) Studies in the British *Epipactis*. V. *E. leptochila Watsonia* **5**(3): 127–135.

APPENDIX

LIST OF PRINCIPAL RECORDERS

a. *Individuals:*
D. J. Allen; V. B. Almond; D. E. Ansley; K. Arscott; O. G. Ashley; C. J. Baker; R. A. Barr; E. Bax; R. Bell; A. J. C. Beddow; G. A. Berresford; J. A. R. Bickford; I. M. Blackford; A. Bonham-Carter; B. Boulton; D. M. Brewer; M. Brill; J. Brooker; A. J. Bryant; D. E. Bunce; A. Burns; D. M. Carter; M. Chambers; M. Chandler; G. W. Chapman; W. M. Clark; C. J. M. Clarke; M. E. Chartres; J. R. Collman; E. Cowling; L. Crombie; R. S. Cropper; D. A. Curry; R. W. David; J. Davie; E. Deighton; J. Dewey; A. Dunn; M. E. Dunsford; P. Eagle; B. Eaton; D. M. Ellis; G. Elwell; A. S. Ferguson; G. Franklin; H. F. Frost; R. G. Furber; V. E. Gale; P. P. Gammon; D. Gepp; E. Godfrey; S. Goodfellow; D. E. M. Gordon; B. J. Gregory; D. Grose; G. H. Gush; A. M. Hall; A. S. & E. D. Hallpike; A. P. S. Hamilton; P. K. Hann; M. L. Hatch; G. F. C. Hawkins; J. J. Haywood; J. M. Heap; G. Hearnden; H. Hearne; S. Heslop; M. Hickmott; C. E. Hicks; E. M. Hill; P. M. Hill; M. C. Hockaday; C. M. Hodgson; E. M. Howard; E. M. Hubbard; O. D. Hunt; H. G. Hurrell; R. B. Ivimey-Cook; M. Jaques; K. Jefferies; J. M. Jenkins; C. Jones; W. A. Jones; S. L. Jury; J. G. Keylock; G. F. Klepp; J. T. H. Knight; R. G. B. Laidlaw; K. Laver; K. M. Lawder; B. Leakey; J. Lethbridge; K. G. Lethbridge; M. Lethbridge; F. D. Mack; E. T. Mold; F. E. Moysey; H. R. McDouell; M. Nicholls; M. L. Page; P. M. Parker; C. G. Parkerwood; M. Parkinson; M. A. Paske; P. Pearce; R. Peterken; M. Pool; B. R. Poole; E. Potter; J. L. Presland; M. C. F. Proctor; D. C. Prowse; A. R. Radcliffe-Smith; J. S. Rees; A. T. Reid; N. Richards; J. A. Rickard; M. Rickard; J. Robertson; M. Robins; P. A. Robinson; R. Robinson; R. G. B. Roe; S. Rogers; M. J. Russell; S. Russell; H. A. Sandford; J. F. D. Scott; M. H. Scott; I. L. Scott-Elliot; H. E. W. Selby; C. H. Shere; A. G. Side; E. B. Slade; R. J. Sleigh; D. I. Smart; J. Southcott; G. M. & M. F. Spooner; P. C. Stanton; C. Steele; G. S. Steele-Perkins; M. Stile; V. S. Summerhayes; E. W. Sutcliffe; C. Sutton; E. D. Tallant; M. R. Taylor; R. G. Taylor; M. Thompson; R. Thorne; P. Touch; M. L. Trahain; W. H. Tucker; M. Tulloh; M. A. Turner; V. M. Vallins; V. M. Walker; M. J. D. Wall; T. J. Wallace; S. D. Ward; R. F. Warren; M. A. Warren; G. E. C. Waterhouse; D. Watt-Smyrk; R. L. Weatherhead; J. Webster; G. Wedd; K. G. R. Wheeler; W. H. T. White; J. P. Widgery; D. L. Wigston; P. Wilkins; M. Williams; S. I. Wilsdon; A. Wilson; C. M. Wilson; H. G. D. Woods; J. A. Wyatt; M. J. Wyatt; O. E. Young;

b. *Organisations:*
Bicton College of Agriculture; Botanical Society of the British Isles; College of St. Mark & St. John, Plymouth; Devon Trust for Nature Conservation; Devonshire Association (Botanical Section); Exeter Natural History Society; Field Studies Council (Slapton Ley Field Centre); Institute of Terrestrial Ecology (Biological Records Centre); Plymouth City Museum; South West Naturalists Union; University of Exeter (Department of Biological Sciences; Herbarium; National Vegetation Survey). Several branches of the Women's Institute and a number of schools in the county also contributed records.

LYCOPODIACEAE

Huperzia selago (L.) Bernh. ex Schrank & Mart.   Fir Clubmoss
(*Lycopodium selago* L.)
A montane species which may also occur on sloping sites in lowland habitats. Scattered over heaths and moors, and in crevices in tors. Rare on Dartmoor, with only single records from Exmoor and E. Devon. (19)

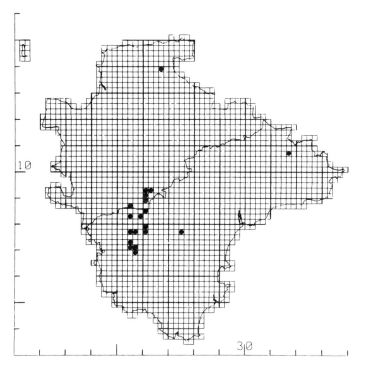

Lycopodiella inundata (L.) Holub   Marsh Clubmoss
(*Lycopodium inundatum* L., *Lepidotis inundata* (L.) C.Börner)
A very rare lowland species occurring on damp peat on heaths and moors, and whose distribution is very susceptible to drainage. Its habitat on Harpford Common has recently been considerably disturbed and it is doubtful if it survives there, though it may have already become extinct during the drought of 1976. There are recent and apparently new Dartmoor records on tinner's waste on Fox Tor Mire, on china-clay waste on Smallhanger Down, and also at Cadover Bridge (Wigston, 1979a, 1981). (6)

Lycopodium clavatum L.   Stag's-horn Clubmoss
A montane species of damp heaths and heathy grassland. It is now quite rare on Dartmoor, and there are only single records from Exmoor and the Blackdown Hills in E. Devon. (6)

Diphasiastrum alpinum (L.) Holub, (*Lycopodium alpinum* L., *Diphasium alpinum* (L.) Rothm.), the Alpine Clubmoss, is an arctic-alpine species of heaths and moors. Lowland records are usually referred to the following taxon, and there is a possible Devon record in Herb. Hiern, ex Herb. W.S.Hoare, from Dartmoor. The plant has not been seen recently and is probably extinct.

Diphasium x issleri (Rouy) Holub, (*Lycopodium alpinum* L. var. *decipiens* Syme ex Druce, *D. alpinum* x *complanatum*), has a more lowland distribution than the only one of its supposed parents which is known to occur in Britain. The only Devon record from near Chagford is very old, and needs confirmation.

ISOETACEAE

Isoetes lacustris L.   Quillwort
A northern species confined to dystrophic (base-poor) ponds and reservoirs, although it is more tolerant of nutrients than the next species. It has been recorded from Burrator Reservoir, in S.W. Devon. (2)

Isoetes echinospora Durieu   Spiny-spored Quillwort
(*I. setacea* auct.)
Strictly confined to dystrophic ponds and reservoirs, usually over peaty substrata. Very abundant submerged in several reservoirs on Dartmoor, often forming continuous carpets, and probably on the increase as such habitats are developed. (8)

EQUISETACEAE

Equisetum variegatum Schleich. ex Weber & Mohr
Variegated Horsetail
A species of montane calcareous mires which also occurs in dune-slacks along the west coast. Apparently confined to Braunton Burrows, where the plants are quite variable, some being small and prostrate and others larger and erect; the cause of this variation is not clear. There are no recent records from S. Devon. (6)

Equisetum fluviatile L.   Water Horsetail
In shallow water and damp ground at the margins of lakes, ponds and ditches. Abundant in some habitats, and locally common throughout the county, though its ecological preferences are not clear. (168)

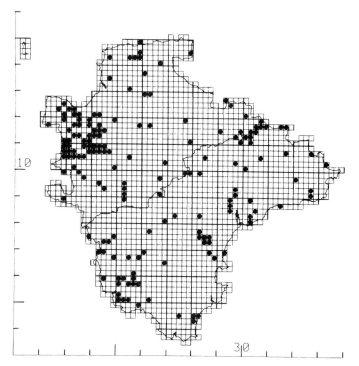

Equisetum palustre L.   Marsh Horsetail
A widely distributed species occurring largely in marshy areas with a supply of base-rich water and absent from peaty habitats. Not uncommon throughout the county, but rarely plentiful. (258)

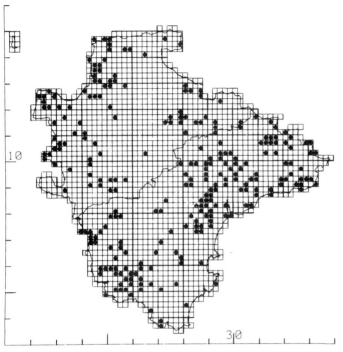

Equisetum arvense L.   Common Horsetail
Widespread and sometimes abundant in hedges and waste places usually on mineral soils, and also as a persistent garden weed. It occurs frequently in dune systems, but is absent from peat-dominated habitats, and hence from the higher moors. (889)

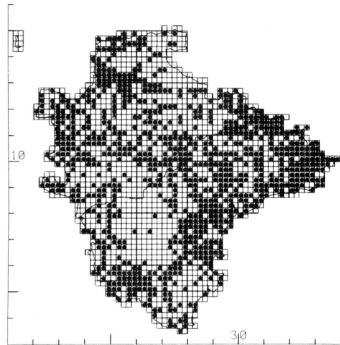

Equisetum sylvaticum L.   Wood Horsetail
Quite widely distributed in damp, shaded roadside ditches and damp woods, often on peaty soils, and persisting where such woods used to occur, more rarely in wet heaths. Mainly in the east and north-west of the county, but nowhere abundant. (28)

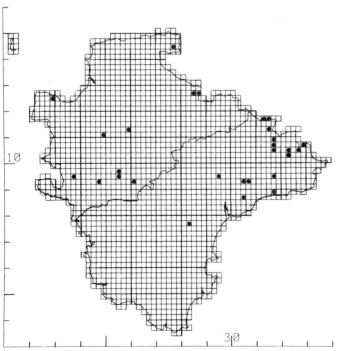

Equisetum x litorale Kühlew. ex Rupr., (*E. arvense* x *fluviatile*), occurs occasionally with the parents, but is rarely recorded. (3)

Equisetum telemateia Ehrh.   Great Horsetail
Locally abundant in damp places on heaths and moors, along roadsides, on sea cliffs and in wet woods and meadows in E. Devon. It requires a soil with a rather high base status, and is usually prominent on heathland only where there are base-rich flushes. (101)

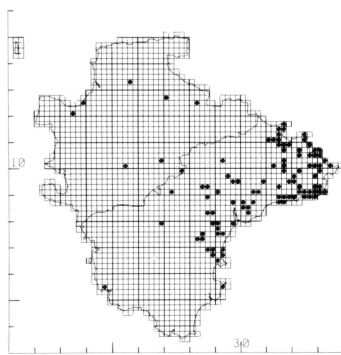

OPHIOGLOSSACEAE

Botrychium lunaria (L.) Swartz   Moonwort
Widely but thinly scattered in old pastures and dry grassland,
most common in fixed dune grassland on Braunton Burrows.
There is a fairly recent record from Lundy, and also near
Lustleigh. The plant has always been rare in Devon, though it
could have been overlooked in the south-east. (5)

Ophioglossum vulgatum L.   Adder's-tongue
In damp pastures, fen and scrub. A species which seems to
come and go, but apparently much less common than formerly,
perhaps as a result of land reclamation, or maybe just overlooked. (17)

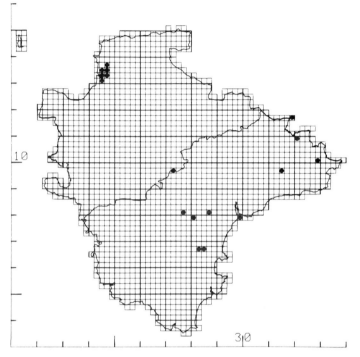

Ophioglossum azoricum C.Presl, (*O. vulgatum* ssp. *ambiguum*
(Coss. & Germ.) E.F. Warb.), occurs in sandy ground near the
sea. It is apparently confined to Lundy where, although it has
not been seen recently, there is no reason to suppose it does not
persist.

OSMUNDACEAE

Osmunda regalis L.   Royal Fern
In bogs and heaths on peaty soil, in wet birch and sallow scrub
and along peaty river banks. It has been recorded from quite a
number of tetrads, especially around the periphery of Dartmoor,
but its status in some of these is doubtful, as it has been much
collected and transplanted into gardens, from which it can
spread naturally. It seems to prefer a moderately base-rich soil,
and is susceptible to excessive drainage. (65)

Osmunda regalis L.   Royal Fern

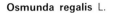
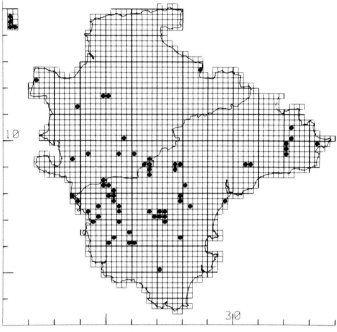

ADIANTACEAE

Adiantum capillus-veneris L.   Maiden-hair Fern
A species commonly found in the Mediterranean region, and
often grown in gardens or as a house plant. Its native habitats
include damp sea cliffs and wet calcareous substrata, and it
probably survives in a genuinely wild state in Devon only where
such habitats are out of reach, as on the cliffs west of Ilfracombe
and at Anstey's Cove, Torquay. It is quite well established on
walls in parts of E. Devon. (8)

Cryptogramma crispa (L.) R.Br. ex Hook.   Parsley Fern
An arctic-alpine species usually restricted to siliceous soils on
the highest moors. There is a single record from Dartmoor, on
the remains of a cottage wall. (1)

HYMENOPHYLLACEAE

Hymenophyllum tunbridgense (L.) Sm. Tunbridge Filmy-fern
On moist surfaces and in the crevices and fissures of shaded,
acid rocks, usually with overhanging trees. Local in the valley
woodlands and on at least 9 tors on Dartmoor. It also occurs on
the north coast, in the vicinity of Lynton and Watersmeet. (23)

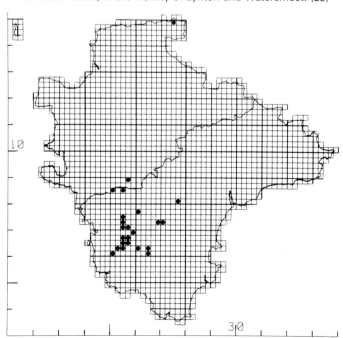

Hymenophyllum wilsonii Hook. Wilson's Filmy-fern
In similar habitats to the preceding species, but able to
withstand greater exposure and higher light intensities; the two
species rarely grow intermingled. It has been found on at least
29 tors on Dartmoor, but is rare in the woodlands; there is a
single record from Exmoor (Watersmeet). (30)

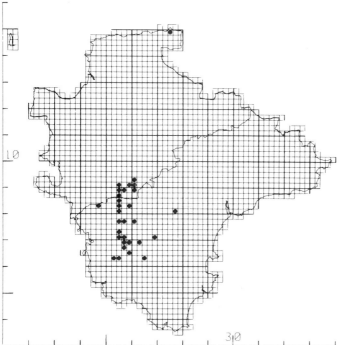

THELYPTERIDACEAE
Oreopteris limbosperma (All.) Holub
Lemon-scented Fern, Mountain Fern
(*Dryopteris oreopteris* (Ehrh.) Maxon, *Thelypteris limbosperma*
(All.) H.P.Fuchs)
A northern species which prefers flowing ground-water and is
chiefly found in the vicinity of streams on acid soils. It is not
uncommon on Dartmoor, especially in some of the higher
woodlands, and there are some records from Exmoor. (138)

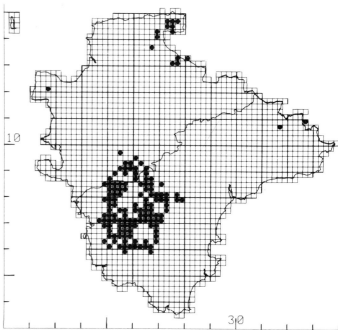

HYPOLEPIDACEAE

Pteridium aquilinum (L.) Kuhn Bracken
A widespread and cosmopolitan species, most commonly
occurring on heaths and in acid grassland, but also frequent in
woods, hedges and waste places. It avoids waterlogged ground
and becomes sparse above about 450 m (1400 ft.), but has been
recorded up to 490 m (1575 ft.) on Dartmoor. It tends to be
absent from highly agricultural regions. (1704)

Thelypteris thelypteroides Michx Marsh Fern
(*Dryopteris thelypteris* (L.) A.Gray, *T. palustris* Schott)
A northern continental species of marshes and fens which has
always been rare in Devon. The only recent record is one quoted
in Jermy *et al.* (1978), from the vicinity of Haldon. (1)

Phegopteris connectilis (Michx) Watt Beech Fern
(*Dryopteris phegopteris* (L.) C.Chr., *Thelypteris phegopteris* (L.)
Slosson)
A northern species of stream-sides, damp woods and shaded
rocky places, always on acid soils. It occurs sporadically in
elevated habitats on Dartmoor, and also on Exmoor, but seems
to have become less frequent. (28)

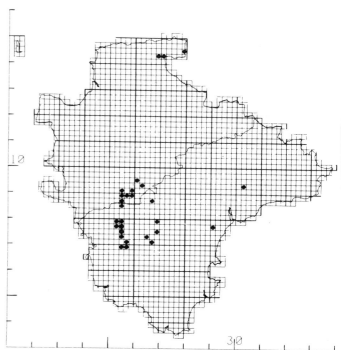

ASPLENIACEAE

Asplenium marinum L.   Sea Spleenwort
Characteristic of walls and the crevices of sea cliffs, and usually within reach of sea spray. It occurs more rarely further inland, in estuaries and habitats exposed to the prevailing south-westerly winds. Moderately common in suitable habitats, along both coasts. (55)

Two subspecies have been described by Lovis (1963): Ssp. **trichomanes** is a montane form which avoids calcareous rocks. Ssp. **quadrivalens** D.E.Meyer emend. Lovis is the common form on calcareous rocks and mortared walls. Details of the morphological differences are given by Lovis (l.c.). Both subspecies occur in suitable habitats in Devon, although details of the distribution patterns remain to be worked out.

Asplenium billotii F.W.Schultz   Lanceolate Spleenwort
(*A. obovatum* auct., *A. lanceolatum* Huds.)
A southern Atlantic species which occurs quite commonly in S.W. England, usually on rocks and walls, and in hedgebanks near the sea. It is quite extensively distributed on old walls along the western edge of Dartmoor and along the South Hams coast. (56)

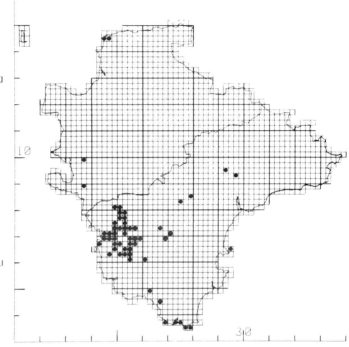

Asplenium trichomanes L.   Maiden-hair Spleenwort
On rocks, walls and hedgebanks; common and abundant throughout the county, though absent from some localities for no very obvious reason, and not on any tors on Dartmoor. (1045)

Asplenium adiantum-nigrum L.   Black Spleenwort
On rocks, walls and in dry hedgebanks, where it may reach a considerable size. Quite widely distributed, perhaps especially in relatively base-rich habitats, and absent from Dartmoor tors. (1289)

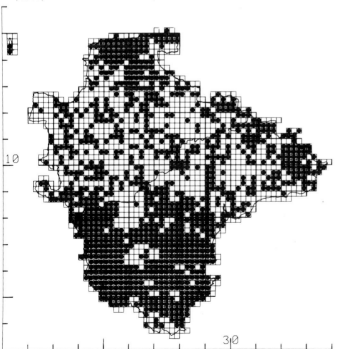

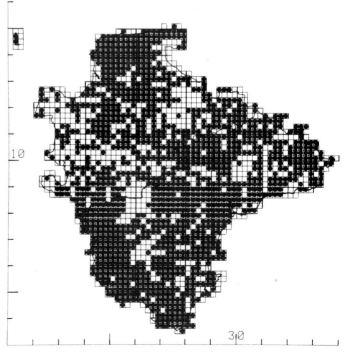

5

Asplenium septentrionale (L.) Hoffm. Forked Spleenwort
A northern species confined to crevices in acid rocks. It has been reported from near Lynton, and also west of Chudleigh, but the only recent record is of a single small plant from a valley near Hennock; it is possible it still persists in similar habitats along the eastern edge of Dartmoor, and may be found especially around old mine sites. (1)

Asplenium x alternifolium Wulf., (*A. septentrionale* x *trichomanes*), has been reported "from acid rocks near Lynton"; the locality appears to be in Somerset.

Asplenium ruta-muraria L. Wall Rue
A widespread species, usually occurring on man-made habitats such as walls and bridges, but also found in rock crevices, with a strong preference for calcareous substrata. Not as ubiquitous as might be expected, and absent from many apparently suitable habitats. (634)

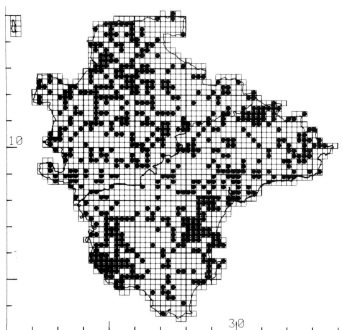

Phyllitis scolopendrium (L.) Newm. Hart's-tongue Fern
(*Asplenium scolopendrium* L.)
A southern Atlantic species largely confined to base-rich habitats. Common and generally distributed in woods and hedgerows, and on shaded rocks and walls; not so common in more agricultural districts. (1475).

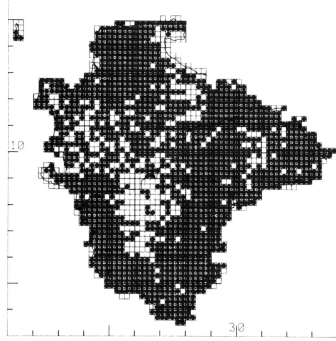

X Asplenophyllitis jacksonii Alston
(*Asplenium adiantum-nigrum* x *Phyllitis scolopendrium*)
Only known from Devon, Cornwall and the Channel Islands, this hybrid is distinguished by its simply pinnate, triangular fronds. It has been recorded from Hartland, and from 2 other localities. (3)

ATHYRIACEAE

Athyrium filix-femina (L.) Roth Lady Fern
A common and often abundant species of damp woods and the margins of rivers and streams, but strictly avoiding calcareous substrata. It is very common in the northern and western parts of the county, much less so in the south and east, and in agricultural regions. (1223)

Ceterach officinarum DC. Rusty-back Fern
In the crevices of limestone rocks and especially on walls made with mortar, but much less frequent when these have been repaired with cement. Not uncommon, and fairly generally distributed, but absent from many apparently suitable habitats. (305)

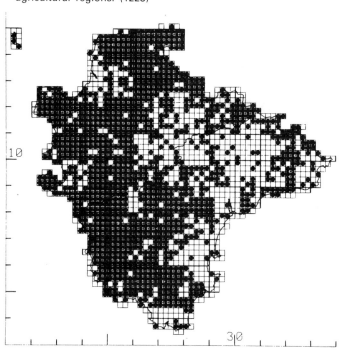

Cystopteris fragilis (L.) Bernh.   Brittle Bladder-fern
A montane species of base-rich shaded rocks and walls. Very rare in Devon, and apparently decreasing, with only isolated recent records. (3)

ASPIDIACEAE

Polystichum aculeatum (L.) Roth   Hard Shield-fern
(*P, lobatum* (Huds.) Chevall.)
In woods, hedgebanks and shaded places, preferably on base-rich substrata. Widely distributed but apparently rare and perhaps under-recorded, with only very few plants at any one site. (122)

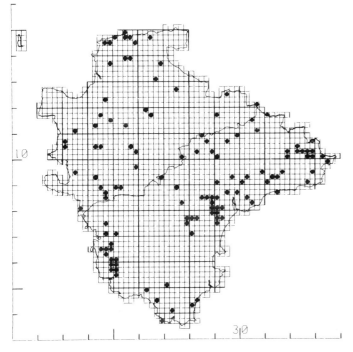

Polystichum x bicknellii (Christ) Hahne, (*P. aculeatum* x *setiferum*), has been recorded from near Plymouth, and one locality in N. Devon, where the parents grow together, but it is often difficult to distinguish from *P. aculeatum.* (2)

Dryopteris filix-mas (L.) Schott   Male Fern
Common and widespread, occurring in woods and hedgerows, along roadsides and in waste places. It has no marked ecological preferences, though often does better on base-rich soils. It is absent from the higher moors and rather infrequent on the heavier soils of the Culm. (1566)

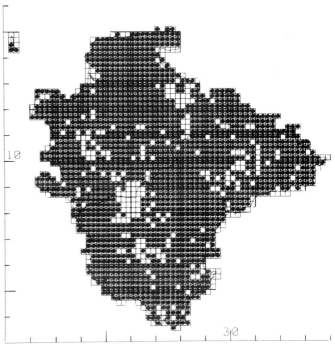

Polystichum setiferum (Forsk.) Woynar   Soft Shield-fern
A southern Atlantic species of woods and especially hedge-banks, most commonly on base-rich soils. Locally common, and in some districts the most abundant hedgerow fern, but rare or absent in others. (1059)

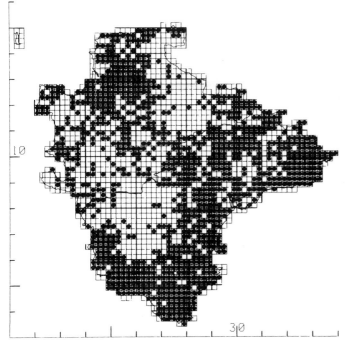

Dryopteris affinis (Lowe) Fraser-Jenkins
(*D. pseudomas* (Woll.) Holub & Pouzar, *D. filix-mas* var. *paleacea* (Don) Druce, *D. borreri* Newm.)
Particularly common in oceanic areas, especially on acid, clayey soils. Widespread in Devon, and characteristic of the damp woodlands on the Culm clays, where it may reach a consider-able size. It can be found on 55 tors on Dartmoor. (915)
Our plant is ssp. **robusta**.

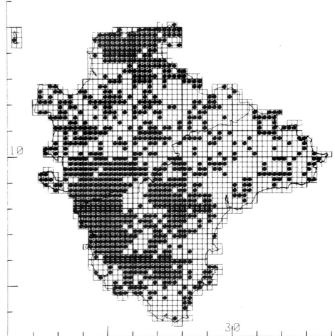

Dryopteris x tavelii Rothm., (*D. filix-mas* x *affinis*), is intermediate between its parents and not easily distinguishable from either; it has been recorded from several places near Ilfracombe and around Torbay, and probably occurs elsewhere. (6)

Dryopteris carthusiana (Vill.) H.P.Fuchs   Narrow Buckler-fern (*D. spinulosa* auct.)
A northern species found chiefly on banks and in damp woodlands; it is scattered throughout the county, but never abundant where it occurs. Some records could be the result of confusion with forms of *D. dilatata*. (52)

Dryopteris x deweveri (Jansen) Jansen & Wachter, (*D. dilatata* x *carthusiana*) is said to be quite common where the parents grow together, and is intermediate between them in characters. It has been recorded from 2 sites to the east of Dartmoor, and probably occurs elsewhere. (2)

Dryopteris aemula (Ait.) O.Kuntze   Hay-scented Buckler-fern
In damp hedges, woodlands and rock crevices on tors; chiefly in the west and north-west of the county and on Lundy, where it is locally not uncommon. (94)

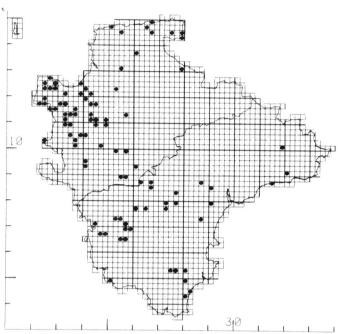

Gymnocarpium dryopteris (L.) Newm., (*Thelypteris dryopteris* (L.) Slosson, *Dryopteris linneana* C.Chr.), the Oak Fern, is a rare plant of damp woods and shaded rocks on acid soils. It has not been seen in recent years in any of its stations around Dartmoor or in the South Hams, though it still occurs in Somerset.

BLECHNACEAE

Dryopteris dilatata (Hoffm.) A.Gray   Broad Buckler-fern
(*D. austriaca* (Jacq.) Woynar)
Widely distributed among rocks on heaths and moors, in woodlands and in hedges. It often attains considerable size, and is rather variable. Generally common. (1415)

Blechnum spicant (L.) Roth   Hard Fern
Widely distributed on well-drained acid soils, on heaths and moors as well as in hedgebanks and woodlands. Very common in suitable habitats. (1202)

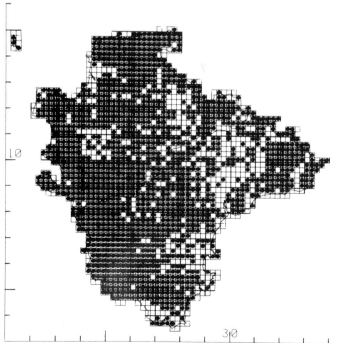

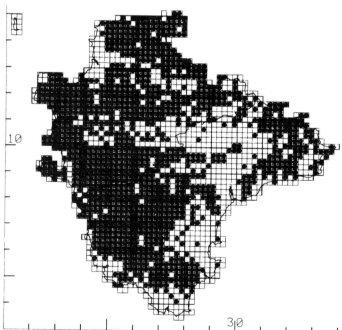

POLYPODIACEAE

Polypodium vulgare L.   Polypody
Occurs commonly on walls, rocks and in hedgerows, and sometimes as an epiphyte on trees, especially oak. (1669)

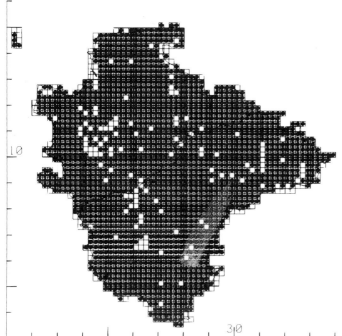

The species is frequently split into three, the segregates being treated as either species or subspecies:

Polypodium australe Fée, (*P. vulgare* L. var. *serratum* Willd.) is usually restricted to calcareous rocks and soils; it occurs on the limestone outcrops behind Torquay, at Chudleigh, by the upper ferry at Dartmouth and near Plymouth, while there is a single record from N. Devon. This species is diploid (2N).

Polypodium vulgare L. s.s. occurs on walls and in crevices of acid rocks, and frequently as an epiphyte. It is usually found above about 200 m, and is the commonest form on the higher moors and on tors. This species is tetraploid (4N).

Polypodium interjectum Shivas, (*P. vulgare* L. ssp. *prionodes* Rothm.), is the common lowland form; it grows on rocks, walls and in hedges, and sometimes as an epiphyte, and may reach a considerable size. It is an allopolyploid (6N) and is believed to have arisen from a hybrid between the two previous species.

Polypodium x mantoniae (Rothm.) Shivas, (*P. interjectum* x *vulgare*), is intermediate morphologically between its parents. It has been recorded from Lundy, but can probably be found wherever the parents grow together.

MARSILIACEAE

Pilularia globulifera L., the Pillwort, usually grows in the margins of lakes and pools on peaty, acid soils. It was recorded in 1829 on Woodbury Common, has not been found since and is undoubtedly extinct.

SALVINIACEAE

Azolla filiculoides Lam.
Introduced; a native of America, now naturalised in several places, particularly in the Tiverton Canal, where it is often locally abundant, but varies considerably in quantity from year to year. It also occurs in ditches and artificial ponds, to which it may be carried either by waste water or by birds. (11)

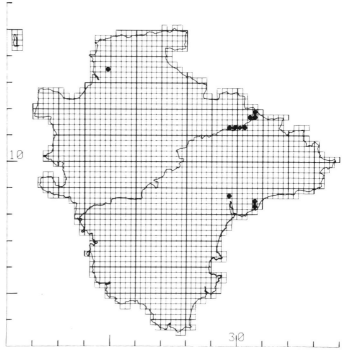

PINACEAE

Picea abies (L.) Karst., the Norway Spruce, and **Picea sitchensis** (Bong.) Carrière, the Sitka Spruce, are both planted quite frequently, the latter especially on Dartmoor. Although young plants may appear in the vicinity of the parent, neither can be said to be truly naturalised.

Larix decidua Mill.   European Larch
Quite frequently planted and sometimes naturalised. Widely scattered over the county, usually in plantations or woods. (330)

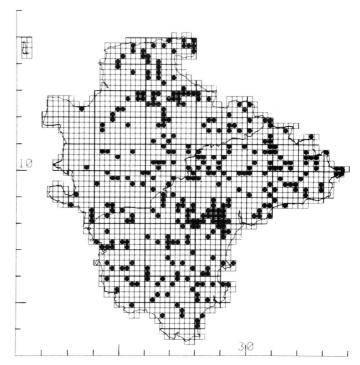

Larix kaempferi (Lamb.) Carrière   Japanese Larch
(*L. leptolepis* (Sieb. & Zucc.) Endl.)
In plantations and as single trees in woods and hedges; not
infrequently planted, but scarcely naturalised. (48)

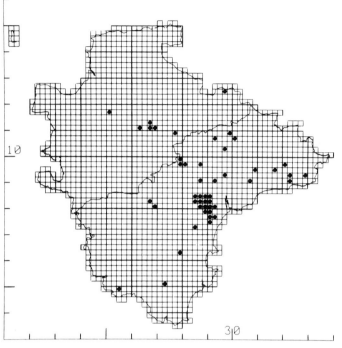

Larix x eurolepis Henry, (*L. decidua* x *kaempferi*), is planted
quite frequently; seedlings usually only occur in forests or
where the parents are planted together.

Pinus sylvestris L.   Scots Pine
Introduced in Devon. Widely planted and found in either woods
or scrub or as single trees in hedges. Quite common all over the
county, usually in rather base-poor habitats, where it may seed
itself. (616)

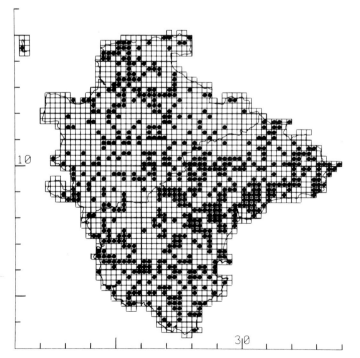

Several other species of **Pinus,** especially **P. mugo** Turra, the
Mountain Pine, **P. nigra** Arnold ssp. **nigra,** the Austrian Pine and
ssp. **laricio** (Poir.) Palibin, the Corsican Pine, have been planted,
sometimes on a considerable scale; they often propagate
themselves in the immediate vicinity of their parents. **P. pinaster**
Ait., the Maritime Pine, is sometimes planted in rather poor soils
or near the sea and can be more or less naturalised.

Pseudotsuga menziesii (Mirb.) Franco   Douglas Fir
Quite frequently planted in plantations and woodlands, but
scarcely naturalised. (46)

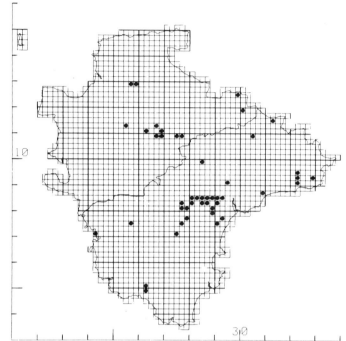

Other conifers which have been planted include **Tsuga heterophylla** (Rafin.) Sarg., the Western Hemlock, **Sequoia sempervirens** (Lamb.) Endl., the Redwood, and **Thuja plicata,** the
Western Red Cedar, and several species of **Abies**. These are
mostly found in parks but sometimes grown for forestry on
a small scale. Species of **Cupressus** and **Chamaecyparis,**
especially **Chamaecyparis lawsoniana** (A.Murr.) Parl., the
Lawson's Cypress, are quite frequently grown in parks and
gardens, and may be found rarely as isolated plants in
semi-natural habitats, often from wind-borne seed.

TAXACEAE

Taxus baccata L.   Yew
Perhaps native in woods and scrub on the chalk, but frequently
planted and widely distributed, usually fairly near habitations
and especially characteristic of churchyards. Bird-sown plants
occur frequently in scrub and hedges and sometimes on walls
and bridges. (208)

Salix alba L.   White Willow
Perhaps native; it occurs on river banks, stream-sides and in
damp woodland, apparently preferring more base-rich soils
than *S. fragilis*. Widely distributed, but never common and
probably often planted. (97)

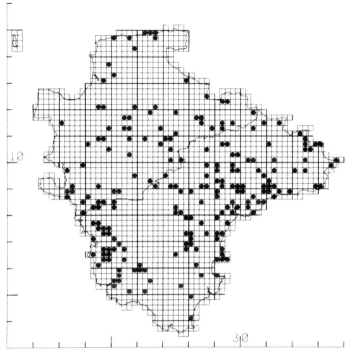

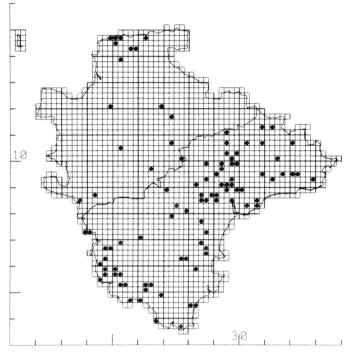

SALICACEAE

Salix fragilis L.   Crack Willow
Most commonly found by streams and rivers, and sometimes in
wet marshes; widely distributed, but probably often planted.
(170)

Salix triandra L.   Almond Willow
Along streams and rivers and in marshy habitats; not often
recorded and probably quite rare. Most frequent in the Exe and
Tamar valleys, where it is probably often planted. (16)

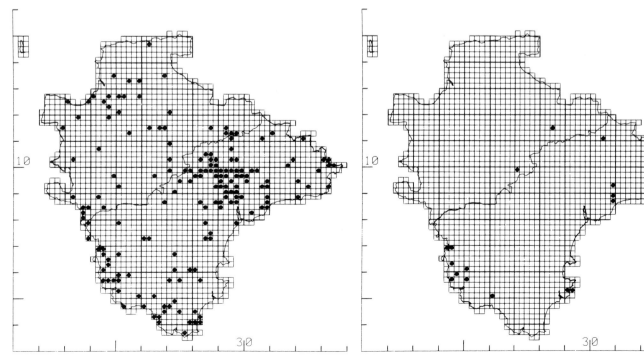

11

Salix cinerea L.   Common Sallow
(inc. *S. atrocinerea* Brot.)
The commonest of the willows, widely distributed in damper
habitats in woods and hedges and on heaths, by ponds and
streams, and in marshy places. Common throughout the
county, and often an early coloniser of neglected marshy fields
which later become wet woodland. (1453)
Our plant is ssp. **oleifolia** Macreight.

Salix caprea L.   Goat Willow
Occurs commonly in woods, hedges and on waste ground;
quite widely distributed in damp or marshy habitats, and sometimes in drier places as well, and rather more lowland than the
two previous species. Generally in better-drained and more
calcareous habitats than *S. cinerea*. (921)

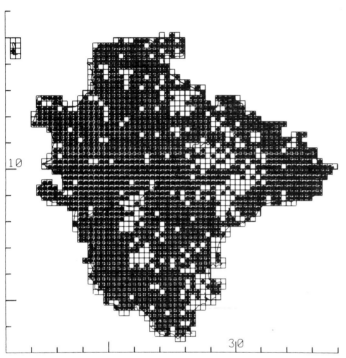

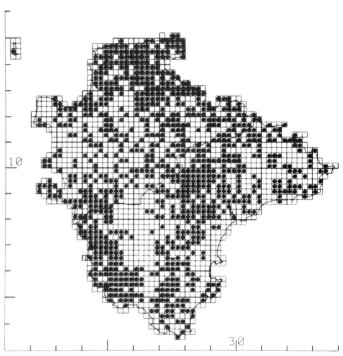

Salix aurita L.   Eared Sallow
Widely distributed on neutral or rather acid soils in woods,
hedges and scrub. Quite frequent in damper habitats in N.W.
Devon, and also on heaths in E. Devon, but generally rather less
common than it used to be. (665)

Salix repens L.   Creeping Willow
Not uncommon in wet moorland habitats in the north and west
of the county, and also frequent on heathy commons in the east;
otherwise rare, mostly in moorland. (155)

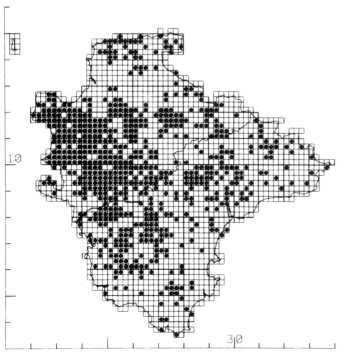

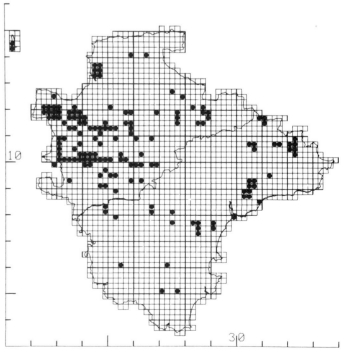

Ssp. **argentea** (Sm.) A. & G.Camus, (*S. arenaria* L.), is confined
to maritime dune systems. It is common in the dune-slacks of
Braunton Burrows and occurs in similar habitats elsewhere.

Salix viminalis L.   Common Osier
Commonly planted as an osier, it occurs by streams and in
marshes, fens and roadside hedges, as well as artificial habitats.
Quite frequent, but native plants are rather rare. (80)

Populus alba L.   White Poplar
Introduced; a native of Europe. Frequently planted in woods and
plantations, and sometimes found as isolated trees. Although
seedlings may establish for a short while, it does not appear to
be truly naturalised. (18)

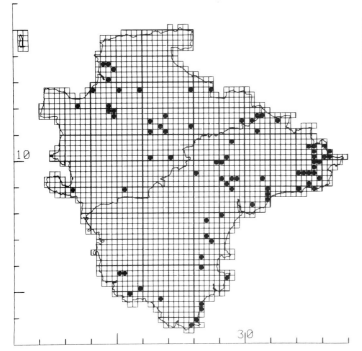

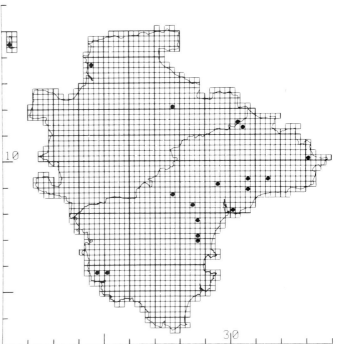

Salix purpurea L.   Purple Osier
This has been recorded near the railway bridge at Totnes, from a
similar site at North Tawton, and on railway sidings; it is
certainly introduced, but its provenance is not known. (3)

Salix pentandra L., the Bay Willow, is said to have been planted
in scattered localities along streams and in marshes, but there
are no recent records.

Salix Hybrids
Many species of **Salix** form hybrids readily, and quite a number
of these have been recorded from Devon, but it has been
possible neither to reassess their status nor to discover if they
persist in their original localities.
Salix x ambigua Ehrh., (*S. aurita* x *repens*), is recorded from
heathy scrub and wood margins from both vice-counties;
Salix x capreola A.Kerner ex Anderss., (*S. aurita* x *caprea*), has
been reported from Devon without locality; it occurs in woods,
scrub and hedges in much of Britain;
Salix x mollissima Hoffm. ex Elwert., (*S. triandra* x *viminalis*), is
often planted in southern Britain, though it seems unlikely to
occur naturally;
Salix x multinervis Doell., (*S. aurita* x *cinerea*), is probably not
uncommon in Devon, as it is quite frequent in scrub and wood
margins on acid soils over much of Britain;
Salix x reichartii A.Kerner, (*S. caprea* x *cinerea*), occurs in
similar habitats to the previous hybrid, and is also probably
quite frequent in the county;
Salix x rubens Schrank, (*S. alba* x *fragilis*), is recorded from S.
Devon, but its distribution is not known;
Salix x sericans Tausch ex A.Kerner, (*S. caprea* x *viminalis*), is
recorded from hedgerows, scrub and waste ground in much of
Britain, and has been found at Teignmouth;
Salix x smithiana Willd., (*S. cinerea* x *viminalis*), occurs in
hedges, scrub, osier beds and waste ground over much of
Britain, and has been reported from both vice-counties;
Salix x speciosa Host., (*S. fragilis* x *triandra*), which is very
similar to *S. fragilis,* is well known from S. Devon.

Populus canescens (Ait.) Sm.   Grey Poplar
Introduced in Devon. Generally found as a planted tree in wet
woodland and hedges. Not at all common, though recorded
from a number of sites throughout the county. (59)

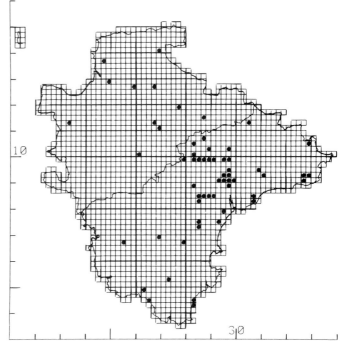

Populus tremula L.   Aspen
Widely distributed in woods and scrub, especially on clayey soils. Never common and probably planted in many sites, but tending to spread by suckers. (144)

Populus x canadensis Moench, (*P. deltoides* Marsh x *nigra*), the Black Italian Poplar, is occasionally planted, as it is one of the fastest-growing poplars. There are several cultivars some not readily distinguishable from *P. nigra*. (16)

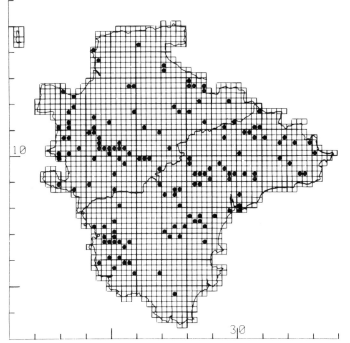

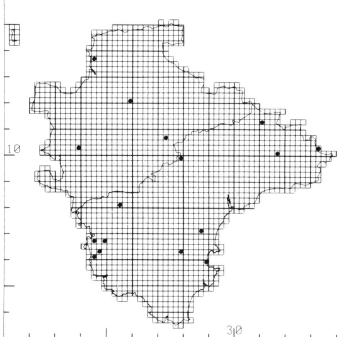

Populus x gileadensis Rouleau   Balm of Gilead
Introduced; of unknown origin. Sometimes planted by streams and in wet woodland, and also spreading to some extent by suckers. (1)

Populus nigra L.   Black Poplar
Introduced in Devon. Planted in several localities on streamsides and in damp scrub, but not naturalised. Some records may be the result of confusion with cv. *italica* Duroi, (*P. italica* (Duroi) Moench), the Lombardy Poplar, which is often planted. (64)

MYRICACEAE

Myrica gale L.   Bog Myrtle, Sweet Gale
Locally abundant in lowland peat bogs and wet heaths, but very much less common than formerly as a result of land drainage and the destruction of heathland. Most frequent on the lowland heaths east of Dartmoor, and also occurring on the Pebble-bed commons in the east of the county. (22)

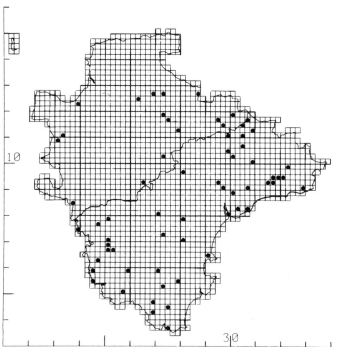

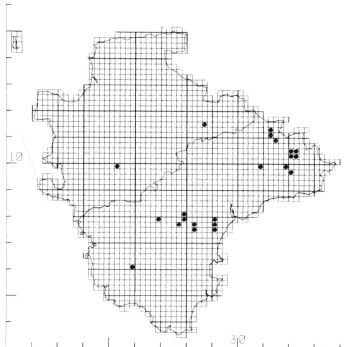

JUGLANDACEAE

Juglans regia L. Walnut
Introduced; a native of S. Europe and W. Asia. Occasionally planted, sometimes for its fruits or as a decorative tree; not naturalised. (8)

BETULACEAE

Betula pendula Roth Silver Birch
Common and widely distributed in woods, scrub and on heaths, and particularly abundant on light dry acid soils and shallow peat. Not so frequent in the north-west, where it is largely replaced by *B. pubescens*. (865)

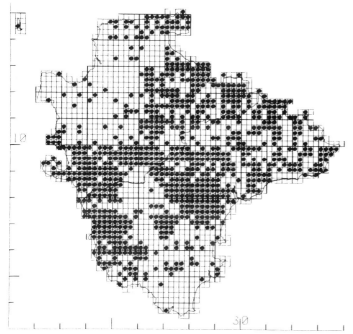

Alnus glutinosa (L.) Gaertn. Alder
A major component of the wooded margins of streams and rivers, but also occurring in wet woods. Common and generally distributed, though not at high altitudes and rather rare near the coast. (1223)

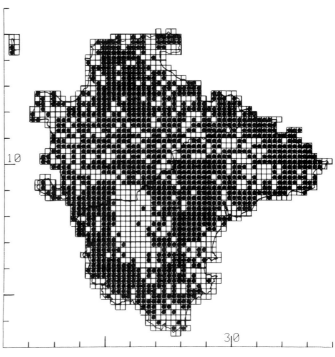

Betula pubescens Ehrh. Birch
Common and widely distributed in woods and on heaths, and able to withstand rather wetter or colder soils than *B. pendula*, but the two species often grow together. (642)

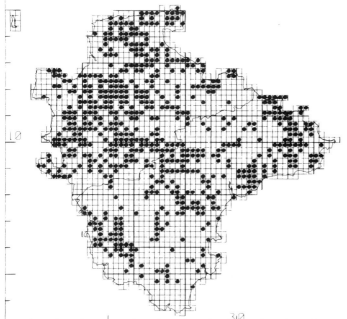

The hybrid between these two species has not been recorded for the county, but it is extremely difficult to recognise.

CORYLACEAE

Carpinus betulus L. Hornbeam
Locally common in woods and hedgerows; perhaps often planted in hedges, as it is often found in almost pure stands. Widespread, and fairly common in the west, but only occasional in the south-east. (180)

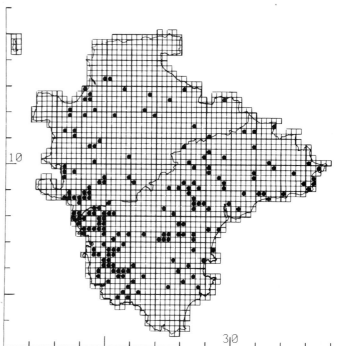

Corylus avellana L.   Hazel
A very common species of hedges, scrub and as an understorey
in woods, especially on the more base-rich soils. Throughout
the county, generally avoiding the high ground of Dartmoor and
Exmoor though reaching over 300 m (1000 ft.) in the West
Okement valley, and also rather less common in the immediate
vicinity of the coast. (1635)

Castanea sativa Mill.   Spanish Chestnut, Sweet Chestnut
Introduced; a native of Europe. Quite frequently planted in
woodlands and elsewhere, and apparently naturalised in some
places, preferring rather acid but well-drained soils. Most
frequent in the southern half of the county. (532)

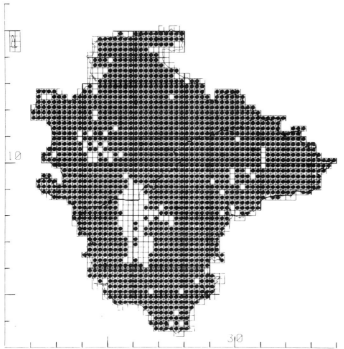

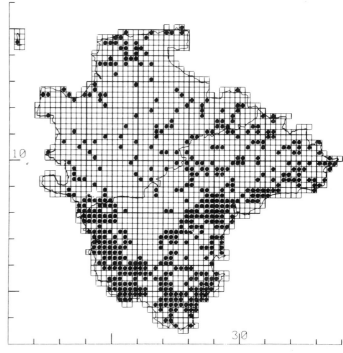

FAGACEAE

Fagus sylvatica L.   Beech
Probably introduced in Devon, but a common and widely
distributed tree which locally forms pure woodland stands, is
rather frequent in acid woods around Dartmoor, and is also a
component of lowland deciduous woodland. Much planted for
hedges, shelter belts and snow-breaks in N. Devon, including
Exmoor, to a lesser extent elsewhere. (1548)

Quercus ilex L.   Holm Oak
Introduced; a native of the Mediterranean region. Commonly
planted and quite extensively naturalised, particularly in coastal
districts, e.g. in the Axmouth-Lyme Regis Undercliffs Nature
Reserve and around Torquay, as it withstands salt-laden air.
(138)

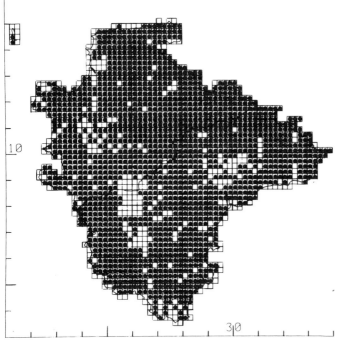

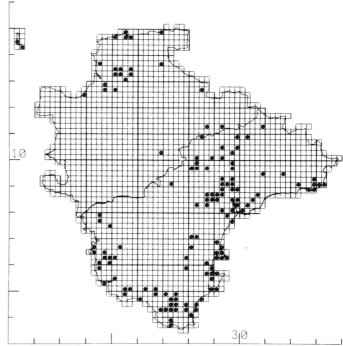

Quercus cerris L. Turkey Oak
Introduced; a native of Europe. Not uncommonly planted and sometimes naturalised. Intermediates between this species and *Q. petraea* appear to be not uncommon where the parents grow together. (278)

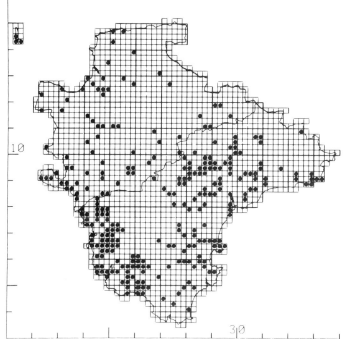

Quercus petraea (Matt.) Liebl. Durmast Oak, Sessile Oak
An important component of woodlands on the more acid soils, especially in steep-sided valleys down to sea-level in the south-west. Dominant on the Culm, and locally on acid soils in E. Devon. Quite common in scrub and hedgerows, but less so than *Q. robur*. (702)

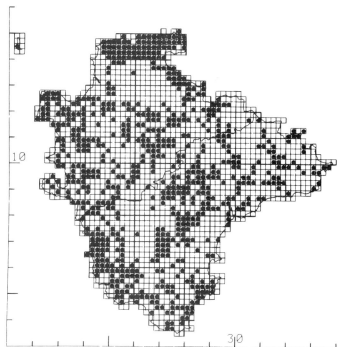

Quercus robur L. Common Oak, Pedunculate Oak
Common and widely distributed in woods, scrub and hedgerows. It tends to predominate on the granite, and on the better soils in the lowlands, and is by far the commonest species of the uplands west of Dartmoor forming almost pure woods in a few sheltered valleys in higher parts of the moor. (1549)

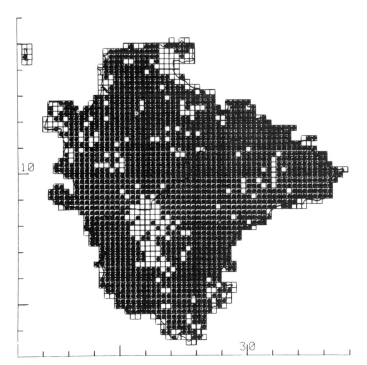

The problem of distinguishing between these two species of *Quercus* was highlighted by Wigston (1975), though it has long been known that intermediates between them occur (these have been placed in **Quercus x rosacea** Bechst.). The situation has been shown to be more complex than this, and that while it is possible to recognise populations which can be described as 'good *robur*' or 'good *petraea*', all stages of intermediates between these exist as a result of hybridisation and back-crossing or introgression towards both parents. This is particularly true of hedgerow plants which, although they can often be assigned to one or other of the parent species without too much difficulty, frequently show some intermediate characters.

Species of the genus **Nothofagus**, which is native in Australasia and S. America, are being cultivated on an increasing scale as their suitability for forestry becomes apparent. As they seem to grow rapidly and well, it must only be a matter of time before some become naturalised. **Nothofagus dombeyi** (Mirbel) Blume, a native of Chile, has been planted at Tavistock (Wigston, 1979b).

ULMACEAE

Ulmus glabra Huds.   Wych Elm
Widely distributed throughout the county, in woods, scrub and
hedgerows, but never common, though sometimes locally
frequent. (627)

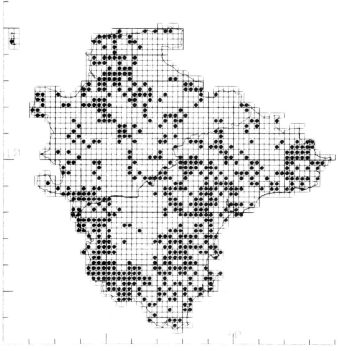

Ulmus minor Mill.   Elm
(*U. glabra* Mill. non Huds., *U. carpinifolia* G.Suckow, *U. stricta*
(Ait.) Lindl.)
Recorded from quite a number of sites, chiefly in W. Devon, and
mostly as *U. stricta*, the Cornish Elm (*U. carpinifolia* var.
cornubiensis (Weston) Rehd.). It is also not uncommonly
planted, e.g. around Exeter. (107)

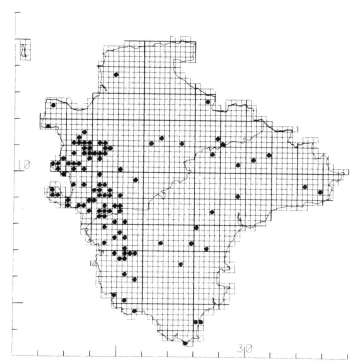

Ulmus procera Salisb.   English Elm
In woods, scrub and especially hedgerows, where it may form
substantial trees. Widely distributed, but particularly frequent in
the south and east, though largely killed by Dutch Elm disease in
the 1970's. (898)

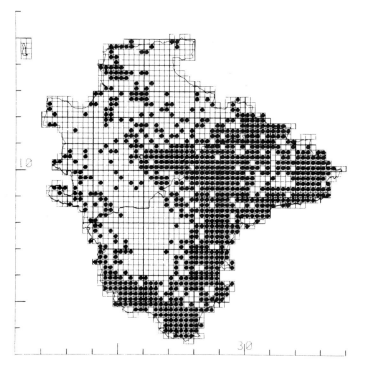

The Jersey Elm, (*U. glabra* x *minor, U.* x *hollandica* x *angustifolia*) has been recorded from S. Devon, but is widely planted. A
hybrid between *U. glabra* and *U. stricta* has been recorded from
Doddiscombsleigh, but in view of the variability of the latter
parent, its identity must be considered suspect. Many of the
parents of the elm hybrids are now included within the concept
of *U. minor* and in consequence, the hybridisation pattern has
been much simplified.
As a result of the recent outbreak of Dutch Elm Disease, many of
the arboreal elms have been killed and those that remain are
continuing to be attacked, though at a decreasing rate. Hedgerow plants, with their small trunks, appear to be less susceptible, though they are not immune. There is evidence for some
regeneration of *U. procera* from suckers and epicormic shoots,
while *U. glabra* appears less susceptible than *U. procera*. It is
clear that the disease will leave the elm population of the county
very much reduced, but it is not yet possible to predict the
structure of the population or distribution of the species.

18

CANNABACEAE

Humulus lupulus L.   Hop
In hedges and waste ground, frequently only noticeable later in the year when it climbs the stay-wires of telegraph poles and other supports. Quite common and widely distributed, but probably less frequent than formerly, when it was often cultivated for local use in brewing. (265)

Urtica urens L.   Small Nettle
In fields, cultivated places and waste ground; widely distributed and fairly frequent around the Exe estuary, but generally not common, no doubt reflecting changes in agricultural practices over the years. (139)

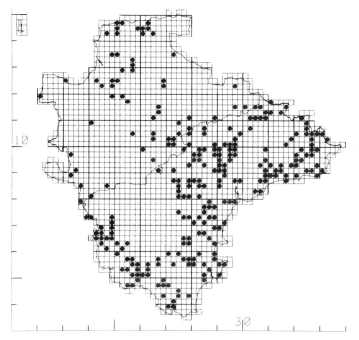

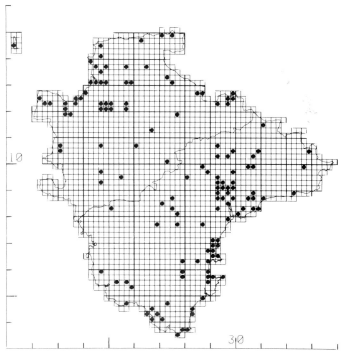

Cannabis sativa L., the Hemp, is a casual, occasionally found in waste places or as a bird-seed alien, and sometimes, illegally, cultivated.

Urtica pilulifera L., the Roman Nettle, is a very rare annual alien for which there are no recent records.

URTICACEAE

Urtica dioica L.   Stinging Nettle
Common and generally distributed in woods, scrub, the margins of fields and in waste places. Particularly characteristic of nitrogenous and phosphate-rich habitats, and thus common around farmsteads, rubbish dumps and under rookeries, etc., and also on the moors where animals congregate for shelter or food. Throughout the county, though local on the moors. (1751)

Parietaria judaica L.   Pellitory-of-the-Wall
(*P. diffusa* Mert. & Koch)
On old walls and the sides of buildings, occasionally in rocky hedgebanks and also on natural rock outcrops on Berry Head. Local, though often abundant where it occurs, and absent from many apparently suitable habitats, especially in the middle of the county; it has been suggested it may respond to maritime influences. (341)

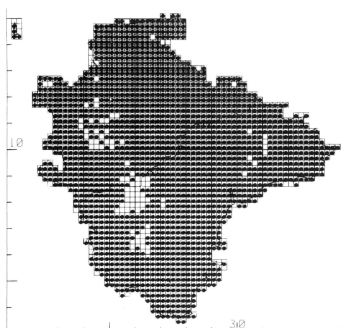

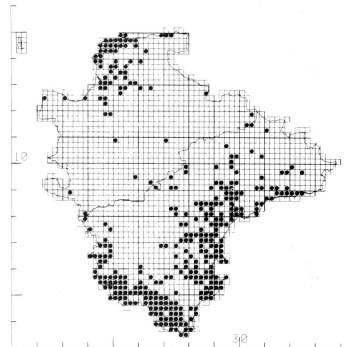

Soleirolia soleirolii (Req.) Dandy
                    Mind-your-own-business, Mother-of-thousands
(*Helxine soleirolii* Req.)
Introduced. A native of the Mediterranean region which has been commonly planted in rock-gardens and cool greenhouses, whence it has become naturalised in damp wall crevices and banks. Local, mainly in the vicinity of villages or habitations. (144)

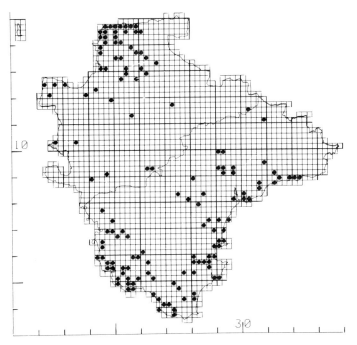

LORANTHACEAE

Viscum album L.   Mistletoe
Semi-parasitic on the branches of various, usually deciduous, trees, especially apple and poplar. Very local in its distribution, and apparently much less frequent than formerly. Some records are no doubt introductions from imported plants. (14)

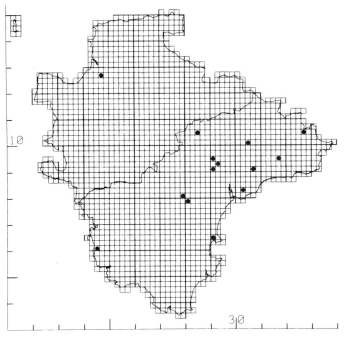

ARISTOLOCHIACEAE

Asarum europaeum L. and **Aristolochia clematitis** L. were both recorded in Fl. Dev., but there are no recent records and both were probably escapes from cultivation.

POLYGONACEAE

Polygonum oxyspermum Meyer & Bunge ex Ledeb.
                                                    Ray's Knotgrass
(*P. raii* Bab.)
On sandy and shingly shores, and waste places near the sea. At one time quite common, particularly in S. Devon, but now rarely seen. Probably suffering from disturbance on much-frequented beaches, though it may have been under-recorded as a result of its similarity to *P. aviculare*. (6)
Our plant is referred to ssp. **raii** D.A.Webb & Chater.

Polygonum aviculare L.   Knotgrass
Common and widely distributed on waste and cultivated ground, roadsides and especially characteristic of gateways and other trampled habitats. It also occurs on shores, but is absent from the higher moors. (1521)

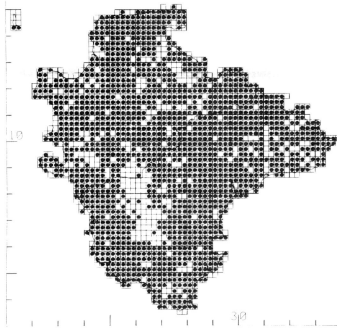

Polygonum arenastrum Bor.   Small-leaved Knotgrass
(*P. aequale* Lindm.)
In generally similar habitats to *P. aviculare*, particularly in cultivated ground, roadsides and waste places, though perhaps preferring drier sites. The paucity of records could be genuine, but probably reflects confusion with the previous species. (27)

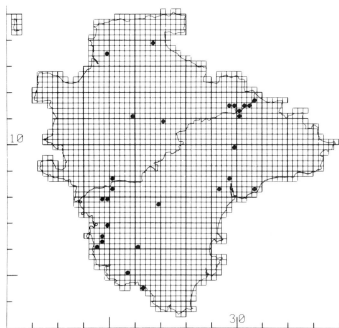

Polygonum mite Schrank
In marshy ground and beside streams and ditches. Apparently very rare, with only a single record from Harpford, by the R. Otter, in 1957. It has, perhaps, been confused with *P. hydropiper.* (1)

Polygonum hydropiper L.   Water-pepper
In damp and wet places, especially by the sides of ditches and streams. Common and widely distributed and, although at times abundant, perhaps less common than formerly as a result of land drainage. (1047)

Polygonum lapathifolium L.   Pale Persicaria
(inc. *P. nodosum* Pers., *P. pectinale* (Stokes) Druce)
In damp waste places and cultivated ground, and by streams and ponds. Moderately common, especially in the north-west of the county, but considerably less so than formerly, and absent from many areas. (306)

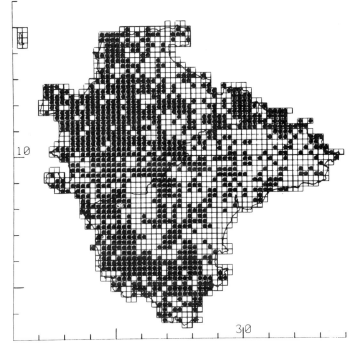

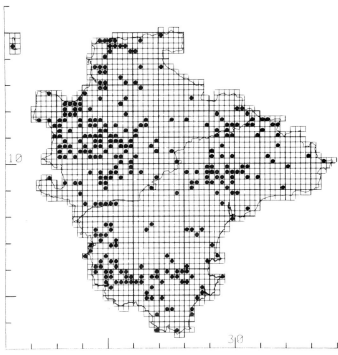

P. nodosum, the Large Persicaria, has been recorded from marshy places and waste ground at Braunton, Plymstock and in the Exe valley, but not recently. It is probably best regarded as a variant of *P. lapathifolium.*

Polygonum x lenticulare Hy, (*P. lapathifolium* x *persicaria*), has been recorded from S. Devon, but as both its parents are very variable, should be treated with much reserve until confirmed.

Polygonum amphibium L.   Amphibious Bistort
In ponds, canals and slow-flowing rivers, sometimes stranded by falling water levels; the erect form may occur along their margins. Local, but not uncommon in suitable sites and occasionally abundant. (72)

Polygonum persicaria L.   Spotted Persicaria
Common and fairly widely distributed in waste places and especially in cultivated ground on damper soils; absent from heaths and moorland. (1221)

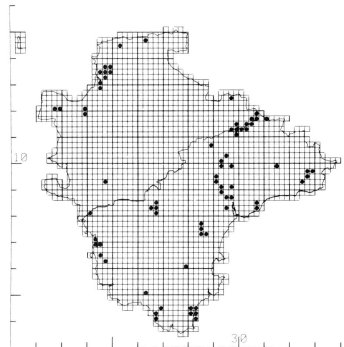

Polygonum bistorta L.   Snake-root
In damp meadows and pastures, sometimes by roadsides,
especially on acid soils. Most common in the north and west,
otherwise rather local; some records could be garden escapes.
(83)

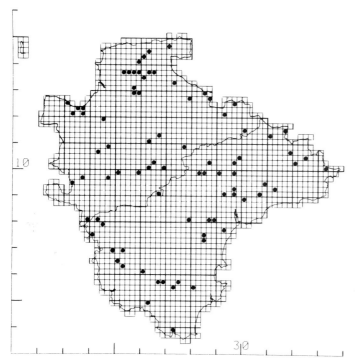

Polygonum campanulatum Hook.f.
Introduced; a native of the Himalayas which is sometimes
grown in gardens. There are records from Lustleigh and
Chudleigh Knighton, but it only seems to have persisted in the
former locality. (1)

Polygonum maritimum L., the Sea Knotgrass, has not been seen
at Braunton Burrows for several years, and it is probably now
extinct in Devon. **Polygonum minus** Huds., the Small Persicaria,
which used to occur in sandy and gravelly ground at Cullompton and Slapton, may still persist at Slapton, but has not been
found recently. **Polygonum sagittatum** L., which was collected
at Widecombe in 1940, and **Polygonum amplexicaule** D.Don,
which was collected in 1955 at Bicton, have not been seen since.

Fallopia convolvulus (L.) A.Löve   Black Bindweed
(*Polygonum convolvulus* L., *Bilderdyckia convolvulus* (L.) Dum.)
A weed of waste places, arable land and gardens. Not uncommon, and probably a persistent weed where it occurs, but rather
local. (404)

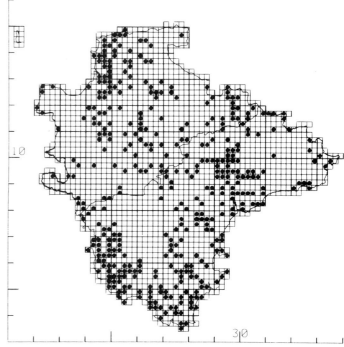

Polygonum polystachyum Wall. ex Meissn.
Introduced; a native of the Himalayas which probably escaped
from cultivation and has now become quite widely naturalised,
but it is not common, except along the old railway track between
Barnstaple and Lynton. (58)

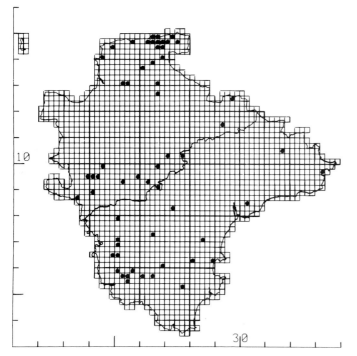

Fallopia dumetorum (L.) J.Holub, (*Polygonum dumetorum* L.,
Bilderdyckia dumetorum (L.) Dum.), is not known to occur in
Devon and all records are erroneous.

Bilderdyckia aubertii (L.Henry) Moldenke   Russian Vine
(*Polygonum baldschuanicum* auct.)
Introduced; a native of China and Tibet which is cultivated as a
vigorous woody climber. It has become naturalised in several
localities. (10)

Reynoutria sachalinensis (F. Schmidt) Nakai
(*Polygonum sachalinensis* F.Schmidt)
Introduced; a native of E. Asia which has become naturalised to
a limited extent. It appears as difficult to control as *R. japonica,*
but does not, as yet, present as serious a problem. (16)

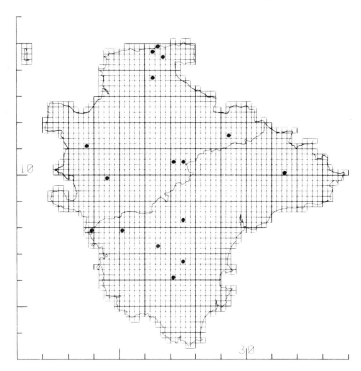

Reynoutria japonica Houtt.
(*Polygonum cuspidatum* Sieb. & Zucc.)
Introduced; a native of Japan which has become extensively
naturalised along roadsides, in scrub and waste places. It may
form dense stands and is becoming a serious and persistent
weed which is spreading rapidly, especially along river banks,
and is very difficult to control. (386)

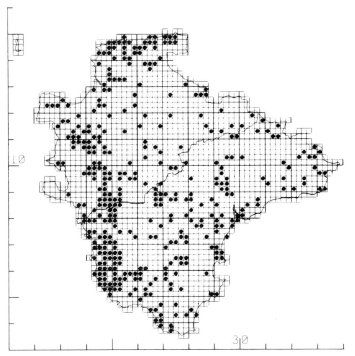

Fagopyrum esculentum Moench   Buckwheat
(*F. sagittatum* Gilib.)
Introduced; a native of Europe. A widely cultivated crop plant
which has been grown to a limited extent as food for pheasants.
Probably not naturalised. (11)

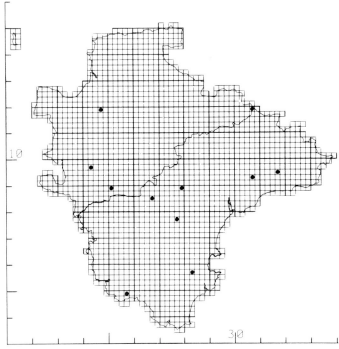

Fagopyrum tataricum (L.) Gaertn. was reported on one occasion
from Woolborough, in 1937; it can occur as a weed with the
previous species.

Rumex acetosella L.   Sheep's Sorrel
Common and widely distributed in dry heathland, poor pastures
and on rocks and walls. Strictly calcifuge, and probably most
common on the higher ground. (991)

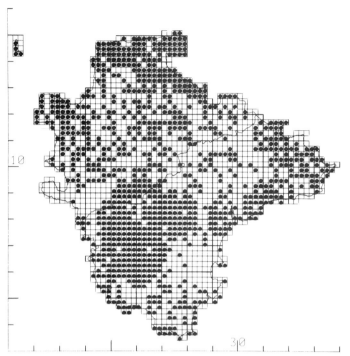

The closely related **R. tenuifolius** (Wallr.) A.Löve, which seems
to be confined to very poor acid soils, has been recorded from
the vicinty of Braunton.

Rumex acetosa L.   Sorrel
Widely distributed in moist meadows, grassland, woods,
hedges and similar habitats, and also occurring in waste
ground. It can be especially luxuriant near the coast. (1700)

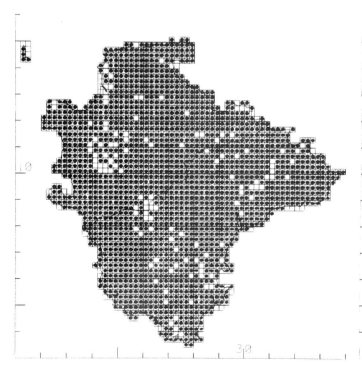

Rumex hydrolapathum Huds.   Great Water Dock
Along the margins of rivers and canals, sometimes in ditches
and other standing water. Never common, and apparently
confined to southern and eastern Devon, and most characteristic of the Exe valley and Slapton Ley. (13)

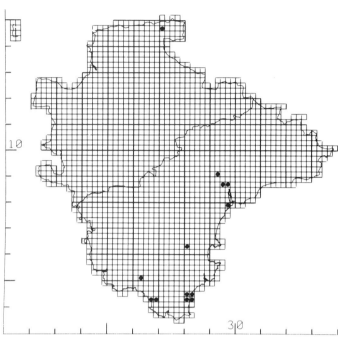

Rumex frutescens Thouars
(*R. cuneifolius* Campd.)
Introduced; a native of S. America which has become natural-
ised in parts of Braunton Burrows. (2)

Rumex alpinus L.   Monk's Rhubarb
Introduced; a native of C. and S. Europe which has been
recorded on one occasion from the eastern edge of Dartmoor.
(1)

Rumex crispus L.   Curled Dock
In pastures and the edges of fields, along roadsides, on shingle
beaches and in waste places, especially near the sea; a
widespread and often abundant plant which can become a
serious agricultural weed. (1233)

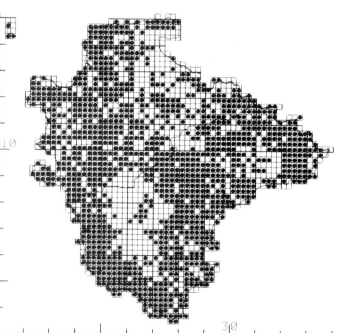

24

Rumex conglomeratus Murr.   Sharp Dock
In damp pastures and grassy roadsides, sometimes in woodlands. Widely distributed throughout the county, but absent
from considerable areas; only consistently present in the
vicinity of Plymouth. (687)

Rumex rupestris Le Gall   Shore Dock
Restricted to sea cliffs, maritime rocks and sandy or stony places
on the sea-shore. Recorded from Plymouth and Slapton, but it
used to be locally plentiful along the coast between Plymouth
and Prawle Point, and it could have been overlooked. (3)

Rumex pulcher L.   Fiddle Dock
In well-drained and base-rich grassland and waste places,
particularly on south- and south-west-facing slopes near the
sea. Quite frequent in S. Devon, and often some distance inland;
much less common in the north. (79)

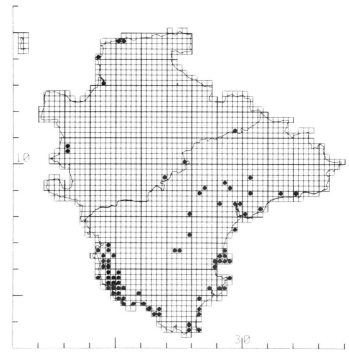

Rumex sanguineus L.   Red-veined Dock
(*R. condylodes* Bieb.)
On waste ground, roadsides and in hedges, and sometimes in
woods or scrub. Common and generally distributed. The
commonest form is var. *viridis*. (991)

Rumex obtusifolius L.   Broad-leaved Dock
Common and widely distributed in fields, roadsides and waste
places. Probably the commonest of the docks, and the most
generally distributed, though absent from the higher moors.
(1605)

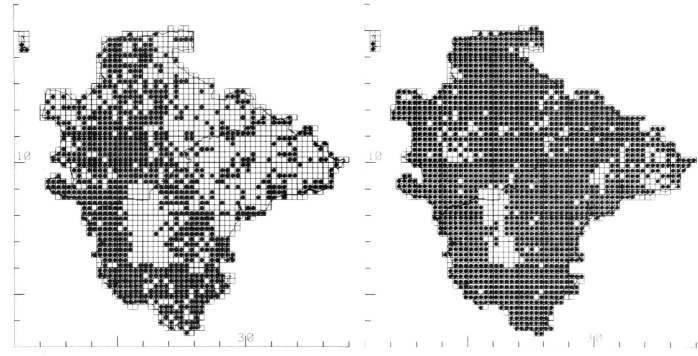

Rumex maritimus L., the Golden Dock, has been reported from Braunton, Exmouth and the Exeter Canal, but there are no recent records and it is probably extinct.

Rumex Hybrids.

Quite a number of *Rumex* hybrids are known to occur in Devon, though with very varying degrees of certainty.

Rumex x dufftii Hausskn., (*R. obtusifolius* x *sanguineus*), is intermediate between its parents and is found in the vicinity of woods. It has been recorded from Chagford.

Rumex x muretii Hausskn., (*R. conglomeratus* x *pulcher*), is very similar to *R. pulcher,* but an authentic specimen has been described from S. Devon (Lousley & Williams in Stace, 1975).

Rumex x ogulinensis Borbás, (*R. obtusifolius* x *pulcher*), is again intermediate between its parents and grows not uncommonly in dry habitats; it has been recorded from Branscombe Mouth, in S.E. Devon.

Rumex x pratensis Mert. & Koch, (*R. crispus* x *obtusifolius, R. x acutus* auct.) occurs commonly with the parents and is said to be quite frequent in the county (Fl. Dev.).

Rumex x pseudopulcher Hausskn., (*R. crispus* x *pulcher*), looks very much like *R. crispus* but has the tepals of its other parent; it has been recorded from dry, warm habitats in S. Devon.

Rumex x ruhmeri Hausskn., (*R. conglomeratus* x *sanguineus*), is rather an uncommon hybrid, but authentic material has been found in S. Devon (Lousley & Williams in Stace, 1975).

Rumex x sagorskii Hausskn., (*R. crispus* x *sanguineus*), is common along roadsides, the edges of woods and waste places in many parts of Britain, and has been found in S. Devon.

Rumex x wrightii Lousley, (*R. conglomeratus* x *frutescens*), has been recorded on one occasion from a dune-slack on Braunton Burrows (Lousley, 1953).

Ssp. **vulgaris,** with its axis conspicuously swollen at the hypocotyl, is cultivated in various forms, including the sugar beet and mangold, and sometimes escapes.

Hybrids between the two subspecies occur readily. As ssp. *maritima* can flower in its first year, hybridisation leads to bolting in field crops, but in general, hybrids are very difficult to recognise and are rarely reported.

Chenopodium bonus-henricus L.   Good King Henry
Introduced; a native of Europe. In waste ground and on roadsides, especially near habitations. In the past it was cultivated as a vegetable, and had become quite widely naturalised, but is now very local and rather rare. (34)

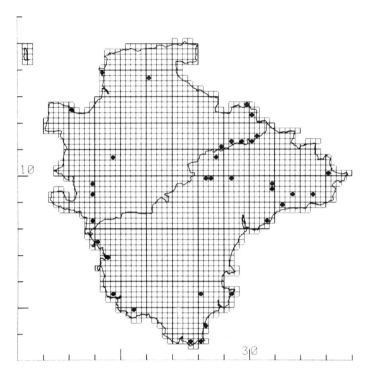

CHENOPODIACEAE

Beta vulgaris L.   Beet
Ssp. **maritima** (L.) Arcangeli, the Sea Beet, is common on rocky headlands, around estuaries and on sea shores. It is abundant in suitable habitats on both coasts, but rarely occurs inland. (183)

Chenopodium rubrum L.   Red Goosefoot
A fairly common weed of cultivated ground and waste places, which also occurs along the shore. It may be quite abundant in some nitrogen-rich habitats. (74)

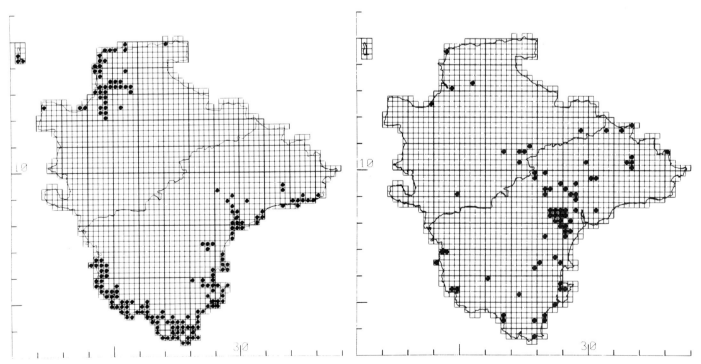

Chenopodium botryodes Sm., a species of muddy estuaries, has not been confirmed in Devon; it closely resembles some forms of *C. rubrum.*

Chenopodium polyspermum L.   All-seed
In nitrophilous habitats in waste and cultivated ground. Rather uncommon, but quite generally distributed. (148)

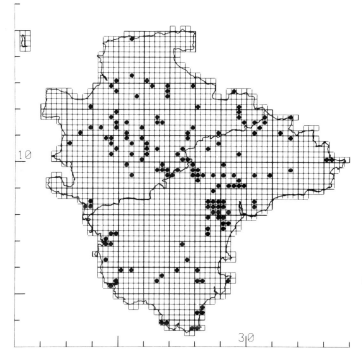

Chenopodium album L.   Fat Hen
A common weed of agricultural land and waste places, especially in nitrogen-rich habitats. A rather variable species, often locally abundant. (1060)

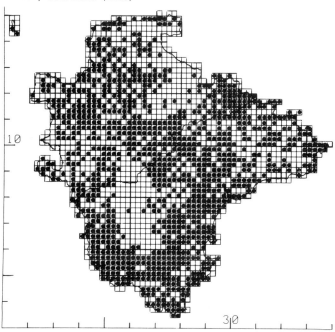

A number of other species of **Chenopodium** have been recorded from time to time. **C. urbicum** L., the Upright Goosefoot, has been reported from nitrogen-rich habitats in various parts of the county; **C. glaucum** L., the Oak-leaved Goosefoot, has also been reported in the past but like **C. opulifolium** Schrad. ex Koch & Ziz, which has been found as a casual along roadsides and in waste places, none of these have been found recently. The only record for **C. hybridum** L. in Devon is very old and probably erroneous, and there is also no evidence for the occurrence of **C. ficifolium** Sm., the Fig-leaved Goosefoot. Several other species have been reported, especially as wool aliens, but none of them seem to have persisted. These include **C. leptophyllum** (Moq.) S.Wats., from N. America, **C. hircinum** Schrad. from S. America, and **C. ambrosioides** L. (*C. anthelminticum* auct.), **C. berlandieri** Moq. and **C. capitatum** (L.) Aschers. from Europe.

Chenopodium vulvaria L.   Stinking Goosefoot
In waste places, arable fields and gardens. Very rare, usually near the sea. (2)

Chenopodium murale L.   Nettle-leaved Goosefoot
In waste places, often near buildings and the coast, particularly on light soils. Rare in the north, and only a little more frequent in the south, and seldom seen nowadays. (36)

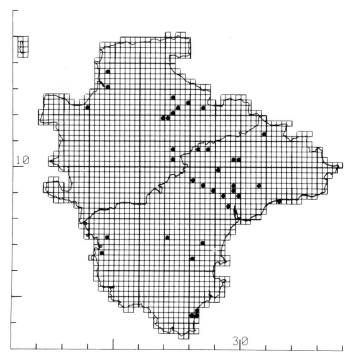

Atriplex hortensis L.   Orache
Introduced; a native of Europe, where it is widely cultivated as a vegetable. Sometimes recorded as a casual, but scarcely naturalised. (1)

Atriplex laciniata L.   Frosted Orache
In sandy and gravelly shores, often as a component of the strandline flora. Very local and rare, but known from Dawlish Warren and Braunton Burrows. (8)

Atriplex patula L.   Common Orache
In cultivated and waste ground and along roadsides, especially near the sea. Very variable, according to the availability of water and nutrients. Fairly common and generally distributed. (484)

Atriplex patula L.   Common Orache

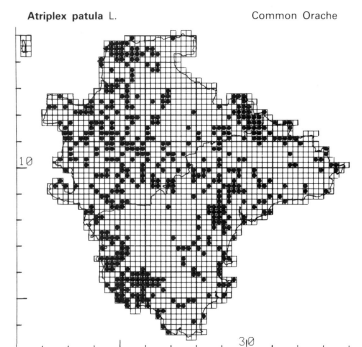

Atriplex glabriuscula Edmonst.   Babington's Orache

Atriplex halimus L. is a shrub which has been planted in a few places around the Exe estuary and elsewhere, and may still persist, but has not been recorded recently. **A littoralis** L., the Shore Orache, probably does not occur in Devon.

Atriplex prostrata Bouch. ex DC.   Hastate Orache
(*A. hastata* auct. non L.)
In waste and arable land, where it may be common and sometimes abundant, especially near the sea. (257)

Halimione portulacoides (L.) Aellen   Sea Purslane
(*Atriplex portulacoides* L.)
In salt-marshes, especially along the margins of drainage channels, and in estuaries, ordinarily flooded at high-water. Locally common and often abundant in suitable habitats. (47)

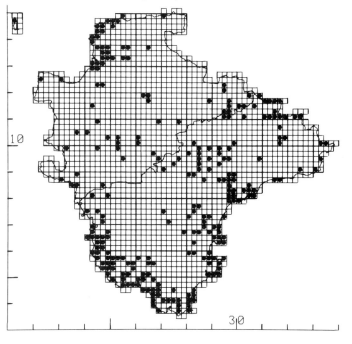

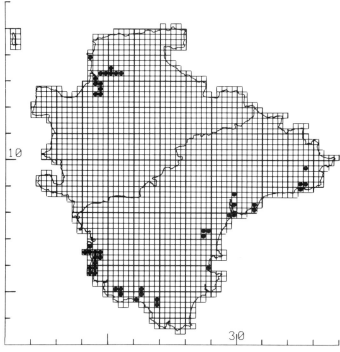

Salicornia
The existing accounts of this very difficult genus are often contradictory, and the limits of the species are far from clear.

Atriplex glabriuscula Edmonst.   Babington's Orache
On coasts, especially sandy shores and estuaries, usually just above high-water mark. Locally common, though some records may refer to one of the two preceding species, with some forms of which it is rather readily confused. (48)

Salicornia europaea L.   Sea Samphire, Glasswort
(inc. *S. stricta* Dum.)
In open sandy mud in salt-marshes and estuaries, usually at the lower levels. Probably not very common, but its distribution is uncertain.

Salicornia europaea L.   Sea Samphire, Glasswort

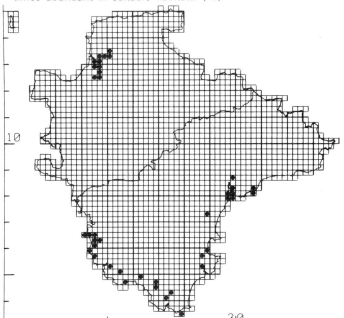

Salicornia ramosissima J.Woods
(inc. *S. smithiana* Moss, *S. prostrata* Pall.)
In salt-marshes and on mud-flats, avoiding the lowest levels.
Generally common in suitable habitats.

Salicornia dolichostachya Moss
The principal coloniser of low-level mud-flats and muddy sand,
and with a very varied habit. Probably not uncommon, and
known to occur in the Exe, Otter and Teign estuaries and
probably more generally distributed, but it is not clear how well
it has been distinguished from *S. europaea*.

Salicornia perennis Mill.   Perennial Glasswort
Not uncommon in the middle levels of salt-marshes around the
south coast, including the Exe estuary, and in the Taw-Torridge
estuary, but its present distribution is not well known.

Salicornia pusilla J.Woods, (*S. disarticulata* Moss), has been
reported from both Dawlish and Braunton (Fl. Dev.), but there is
no recent confirmation of this.

S. x marshallii Druce nom. nud., (*S. pusilla* x *ramosissima*), has
been recorded from the upper levels of a salt-marsh in S. Devon
(Dalby in Stace, 1975).

Suaeda maritima (L.) Dum.   Annual Seablite
In salt-marshes and along strand-lines. Common and sometimes abundant in suitable habitats. (40)

Salsola kali L.   Saltwort
Largely confined to the strand-lines of sandy shores. Most
frequent in N. Devon around Braunton and Northam Burrows;
rare elsewhere, and absent from many apparently suitable
habitats. (17)

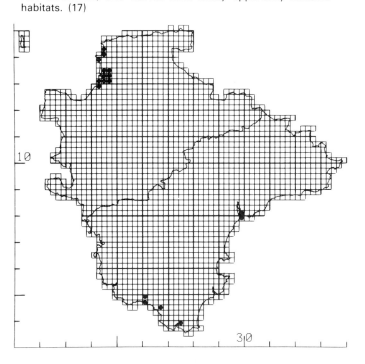

AMARANTHACEAE

Amaranthus retroflexus L.
Introduced; a native of N. America which occurs sporadically as
a garden weed and is sometimes found as a wool alien. (2)

Other species of **Amaranthus** are found occasionally, including
A. caudatus with its long pendent red inflorescences, either as
escapes from cultivation or around rubbish tips.

AIZOACEAE

Carpobrotus edulis (L.) N.E.Br.   Hottentot Fig
Introduced; a native of S. Africa, now naturalised along sea cliffs
in various places along the coasts of both N. and S. Devon, and
often very abundant where it occurs. (16)

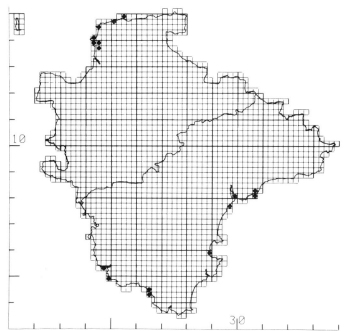

PORTULACACEAE

Montia fontana L.   Water Blinks
Typically a plant of wet habitats, stream-sides, wet flushes and moist pastures, but also occurring in a stunted form on dry banks and hillsides, especially those facing west. Generally common, but always on acid soils. (329)

Montia sibirica (L.) Howell

Four subspecies have been described, of which ssp. *fontana* does not occur in southern England.

Ssp. **chondrosperma** (Fenzl) Walters seems to be the commonest in Devon, in both wet and dry habitats, even though Perring & Sell (1962) give only a few records from the south of the county.

Ssp. **amporitana** Sennen, (*M. fontana* var. *intermedia* Beeby), has been identified from several localities around Dartmoor and Exmoor and elsewhere, but its distribution is not well known.

Ssp. **variabilis** Walters also has a few records, mostly in the north, but it has not been found recently.

These subspecies are separated mostly by the sculpturing on the testa, but this is not infallible, and intermediates occur not uncommonly. Further details can be found in Walters (1953).

Montia perfoliata (Donn. ex Willd.) Howell
(*Claytonia perfoliata* Donn. ex Willd.)
Introduced. A native of N. America, occasionally established on waste and cultivated ground, especially on sandy soils. (2)

Montia sibirica (L.) Howell
(*Claytonia alsinoides* Sims, *C. sibirica* L.)
Introduced; a native of N. America, now widely naturalised in damp woods and shaded stream-sides, occasionally in hedges. It has been spreading rapidly in recent years and can now be found along the banks of most water-courses in the county, especially on Dartmoor and Exmoor. (267)

CARYOPHYLLACEAE

Arenaria balearica L.
Introduced; a native of the western Mediterranean islands which is sometimes grown in rock-gardens and on damp walls. It has become naturalised in scattered localities on walls and in crevices, mostly in S. Devon. (34)

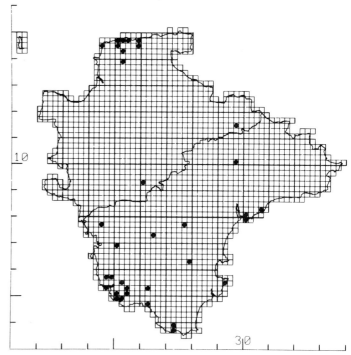

Arenaria serpyllifolia L.   Thyme-leaved Sandwort
A plant of dry, sandy walls and similar habitats. Quite widely distributed but never common, and found mostly in the south. (244)

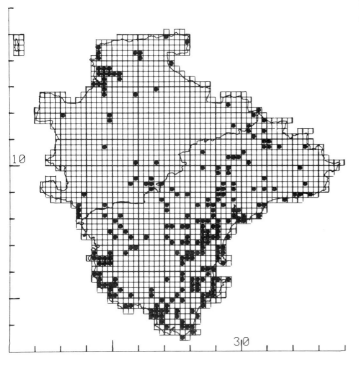

Moehringia trinervia (L.) Clairv.   Three-nerved Sandwort
In damp hedges and well-drained woodland, usually on base-rich soils. Reasonably common in suitable habitats. (740)

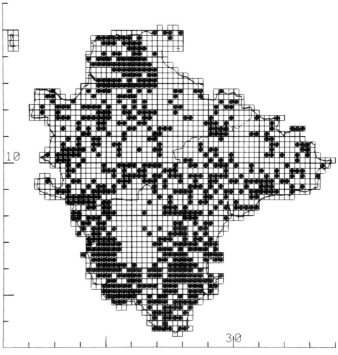

Arenaria leptoclados (Reichenb.) Guss.   Sandwort
In similar habitats to *A. serpyllifolia,* and sometimes more common than this species, with which it is often confused, but apparently local, mostly in the south. (33)

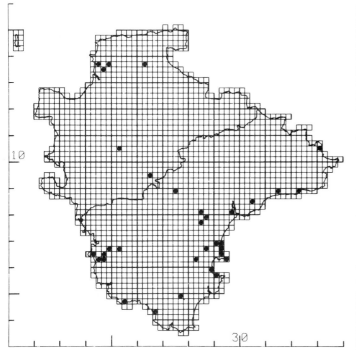

Minuartia hybrida (Vill.) Schischk., (*M. tenuifolia* (L.) Hiern), the Fine-leaved Sandwort, has been recorded from old walls, railway tracks and dry, rocky places; it has not been seen recently in either of its localities at Exeter or Coffinswell.

Honkenya peploides (L.) Ehrh.   Sea Sandwort
(*Minuartia peploides* (L.) Hiern)
On sandy strand-lines and mobile dunes, where it may be locally frequent but varies considerably in amount from year to year. It is found locally on Braunton Burrows and Woolacombe, and on a number of other dune systems in the south of the county. (18)

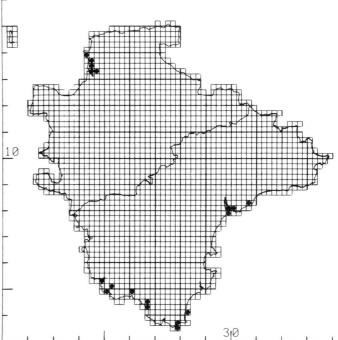

Stellaria nemorum L.   Wood Stitchwort
A northern species, which has its nearest neighbours in the
Severn valley, with a single locality in a dense damp wood near
Watersmeet. (1)

Stellaria media (L.) Vill.   Chickweed
A common weed of cultivated and waste ground, roadsides and
fields; very common and almost ubiquitous, absent only from
open moorland. (1596)

Stellaria holostea L.   Greater Stitchwort
A common plant of hedgerows, roadsides and sometimes in
woodland, preferring not too dense shade. Generally distributed, largely absent from moorland areas, though found in
Wistman's Wood. (1616)

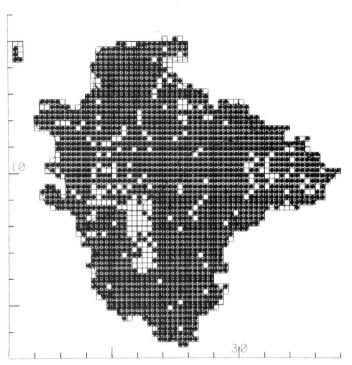

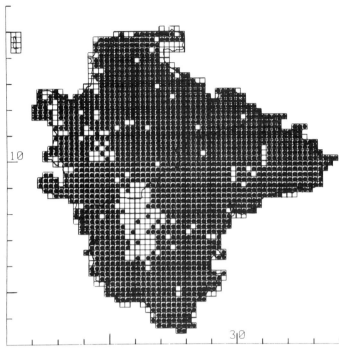

Stellaria pallida (Dum.) Piré   Lesser Chickweed
A very local plant usually found in or near dunes or sandy soil
near the sea. Recorded only from Braunton Burrows, Dawlish
Warren and Anstey's Cove, Torquay. (4)

Stellaria neglecta Weihe   Greater Chickweed
On shaded banks, in hedges and the margins of woods; not
uncommon in hedges on heavy clay soils; rather local, but fairly
generally distributed. (433)

Stellaria alsine Grimm   Bog Stitchwort
(*S. uliginosa* Murr.)
In ditches and stream-sides and bogs on mineral soils, sometimes occurring on the moors. Quite common, and sometimes
abundant in suitable habitats, though apparently absent from
substantial areas in eastern parts of the county. (1107)

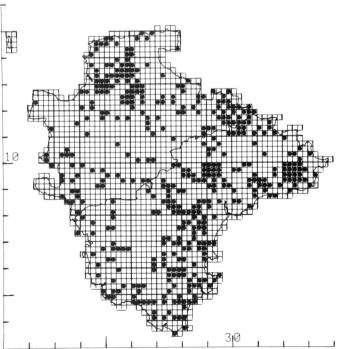

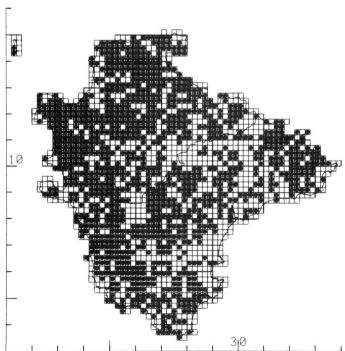

Stellaria graminea L.   Lesser Stitchwort
In drier hedgebanks, acid woods and heathy pastures; quite
common in many parts of the county, perhaps overlooked to
some extent. (1252)

Cerastium arvense L.   Field Mouse-ear Chickweed
Probably introduced; a native of Europe. It occurs on dry sandy
banks, roadsides and in dry grassland. Rare, only known from
sites in N. Devon and to the east of Dartmoor. (3)

Cerastium fontanum Baumg. Common Mouse-ear Chickweed
(inc. *C. holosteoides* Fr., *C. vulgatum* auct.)
This species is widely distributed in Europe. The British forms
are all placed in ssp. **glabrescens** (G.F.W. Meyer) Salman *et al.*
(ssp. *triviale* (Link) Jalas), which is by far the most widespread of
the various infraspecific taxa recognised. It is widely distributed
in Devon, in habitats which include meadows, grassy banks and
sand-dunes, often in well-drained situations. (1657)

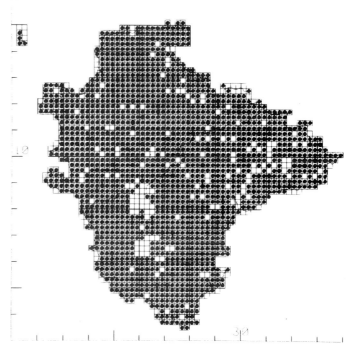

Cerastium tomentosum L.   Dusty Miller
Introduced; a native of S.E. Europe and the Caucasus, commonly grown in rock-gardens and on walls, and frequently
escaping. Quite hardy, but rarely found far from habitations. (97)

Cerastium glomeratum Thuill.   Sticky Mouse-ear Chickweed
(*C. viscosum* auct.)
A common annual of cliffs, walls and roadsides, sometimes in
permanent grassland and sand-dunes. Rather less frequent than
the previous species, but perhaps overlooked, as the two are not
always easy to distinguish when not in flower. (1056)

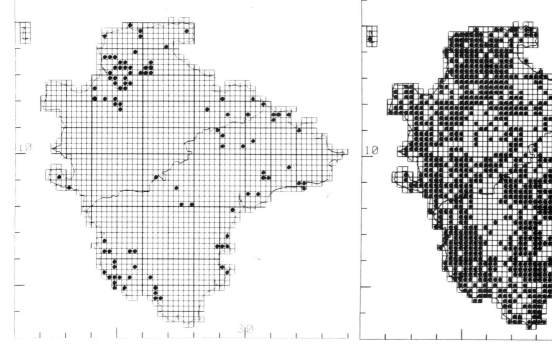

Cerastium semidecandrum L.   Little Mouse-ear Chickweed
In dry, open habitats, most commonly near the coast and in dune systems; more rarely inland, in sandy or well-drained soils. (33)

Cerastium pumilum Curt.   Curtis' Mouse-ear Chickweed
A rare plant of open calcareous grassland, probably now only to be found near the coast at Torquay. (1)

Moenchia erecta (L.) Gaertn., Mey. & Scherb.
Upright Chickweed
A very local plant found in short turf near the sea and in sand-dunes, rarely inland on sandy and gravelly soils, but occurring up to 300 m on Dartmoor. (31)

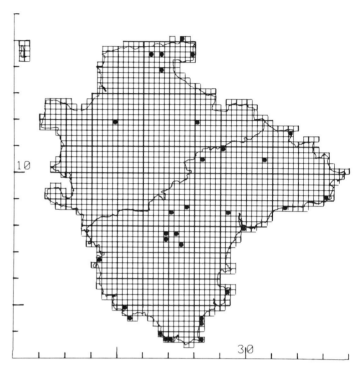

Cerastium diffusum Pers.   Sea Mouse-ear Chickweed
(*C. atrovirens* Bab., *C. tetrandrum* Curt.)
A local plant of dry and usually sandy habitats, most common near the sea or on sea cliffs, more rarely inland, often on walls. Our plant belongs to ssp. **diffusum.** (59)

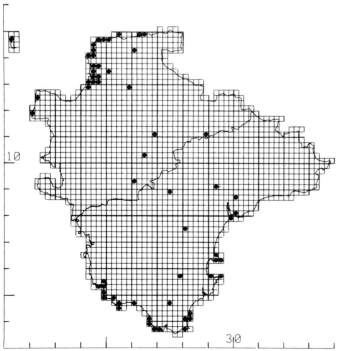

Myosoton aquaticum (L.) Moench   Water Chickweed
(*Stellaria aquatica* (L.) Scop.)
An uncommon species of marshes, ditches and beside rivers and streams. Most frequent in the vicinity of rivers in E. Devon, but also occurring on Braunton Burrows. (56)

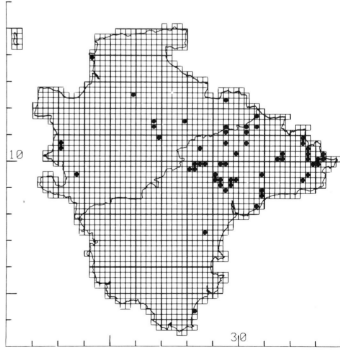

Sagina nodosa (L.) Fenzl   Knotted Pearlwort
Local, in damp heathy and sandy habitats. In quite a number of
localities around Dartmoor, and in dune slacks on Braunton
Burrows. (26)

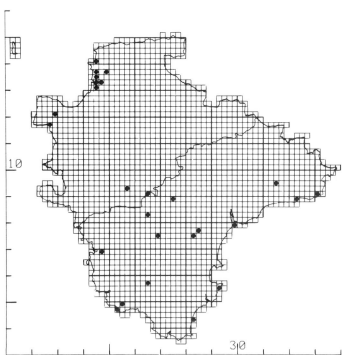

Sagina procumbens L.   Procumbent Pearlwort
On damp ground, banks, paths and waste places; very common
and often abundant on rather poor acid soils. (1138)

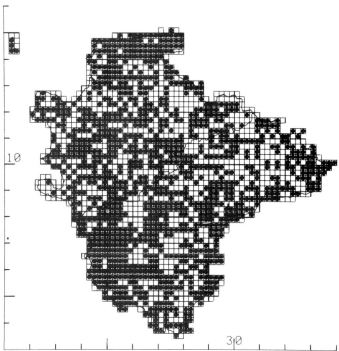

Sagina subulata (Sw.) C.Presl   Awl-leaved Pearlwort
In dry heathy, sandy or gravelly habitats; locally frequent on
Dartmoor, especially on south-west facing slopes, but seem-
ingly less common than formerly. (64)

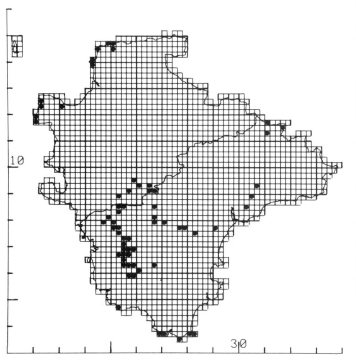

Sagina apetala Ard.   Annual Pearlwort
(inc. *S. ciliata* Fr., *S. reuteri* Boiss.)
Scattered throughout the county, on dry walls, banks and
gravelly places. Used to be a very common species, but either
much under-recorded or much less frequent than it used to be.
(209)

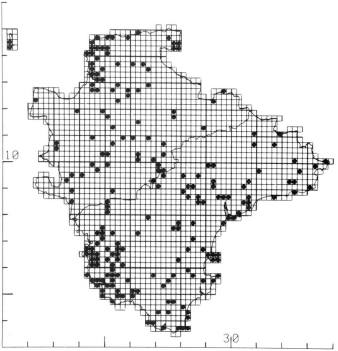

The species formerly separated as *S. ciliata* is now considered to
fall within the range of variation of *S. apetala*; these ciliate forms
tend to have a more coastal distribution. *S. reuteri* is now
considered to be a dwarf form, found in drier habitats.

Sagina maritima G.Don f.　　　　　　Sea Pearlwort
In rock crevices by the sea, on sandy shores and in estuaries. Not uncommon along the south coast and at Braunton Burrows, but apparently absent from habitats east of Torbay. (32)

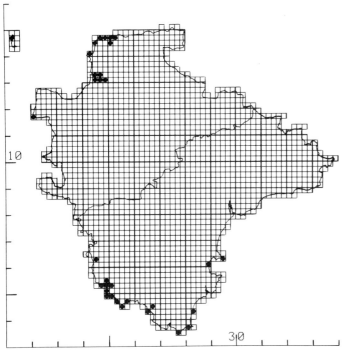

Corrigiola litoralis L.　　　　　　Strapwort
Only known from the damp sandy margins of Slapton Ley, where it is locally abundant. (2)

Scleranthus annuus L.　　　　　　Annual Knawel
In dry, sandy and gravelly fields and waste ground. Rare, mostly in central districts, and locally common to the north of Dartmoor. (22)

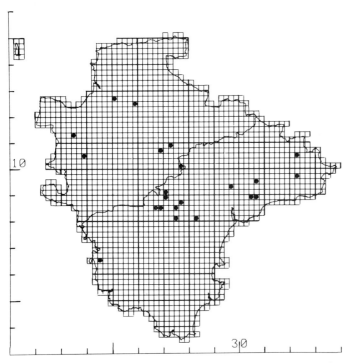

Herniaria hirsuta L., the Hairy Rupture-wort, is a native of Europe which has been reported occasionally from dry or sandy habitats, but there are no recent records. **H. glabra** L., the Glabrous Rupture-wort, is not known to occur in Devon, despite some reports to the contrary, and the same is true for **Illecebrum verticillatum** L., which is, nevertheless, known from both Hampshire and Cornwall.

Polycarpon tetraphyllum (L.) L.　　　Four-leaved All-seed
A very rare species of dry sandy places and roadsides near the sea. It used to be not infrequent between Exmouth and Plymouth; there are post-1930 records from Torbay, but it has only been found recently at Bantham. (1)

Spergula arvensis L.　　　　　　Corn Spurrey
(inc. *S. sativa* Boenn.)
A weed of cultivated and waste ground, especially if this is dry, sandy and rather acid. At one time a frequent cornfield weed, now rarely occurring in such habitats, but still fairly generally distributed. (550)

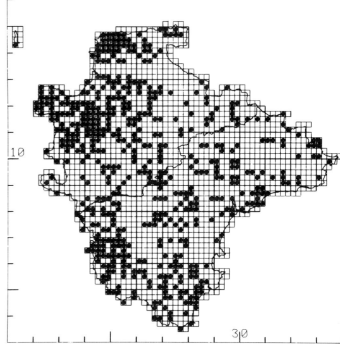

S. sativa used to be separated as a species in which the seeds were tuberculate rather than papillate, but is no longer recognised.

Spergularia rupicola Lebel ex Le Jolis　Cliff Sand Spurrey
On cliffs and rocks in the vicinity of the sea, sometimes on walls, but venturing only a little way inland. Not uncommon along both coasts, more frequent in the south. (107)

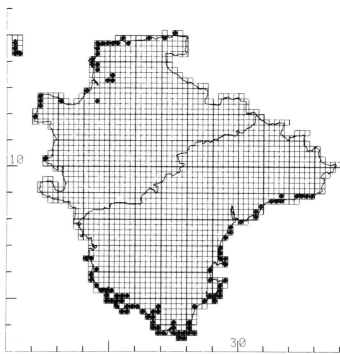

Spergularia media (L.) C.Presl   Greater Sea Spurrey
(*S. marginata* Kittel)
In muddy and sandy habitats in salt-marshes and tidal estuaries, sometimes quite a distance inland. Quite common in suitable habitats. (40)

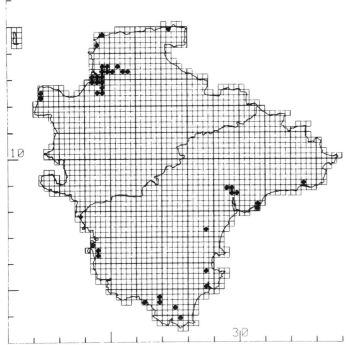

Spergularia rubra (L.) J. & C.Presl
                                        Red Sandwort, Sand Spurrey
(*S. campestris* (All.) Aschers.)
In dry sandy and gravelly places, on roadsides and heaths. Widely scattered, especially around Dartmoor. Not a maritime species, though it is sometimes found near the coast. (77)

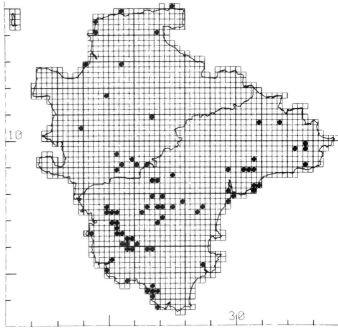

Spergularia bocconii (Scheele) Aschers. & Graeb., Boccone's Sand Spurrey, is a plant of dry coastal sand; there is a single old record from Stokenham, but it has not been seen recently and is probably extinct.

Lychnis flos-cuculi L.   Ragged Robin
A fairly common plant of marshes, wet meadows and ditches. Rather widely distributed in the north-west, but often only occasional where it occurs and less common than formerly. (812)

Spergularia marina (L.) Griseb.   Lesser Sea Spurrey
(*S. salina* J. & C.Presl)
In muddy places, especially salt-marshes and estuaries. In generally similar habitats to the previous species but able to withstand drier situations and sometimes found inland as an adventive. (55)

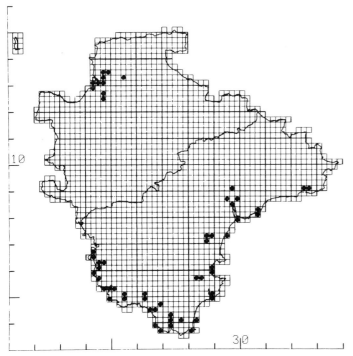

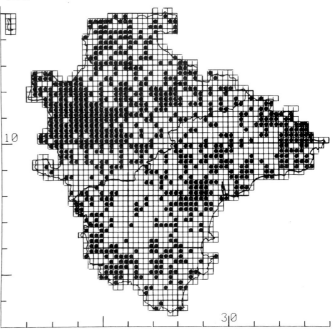

Agrostemma githago L.   Corn Cockle
(*Lychnis githago* (L.) Scop.)
Introduced; a native of the Mediterranean region, formerly quite common as a cornfield weed, but now to be found only very rarely and perhaps always a garden escape. (3)

Silene nutans L. Nottingham Catch-fly
A rare species of maritime cliffs on the Greensand and Chalk in
S.E. Devon, where it is locally frequent. Our plant is sometimes
separated as var. *smithiana* Mon., with broader, more pubes-
cent leaves, and smaller capsules. (5)

Silene vulgaris (Moench) Garcke Bladder Campion
(*S. cucubalus* Wibel, *S. inflata* Sm., inc. *S. maritima* With., *S.
linearis* Sweet)
Quite common on grassy slopes, roadsides and in arable land;
rather infrequent inland and rarely found in any quantity. (246)

Silene noctiflora L. Night-flowering Catch-fly
A weed of arable land, usually on relatively light soils; rare and
local, with very few and scattered records. (4)

Silene alba (Mill.) E.H.L.Krause White Campion
(*Lychnis alba* Mill.)
In hedgerows, roadsides, cultivated land and waste places;
commonest in the south and south-east, and absent from much
of the Culm. (251)

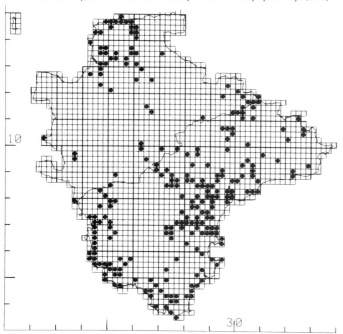

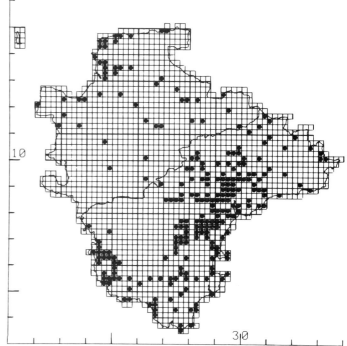

Recent work suggests that several taxa, previously regarded as
species, should be included here:
Ssp. **macrocarpa** Turrill, which was previously referred to *S.
linearis*, has long been established on Plymouth Hoe. It was
probably introduced from Cyprus quite a long, but uncertain,
time ago, and was first recognised by H.W.Pugsley in 1940.

Ssp. **maritima** (With.) A. & D.Löve, the Sea Campion, previously
referred to *S. maritima*, is locally abundant on shingle, maritime
cliffs and similar habitats near the sea. It seems able to resist
competition poorly and is rarely found in dense vegetation.
(121)

Silene dioica (L.) Clairv. Red Campion
(*Lychnis dioica* L.)
In woods, hedgerows and roadsides, perhaps preferring more
base-rich habitats, but very common throughout the county,
absent only from the higher parts of Dartmoor. (1683)

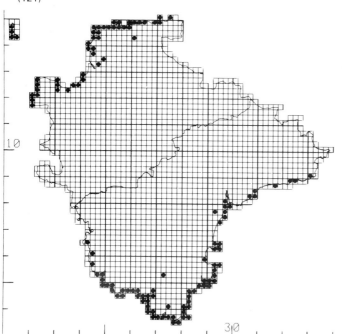

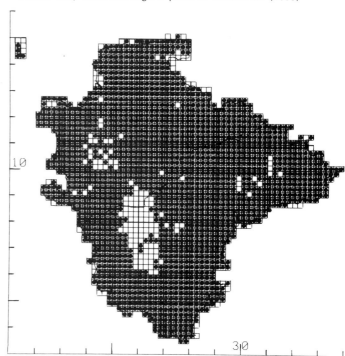

Silene x intermedia (Schur.) nom.prov.
(*S. alba* x *dioica*)
This hybrid is readily recognised by its pink flowers, as well as other characters intermediate between those of its parents, although it often has the more vigorous growth of *S. alba*. It occurs frequently around Exeter and occasionally elsewhere. (14)

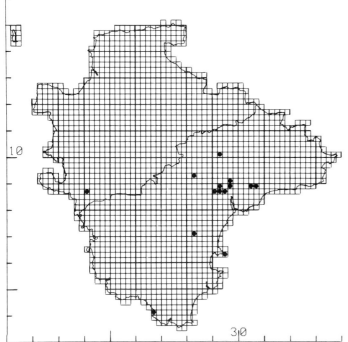

Silene pendula L., the Drooping Catch-fly, was recorded at Exmouth in 1917, but has not been seen since; it is occasionally cultivated. **Silene dichotoma** Ehrh., the Forked Catch-fly, has been recorded as a casual at Exeter, but not seen recently.

Cucubalus baccifer L., the Berry Catch-fly, is an introduced European species which used to occur in thickets on the cliffs at Woody Bay, Martinhoe, but it has not been recorded for many years and is probably extinct.

Saponaria officinalis L.   Soapwort
Introduced; a native of Europe, not uncommon in hedges and along roads, especially in damp habitats, and along streams and rivers. Scattered over the county, usually fairly near habitations. (57)

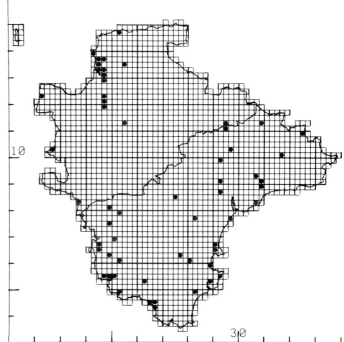

Silene gallica L.   Small-flowered Catch-fly
(inc. *S. anglica* L.)
Probably introduced; a native of Europe. It occurs in sandy or gravelly fields and waste places, sporadically around the periphery of Dartmoor, rarely elsewhere, usually on sand near the coast. (13)

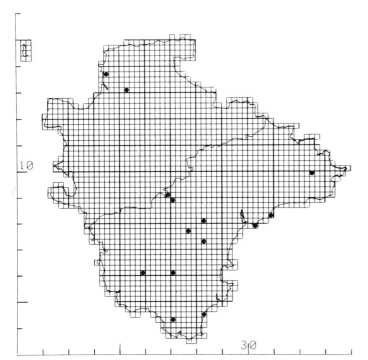

Vaccaria pyramidata Medic.
Introduced; a native of Europe. It has been recorded on one occasion, probably as a garden escape. (1)

Dianthus armeria L.   Deptford Pink
A species of lowland hedgerows and dry sandy places. Very rare, with only a single record since 1963. (1)

Dianthus deltoides L.   Maiden Pink
In waste ground, usually in calcareous habitats. Very rare, with only a single record from Buckfastleigh. (1)

NYMPHAEACEAE

Nymphaea alba Lam. White Water Lily
In lakes and pools, perhaps invariably planted or as an escape from cultivation, though it is said to be native on the R. Clyst. (23)

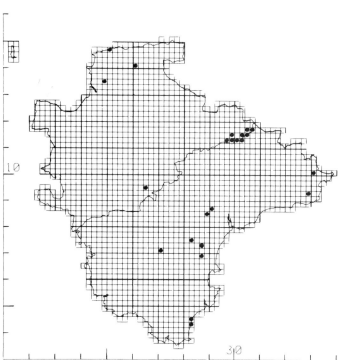

Nuphar lutea (L.) Sm. Yellow Water Lily
In lakes, ponds and streams; almost confined to E. Devon, where it is rather rare. (13)

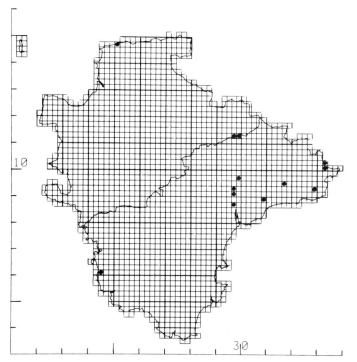

CERATOPHYLLACEAE

Ceratophyllum demersum L. Hornwort
Submerged in streams and slow-flowing water, ditches and old clay workings. Scattered throughout the county, mostly in the south and east, and quite rare. (19)

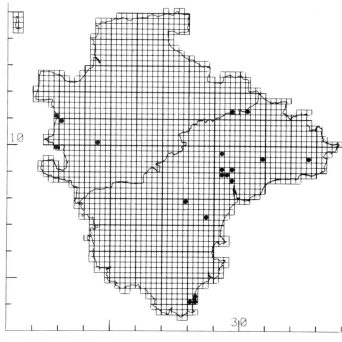

Ceratophyllum submersum L.
Submerged in streams and slow-flowing water. Only known from Slapton Ley, where it is rare. (2)

RANUNCULACEAE

Helleborus foetidus L. Stinking Hellebore
A native plant of wood and scrub on calcareous soils; probably introduced in Devon but possibly native in scrub near Torquay. At one time cultivated as a medicinal herb, and still grown in gardens. (1)

Helleborus viridis L. Green Hellebore
Grows as a native plant on moist calcareous soils; doubtfully native in any of its recorded sites, and not uncommonly cultivated. It has been grown as a medicinal herb. (11)

Our plant is ssp. **occidentalis** (Reut.) Schiffn., with the leaves glabrous beneath.

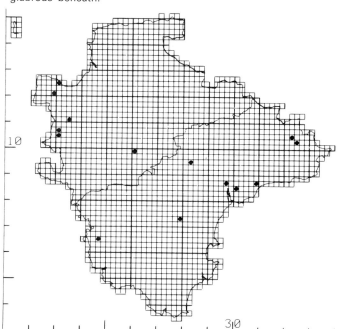

Eranthis hyemalis L., the Winter Aconite, is not infrequently grown in gardens and may escape, but naturalised plants are very rare.

Nigella damascena L., Love-in-the-Mist, is a garden plant which can maintain itself by seed in waste places and rubbish tips, but is scarcely naturalised.

Caltha palustris L.   Marsh Marigold
In wet meadows, marshes and stream-sides, usually on rather clayey soils. Generally distributed in the lowlands, though suitable habitats are rare in some places. (537)

Consolida ambigua (L.) Ball & Heywood, (*Delphinium ambiguum* L., *D. gayanum* Wilmott), the Larkspur, is an introduced annual species which used to be found as a cornfield weed, but is unlikely still to occur as such.

Anemone nemorosa L.   Wood Anemone
In deciduous woodland, especially acid oak woods, and in hedgebanks, usually on damp soils. Often very common where it occurs, but rather local. (434)

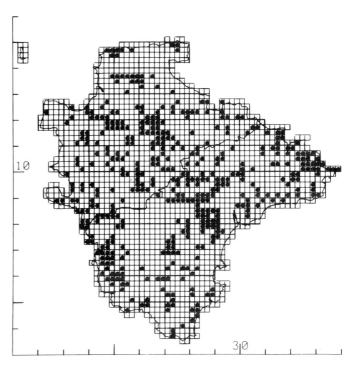

Anemone apennina L.
Introduced; a native of S. Europe, often planted in gardens and occasionally escaping or found with rubbish. (3)

Clematis vitalba L.   Traveller's Joy, Old Man's Beard
In hedgerows, scrub and wood margins; very common in the limestone and chalk regions of E. Devon and around Torbay, scattered elsewhere, especially around habitations or ruined buildings where there are base-rich soils. Usually abundant where it occurs. (370)

Aconitum napellus L.   Monkshood
(inc. *A. anglicum* Stapf)
A woodland plant generally found in moist pastures under alder or beside rivers and streams, usually in alluvial soils. Scattered over the county in suitable habitats, but rare, though locally frequent. (26)

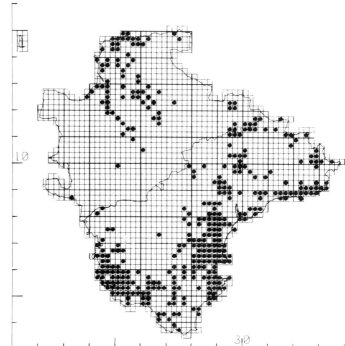

Clematis flammula L.
Introduced; a native of the Mediterranean region. A garden plant which sometimes escapes and can maintain itself for a few years. (3)

Adonis annua L., the Pheasant's Eye, is reported from time to time, but there are no recent records.

Ranunculus repens L.   Creeping Buttercup
Common and abundant in meadows, cultivated land, waste places and roadsides, and also in damp woods. Ubiquitous, and often a troublesome weed. (1741)

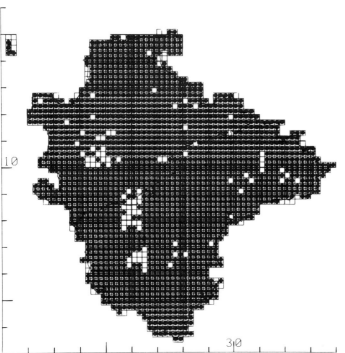

Ranunculus bulbosus L.   Bulbous Buttercup
Most frequent in rather dry, base-rich pastures and grassy waste places, but also in fixed dunes. Generally distributed but rather sparse and apparently absent from much of the north and west. (668)

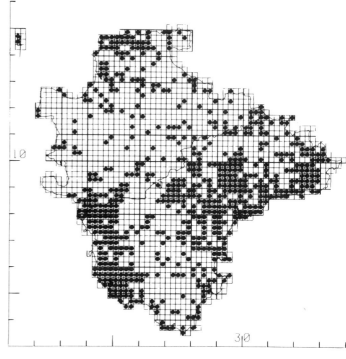

Ranunculus acris L.   Meadow Buttercup
(*R. acer* L.)
Common in damp meadows and pastures, especially on neutral or reasonably base-rich soils. Less frequent than formerly as a consequence of agricultural improvement of pastures. (1469)

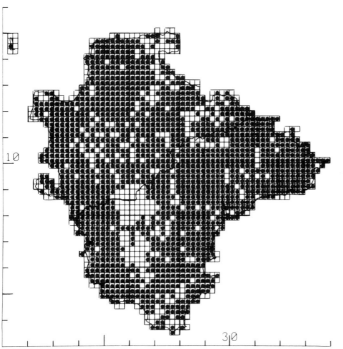

Ranunculus sardous Crantz   Hairy Buttercup
In damp pastures, arable fields and waste ground. Becoming very uncommon, with only scattered records, and much less frequent than formerly, again reflecting changes in agricultural practice. (22)

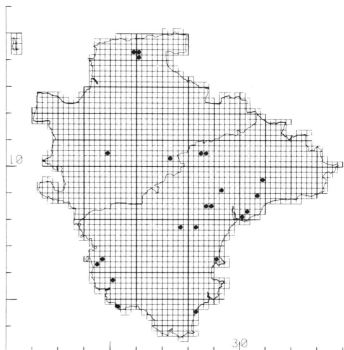

Ranunculus arvensis L.   Corn Buttercup
Perhaps native. Formerly common as a weed of cornfields and
arable land, but now rather rare, and found mostly in S. Devon.
(25)

Ranunculus auricomus L.   Goldilocks
In woodland, mainly on base-rich soils. Absent from the Culm in
mid- and north-west Devon, and another species which has
decreased considerably in recent years. (42)

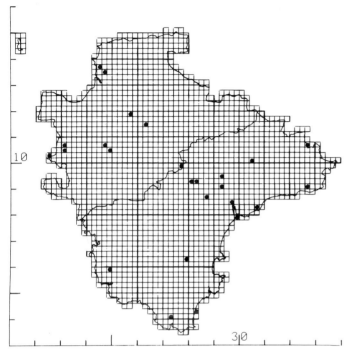

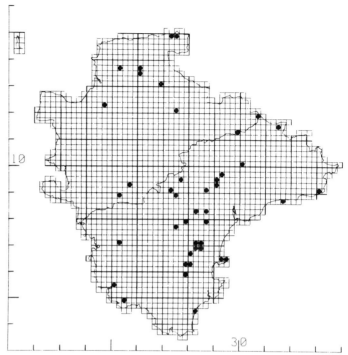

Ranunculus parviflorus L.   Small-flowered Buttercup
A local plant of arable fields and poor pastures and dry, gravelly
places, often fairly near the sea. Scattered, mostly in the south,
but with some records near the N. Devon coast; much less
common than formerly. (108)

Ranunculus sceleratus L.   Celery-leaved Crowfoot
On damp alluvial soils, in marshy meadows and beside ditches
and slow streams. Scattered in several river valleys, especially
in the lower parts of the valleys of the Clyst and Otter, and
around Barnstaple, but nowhere common. (62)

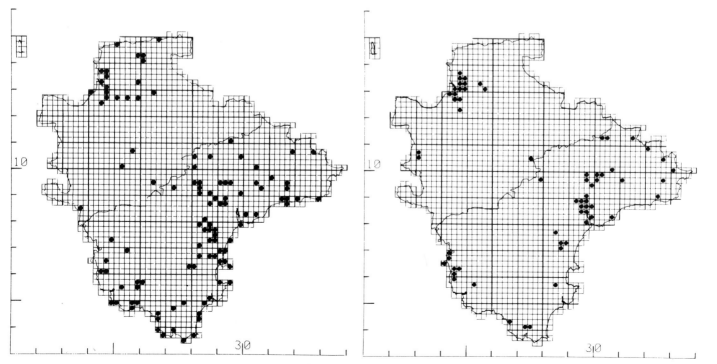

Ranunculus ficaria L.   Lesser Celandine
A common plant of damp woods, roadsides and stream-sides, especially on clayey soils, and as a garden weed. Generally and widely distributed, except on the higher moors. Forms with double flowers are reported occasionally. (1374)

Ranunculus hederaceus L.   Ivy-leaved Water-crowfoot
In springs, ditches and roadside runnels, either on mud or in shallow water. Not uncommon in the vicinity of Dartmoor, but very scattered elsewhere. (286)

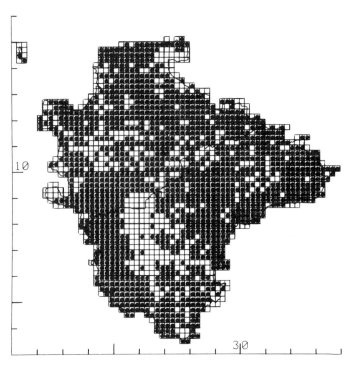

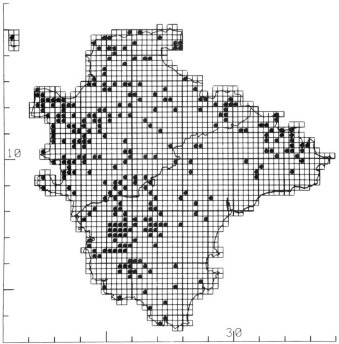

The distribution of ssp. *bulbifer,* which prefers more shaded habitats, is uncertain, but there is a single record for the hybrid *R. ficaria* ssp. *bulbifer* x ssp. *fertilis* from S. Devon (Jones in Stace, 1975).

Ranunculus flammula L.   Lesser Spearwort
In damp meadows and beside ditches and streams, and also abundant in peaty swamps on the moors. Locally common, though less frequent in the south and east. (963)

Ranunculus omiophyllus Ten.   Lenormand's Water-crowfoot
(*R. lenormandii* F.W.Schultz)
Strictly confined to calcifuge habitats, this species is common in pools and running water on Dartmoor and Exmoor and in isolated habitats elsewhere. (303)

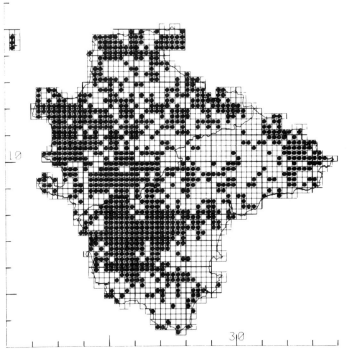

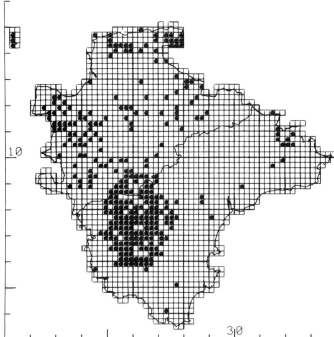

Ranunculus tripartitus DC.   Three-lobed Water-crowfoot
In ditches, and ponds in rather peaty habitats, preferring water
warmed by the sun. Very local and rare, and mostly in the south.
(11)

Ranunculus peltatus Schrank   Common Water-Crowfoot
In lakes, ponds and slow-flowing streams. Scattered over the
county, and fairly frequent in suitable habitats. (39)

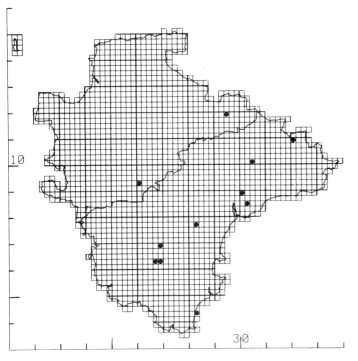

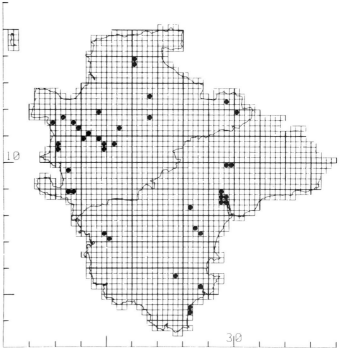

Ranunculus baudotii Godron   Brackish Water-crowfoot
In brackish streams, ditches and ponds in coastal districts or
near estuaries. Mostly around the south coast, and on Braunton
Burrows, and rather rare. (10)

Ranunculus penicillatus (Dum.) Bab.
(*R. pseudofluitans* (Syme) Baker & Foggitt
In fast-flowing streams and rivers. Fairly frequent in rivers in E.
Devon, rather rare in the South Hams. (22)

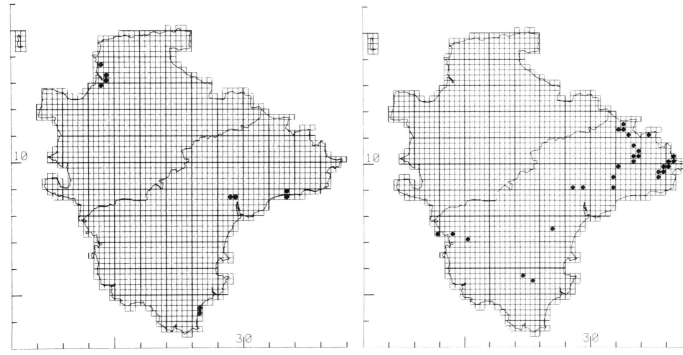

45

Ranunculus aquatilis L.
In ponds, ditches and streams. Rare, but scattered over the county in suitable habitats, mostly in the north. (50)

Ranunculus circinatus Sibth.   Stiff-leaved Water-crowfoot
In ditches, and streams in still or slow-flowing water, often in base-rich areas or where the water has a high mineral content. Very rare, with very scattered records, but occurring in Slapton Ley. (3)

Ranunculus fluitans Lam.   Long-leaved Water-crowfoot
In fairly fast-flowing rivers and streams. Moderately common, especially in the rivers of E. Devon, local elsewhere; not perhaps always distinguished from *R. penicillatus*. (39)

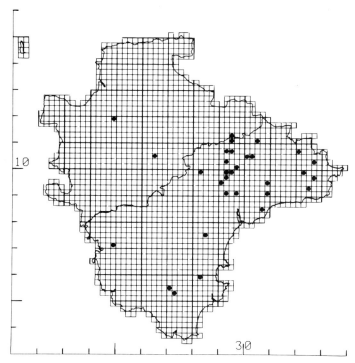

Ranunculus trichophyllus Chaix Short-leaved Water-crowfoot
In ponds, ditches and slow-flowing streams. Quite rare and mostly in the south. (10)

Aquilegia vulgaris L.   Columbine
In woodlands, hedges, and shaded heathland especially near base-rich water. Local, but widely distributed and often abundant where it occurs. Some records are probably of plants which have escaped from cultivation, but it is widely distributed as a native plant and could well be increasing. (188)

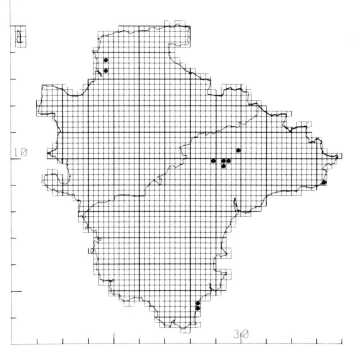

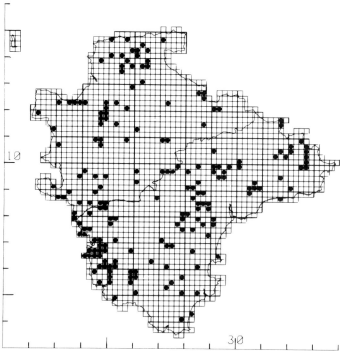

Thalictrum minus L.   Lesser Meadow Rue
Only believed to be genuinely native on the Torbay limestone,
and recorded from Berry Head and near Babbacombe. All other
records are escapes from cultivation. (6)

Thalictrum flavum L.   Meadow Rue
Recorded from moist riverside meadows in the Clyst valley,
near Sowton and Clyst St. Mary, where it is believed native and
has been known for many years. (1)

Mahonia aquifolium (Pursh) Nutt.   Oregon Grape
Introduced; a native of N. America. Quite commonly cultivated,
it can be found as self-sown plants on walls and in waste places,
where it can maintain itself for several years and is perhaps
naturalised. (17)

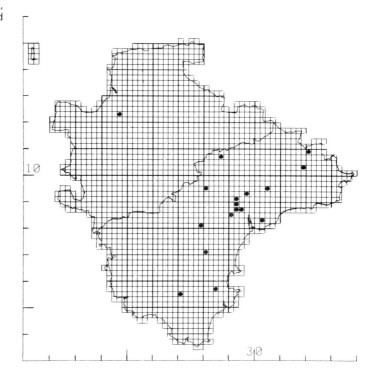

BERBERIDACEAE

Berberis vulgaris L.   Barberry
Probably introduced; a native of Europe. Occurs sporadically in
hedges and is occasionally established in waste places and
elsewhere, usually from cultivated plants. Frequently treated as
an undesirable weed on account of its being the intermediate
host of the wheat rust fungus, *Puccinia graminis*. (26)

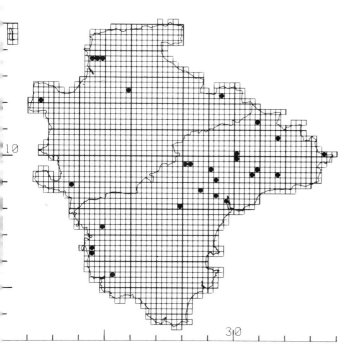

PAPAVERACEAE

Papaver somniferum L.   Opium Poppy
Introduced; a native of Europe. Occurs in waste places and on
rubbish tips, as an escape from cultivation. The form usually
grown is ssp. *somniferum* (inc. ssp. *hortense* (Hussen.) Corb.),
and is not the subspecies from which opium is usually obtained.
(108)

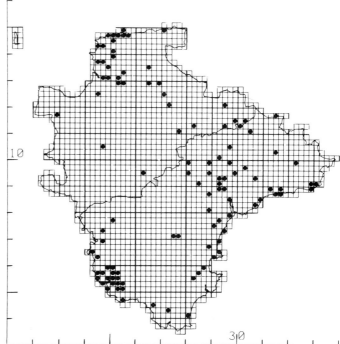

Papaver rhoeas L.   Red Poppy
Perhaps introduced, but native in Europe. A common weed of fields and waste places. Fairly generally distributed, though less frequent in the north and west, and less common than formerly; fields coloured red by the flowers are now quite unusual. (438)

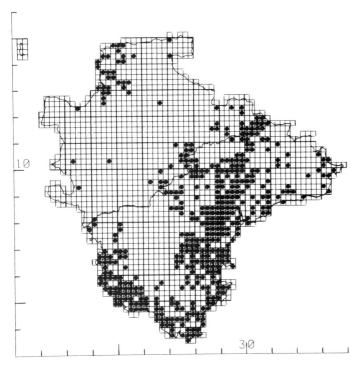

Papaver x nicholsonii Druce n.nud., (*P. rhoeas* x *dubium*), has been recorded from Brixham and Kingswear, but is a non-persistent annual, as it is sterile.

Papaver lecoqii Lamotte   Babington's Poppy
Perhaps introduced, but native in Europe. A rare weed of roadsides and waste places. Formerly rather scattered over the county, now confined to a few sites in N. Devon and near Plymouth. (5)

Papaver argemone L.   Long Prickly-headed Poppy
Perhaps introduced, but native in Europe. A rare annual of arable fields and waste places, recorded recently only from near Exeter and Braunton; it used to be common in the former Braunton bulb-farm. (3)

Papaver hybridum L.   Round Prickly-headed Poppy
Perhaps introduced, native in Europe. A rare weed of arable sandy fields. Formerly common on the Braunton bulb-farm, and thought to be extinct, but it reappeared there in 1980. (1)

Meconopsis cambrica (L.) Vig.   Welsh Poppy
Believed to be native in the vicinity of Exmoor and in the valleys of the Mole and Upper Tamar, and in Lydford Gorge; probably introduced elsewhere, and not infrequent in the vicinity of houses as an escape from cultivation. (129)

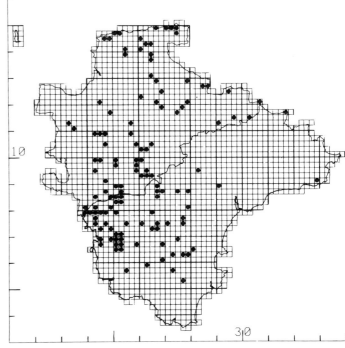

Papaver dubium L.   Long-headed Poppy
Perhaps introduced, but native in Europe. A weed of arable land and waste places which was rather common in the 19th century. It used to be abundant on the Braunton bulb-farm until this ceased operations, and is now rather local in the south and east of the county. (136)

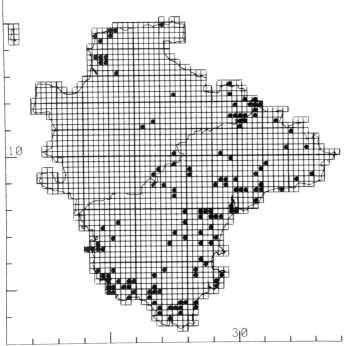

Glaucium flavum Crantz　　　　Yellow Horned-poppy
On shingle and coarse sand along the coast, and also on cliffs in parts of E. Devon. Very local along both coasts and only frequent on Slapton Sands. (23)

Eschscholzia californica Cham., the Californian Poppy, is rather rare as a garden escape which can sometimes be found in the vicinity of rubbish tips, but does not persist.

Corydalis claviculata (L.) DC.
　　　　　　　　　Climbing Fumitory, White Fumitory
In damp and shaded places on granite. A strict calcifuge which is quite common on wooded slopes and valleys of Dartmoor and parts of Exmoor. Local elsewhere, and absent from much of the Culm. (130)

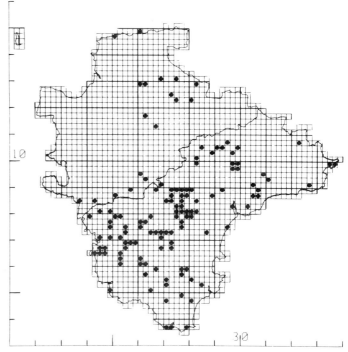

Chelidonium majus L.　　　　Greater Celandine
Perhaps introduced; a native of Europe. Occurs quite frequently and widely throughout the county, often in the vicinity of habitations or farmsteads, at the base of walls, in hedges and churchyards, though rarely in any quantity. It was used as a herbalist remedy for warts and eye diseases, and its distribution perhaps reflects previous cultivation. (288)

Corydalis lutea (L.) DC.　　　　Yellow Fumitory
Introduced; a native of Europe. Not uncommonly naturalised on walls near habitations, and maintaining itself without difficulty. Widespread. (107)

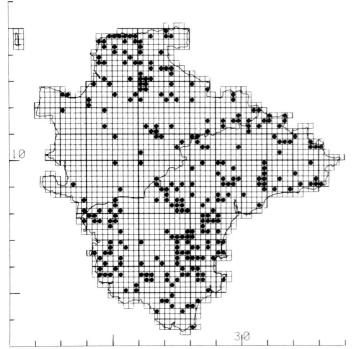

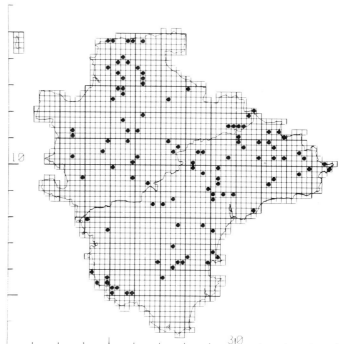

Fumaria capreolata L.   Ramping Fumitory
In cultivated and waste ground and in hedgebanks. Not very common and apparently much less frequent than formerly. Our plant belongs to ssp. **babingtonii** (Pugsl.) Sell, which is endemic in the British Isles. The var. *devoniensis* was first discovered near Morthoe, in 1931. (58)

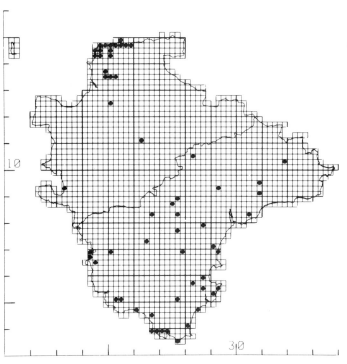

Furmaria bastardii Bor.
Sparsely distributed in waste and cultivated ground, usually near the coast; locally frequent in the north, but quite rare in the south of the county. (11)

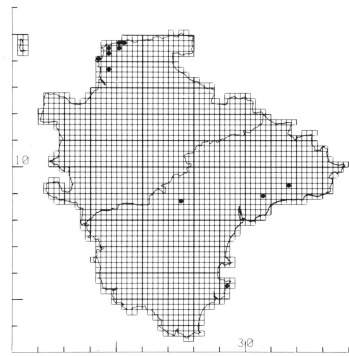

Fumaria purpurea Pugsl.
In waste ground and hedges. First recorded from the vicinity of Ilfracombe, and also known from near Torquay, but is now a rare plant which is endemic to the British Isles. (13)

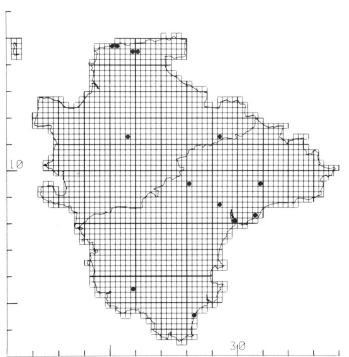

Fumaria muralis Sond. ex Koch
Ssp. **boraei** (Jord.) Pugsl. occurs in cultivated and waste ground, hedges and on walls, and is fairly common and quite generally distributed, though less frequent than formerly. (401)

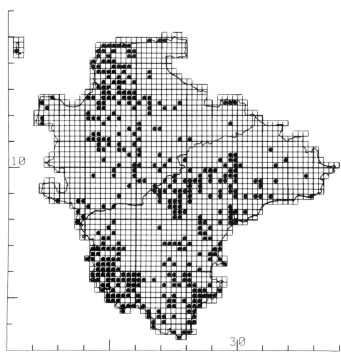

Ssp. **muralis** is a very rare plant of cultivated ground, with a single record from S. Devon (Perring & Sell, 1968).

Fumaria officinalis L.   Common Fumitory
In cultivated and waste ground, especially on the lighter soils.
Not uncommon and quite generally distributed, though less
frequent than formerly. (267)

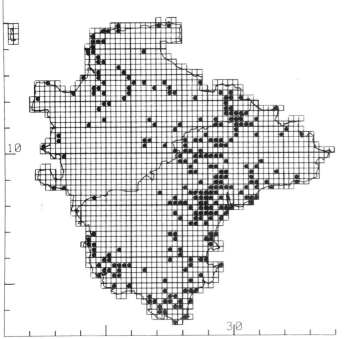

Fumaria martinii Clav. was found on a Salcombe allotment in
1935, but has not been seen since and is undoubtedly extinct.

CRUCIFERAE

Sisymbrium officinale (L.) Scop.   Hedge Mustard
In waste places, cultivated ground and by roadsides, especially
in towns and villages. Common and widely distributed, though
absent from Dartmoor and rather uncommon in the north-west.
(853)

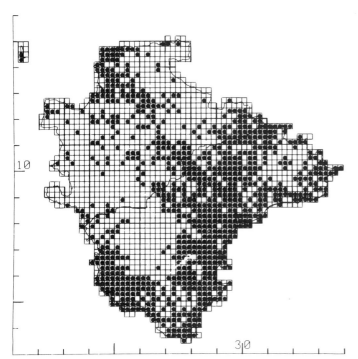

Sisymbrium altissimum L.   Tall Rocket
Introduced; a native of Europe which has become established in
scattered localities in the south of the county, especially along
railway lines and on rubbish tips. (4)

Sisymbrium orientale L.   Eastern Rocket
Introduced; a native of eastern Europe which has become
established on waste ground in the vicinity of rivers, railways
and docks. Very rare except around Exeter and Plymouth. (15)

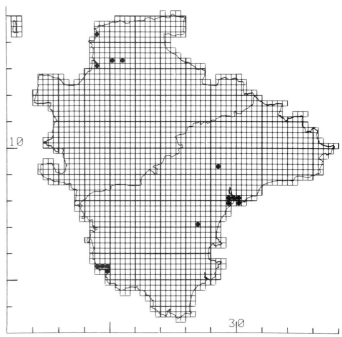

Sisymbrium irio L., the London Rocket, is a doubtful native
which has been found on walls and in waste places, but there
are no recent records. **Descurainia sophia** (L.) Webb ex Prantl,
(*Sisymbrium sophia* L.), the Flixweed, is a European native
which used to be found in the vicinity of quaysides and in waste
places, but is probably now extinct.

Alliaria petiolata (Bieb.) Cav. & Grande
          Garlic Mustard, Hedge Garlic, Jack-by-the-Hedge
(*Alliaria officinalis* Andrz. ex Bieb.)
A common plant of hedgebanks and woods, perhaps preferring
relatively base-rich soils. Generally distributed, though absent
from the higher moors. (1306)

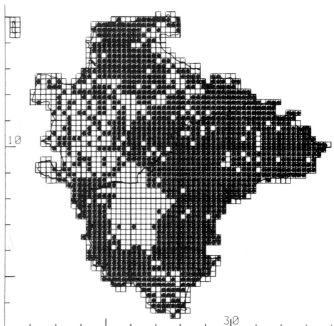

Arabidopsis thaliana (L.) Heynh.   Thale Cress
In sandy waste places, on walls, rocks and cliffs, and sometimes
as a garden weed, always in rather open soils. Quite common,
but seemingly more local than it used to be; a rather insignificant plant and perhaps under-recorded. (395)

Hesperis matronalis L.   Dame's Violet
Introduced; a native of Europe. A garden escape which has
become naturalised in hedgerows and waste places. Scattered
throughout the county, usually near habitations. (48)

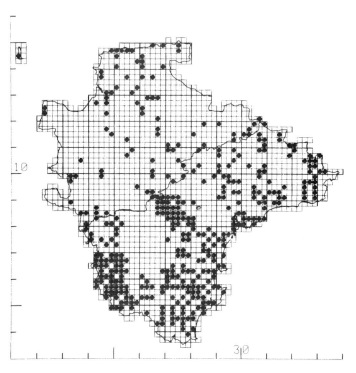

Isatis tinctoria L., the Woad, is an introduced species which
used also to occur as a cornfield weed, but it is no longer
cultivated and is now probably extinct.

Erysimum cheiranthoides L.   Treacle Mustard
Introduced; a native of Europe. A weed of cultivated ground and
waste places which is common in Europe, but which is rare and
local in Devon, though widely scattered. (75)

Cheiranthus cheiri L.   Wallflower
Introduced; a native of the E. Mediterranean region. It readily
establishes itself on sea cliffs, old walls, railway cuttings and
similar situations, and is also found on rubbish tips or with
garden waste. Widely distributed in Europe and very commonly
cultivated. (70)

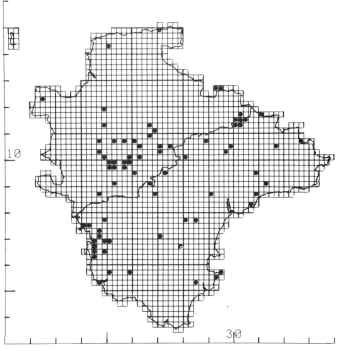

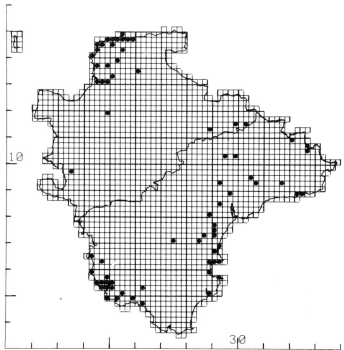

Erysimum repandum L. is a European species which has been
found in the vicinity of the R. Exe, but is probably now extinct.

Matthiola incana (L.) R.Br.   Stock
Introduced; probably native in S. Europe. A rare plant of
maritime cliffs which has been recorded from several localities
along the S. Devon coast, and near Braunton Burrows and
Ilfracombe in the north. Widely cultivated and perhaps (e.g. near
Exeter) an escape from cultivation. The 'Ten-week Stock' is
referable to var. *annua*. (11)

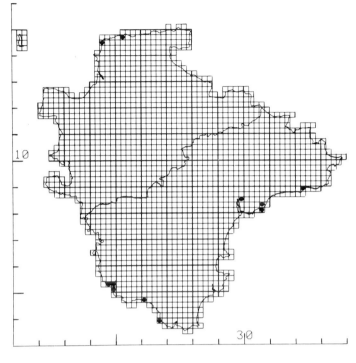

Barbarea vulgaris R.Br.   Yellow Rocket, Winter Cress
Along the margins of streams and wet roadsides, in cultivated
land and hedges. Generally distributed and locally common,
mostly in eastern parts of the county. (261)

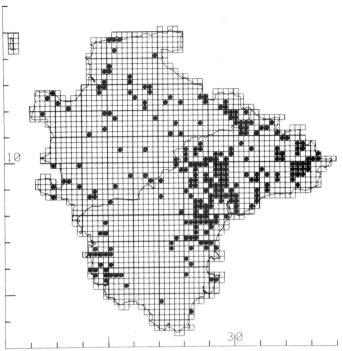

Matthiola sinuata (L.) R.Br.   Sea Stock
A rare plant of sea cliffs and sand-dunes. Confined to Braunton
Burrows and coasts in the vicinity, and increasing in numbers
on the yellow dunes at Braunton. (10)

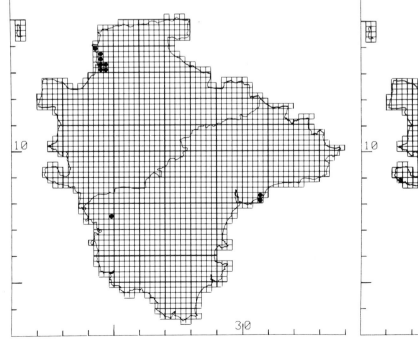

Barbarea verna (Mill.) Aschers. Land Cress, American Cress
Introduced; a native of southern Europe, naturalised over much
of the Continent and now found in waste ground, arable land
and along roadsides in various parts of Devon, but never
common. (51)

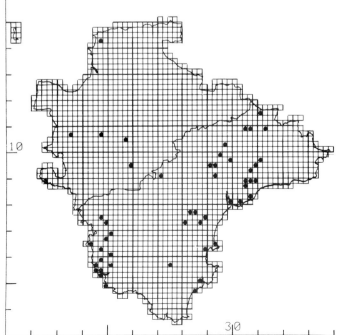

Barbarea intermedia Bor.   Intermediate Yellow Rocket
Introduced; a native of Europe. It occurs rather sporadically on
roadsides, banks and in waste places; the most frequent species
in the south-west of the county. (124)

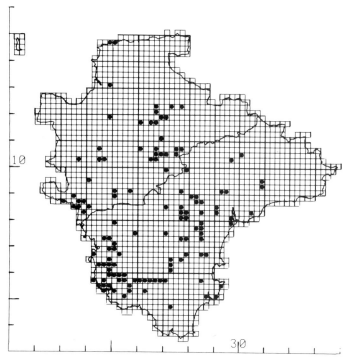

Rorippa islandica (Oeder) Borbás   Marsh Yellow Cress
Usually on alluvial soils on stream and river banks, but very
local. Most frequent along the R. Exe. (28)

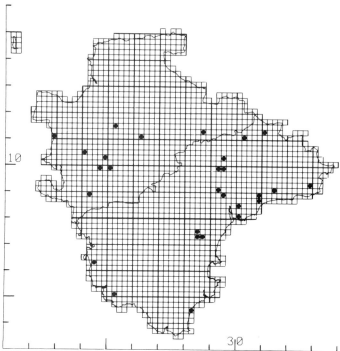

Nasturtium officinale R.Br.   Watercress
(*Rorippa nasturtium-aquaticum* (L.) Hayek)
In springs, streams and ditches where there is running and
preferably base-rich or calcareous water. Common and quite
generally distributed, though absent from the moors and local
in mid-Devon. (806)

Rorippa sylvestris (L.) Besser   Creeping Yellow Cress
In moist ground by streams and rivers; not uncommon in parts
of S. Devon, but rather rare in the north. (53)

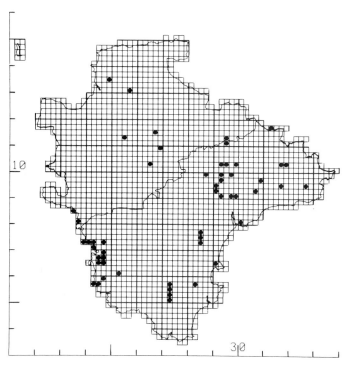

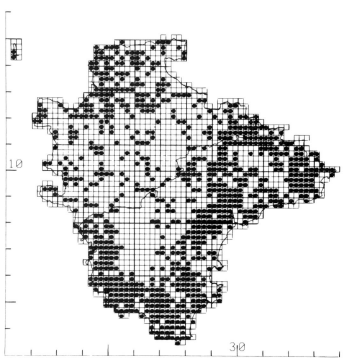

Nasturtium microphyllum (Boenn.) Reichenb.
(*Rorippa microphylla* (Boenn.) Hyl.)
Recorded from various parts of the county, but probably not
always distinguished from the preceding species. It has been
found in several widely scattered localities and probably occurs
elsewhere. (18)

Nasturtium microphyllum (Boenn.) Reichenb.

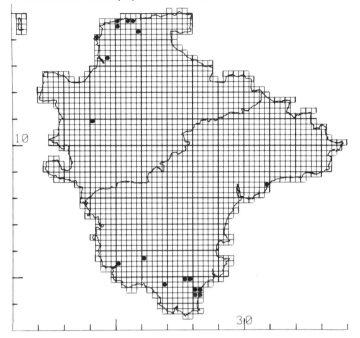

Cardamine flexuosa With.   Wood Bittercress
Common in moist shaded places in woods and by streams. Generally distributed but sometimes difficult to distinguish from some forms of *C. hirsuta*. (1332)

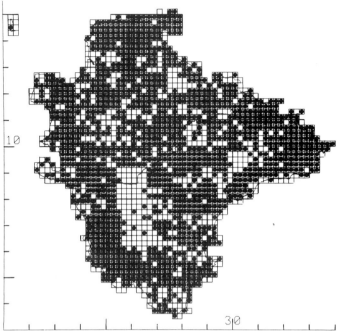

Nasturtium x sterilis (Airy Shaw) nom. prov.
(*N. officinale* x *microphyllum*)
This triploid hybrid is quite common in Britain and includes some of the cultivated watercresses. It has been identified from Barnstaple, Lundy, Ilfracombe and Salcombe, and doubtless occurs elsewhere. (4)

Cardamine bulbifera (L.) Crantz   Coral-wort
(*Dentaria bulbifera* L.)
Introduced; a native of Europe. Recorded from several localities around Exeter, Tiverton and Totnes, but probably always an escape from cultivation and scarcely naturalised. (6)

Cardamine trifolia L.
Introduced; a native of C. Europe. Only known in Trentishoe churchyard, where it is well established. (1)

Cardamine pratensis L.   Lady's Smock, Cuckoo Flower
Common and generally distributed in damp meadows, marshes, roadsides and beside streams. Most specimens appear to fall within *C. palustris* (Wimm. & Grab.) Peterm., with lilac flowers and radical leaves with about 3 pairs of stalked leaflets. Forms with double flowers occur frequently. (1143)

Cardamine x haussknechtiana O.E.Schulz
(*C. flexuosa* x *pratensis, C. hayneana* auct. angl.)
It is possible that this hybrid was recorded (as *C. pratensis* var. *hayneana*) at Malborough in 1935, but no specimen exists.

Cardamine hirsuta L.   Hairy Bittercress
Common on bare ground, banks, cliffs, paths and waste places; an abundant garden weed, usually found in drier situations than *C. flexuosa*. (1140)

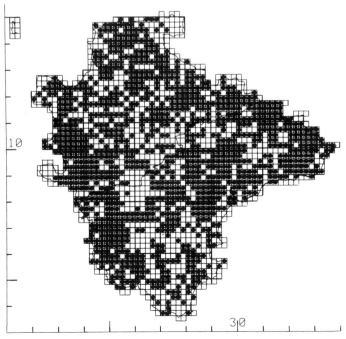

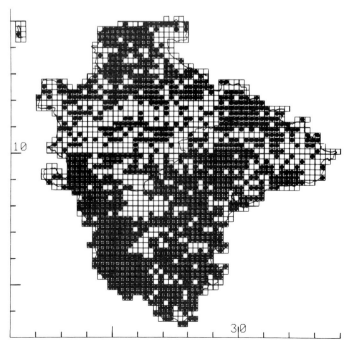

Cardamine impatiens L., the Narrow-leaved Bittercress, which occurs on damp calcareous rocks and soil, and which used to occur in the beds of the R. Teign and R. Bovey and occasionally elsewhere on the Torquay limestone, has not been recorded recently. However, it was always difficult to find and easily confused with related species.

Arabis hirsuta (L.) Scop.   Hairy Rock-cress
Confined to outcrops of the Devonian limestone, in quarries, on walls and other rocky places. Rare and very local. (21)

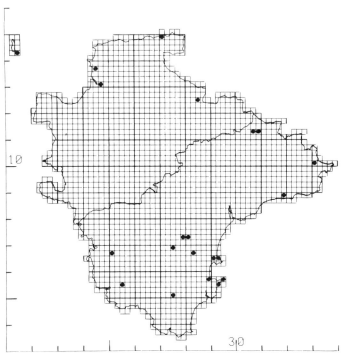

Arabis glabra (L.) Bernh., (*Turritis glabra* L.), the Tower Mustard, has been gathered on two occasions in the past, but was probably brought in from eastern Britain, and is not a normal component of the Devon flora. **Arabis stricta** Huds., (*A. scabra* All.), the Bristol Rock-cress, has been recorded on one occasion as a casual. **Arabis caucasica** Schlecht., (*A. albida* Stev.), the Garden Arabis, is much cultivated in gardens and sometimes escapes but is scarcely naturalised.

Aubrieta deltoides (L.) DC., the Garden Aubretia, is a native of S.E. Europe which is much cultivated in gardens and occasionally escapes into semi-natural habitats.

Lunaria annua L.   Honesty
Introduced; a native of S.E. Europe, frequently grown in gardens and often self-sown around rubbish tips and near habitations, but rarely persisting. (47)

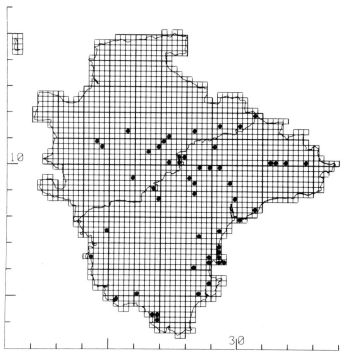

Alyssum alyssoides (L.) L.   Small Alison
Introduced; a native of Europe, now to be found very rarely as a casual in fields and waste places. (3)

Alyssum saxatile L., the Golden Alyssum, is a native of C. Europe much grown in gardens and which occasionally escapes or is found in the vicinity of rubbish tips. **Berteroa incana** (L.) DC., (*Alyssum incanum* L.), has been reported in the past as a casual from cultivated and waste ground, but there are no recent records.

Lobularia maritima (L.) Desv.   Sweet Alison
Introduced; a native of the Mediterranean region which is widely cultivated and frequently escapes, and has become quite widely naturalised on dry walls and in waste places, usually near the sea. (20)

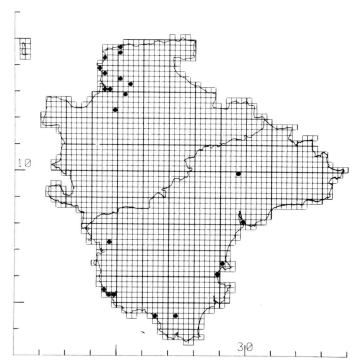

Draba muralis L.   Wall Whitlow Grass
On limestone rocks and walls. Perhaps native in one or two sites
in E. Devon, but introduced elsewhere. Very local and rare. (23)

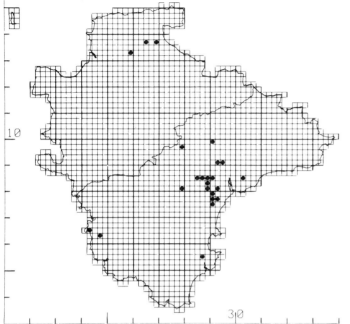

Erophila verna (L.) Chev.   Whitlow Grass
On rocky banks, old walls with lime mortar, sandy ground and
open patches in grassland, especially over limestone. Not
uncommon and widely distributed, particularly in S. Devon, but
probably overlooked, as it flowers very early in the year and is
not very conspicuous. A very variable plant, the minor forms
being perpetuated as they are self-pollinated. (116)

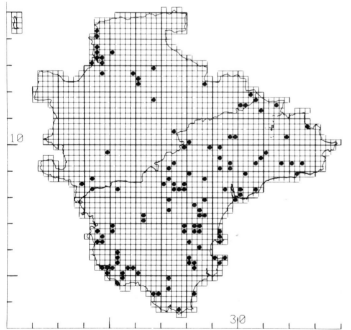

Armoracia rusticana Gaertn., Mey. & Scherb.   Horse-radish
(*Cochlearia armoracia* L.)
Introduced; a native of S.E. Europe. Widely naturalised along
roadsides and in fields and waste places, usually always fairly
damp. Originally cultivated for the condiment prepared from the
roots. Local, but generally distributed. (96)

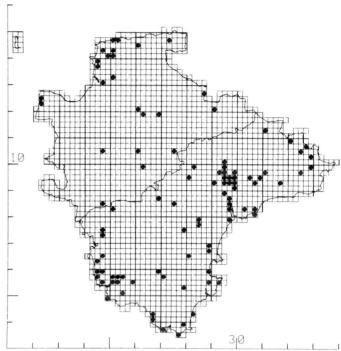

Cochlearia danica L.   Danish Scurvy-grass
Quite common in sandy and rocky places near the sea, mostly
on cliffs, rocks and walls; inland, only along estuaries, but
known to have been brought to Torrington in maritime gravel.
(110)

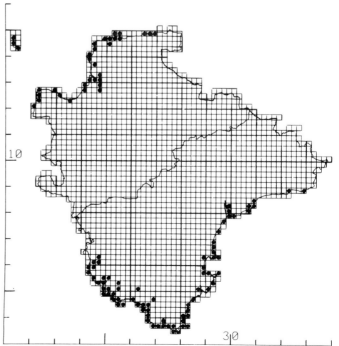

Ssp. **verna** includes forms with an oblanceolate silicula and
leaves with stellate and branched hairs. It is the most generally
distributed taxon.
Ssp. **praecox** (Stevens) Walters, (*E. praecox* Stevens), has forms
with many long simple hairs on the leaves. It was reported from
Dawlish Warren in 1936, but otherwise its distribution is not
known.
Ssp. **spathulata** (Lang) Walters (*E. boerhaavii* (van Hall) Dum., *E.
spathulata* Lang), has relatively short suborbicular siliculae. It
has been recorded from various localities in N. and S. Devon,
including Instow and Saunton, and probably occurs elsewhere.

Cochlearia officinalis L.   Scurvy-grass
On sea cliffs, in maritime grassland and drier parts of salt-
marshes, generally around the coast, but commoner in the
north, tending to be replaced in the south by *C. danica,* though
they occur together on Dawlish Warren. It occurs quite extensively inland in N.W. Devon, on roadsides, in hedges and damp
places. This may be a consequence of previous cultivation,
though the plants are well-established and not near habitations.
(205)

paniculata (L.) Hornem.) is a native of the Near East, widely
naturalised in Europe, which has been found in the past as a
weed, but there are no recent records.

Capsella bursa-pastoris (L.) Medic.   Shepherd's Purse
A common weed of agricultural land and gardens, also on
roadsides and in waste places; absent only from the higher
moors. A variable plant, with many described varieties, which
tend to perpetuate themselves as they are self-pollinated. (138)

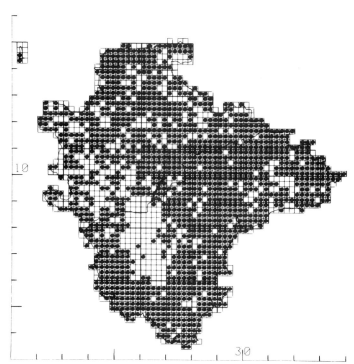

Cochlearia anglica L.   Long-leaved Scurvy-grass
On muddy shores, estuaries and in salt-marshes. Quite frequent
in suitable habitats, and the commonest salt-marsh species. (40)

Teesdalia nudicaulis (L.) R.Br.   Shepherd's Cress
Locally common in sandy and gravelly places, particularly in dry
habitats to the east of Dartmoor and also on Lundy, but with
scattered records elsewhere. (42)

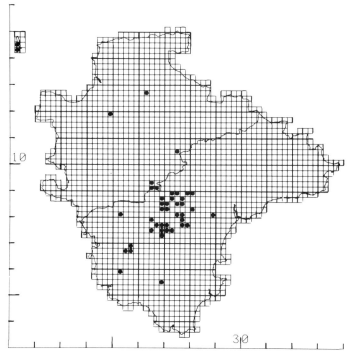

Cochlearia x hollandica Henrard, (*C. anglica x officinalis, C. x
briggsii* Druce), is said to be rather common in salt-marshes
wherever the parents occur together, the one in wetter habitats,
the other in drier. Although not recorded for Devon, there seems
no reason why it should not occur.

Camelina sativa (L.) Crantz, the Gold of Pleasure, is an
introduced species which used to be found as a weed of
agricultural crops, especially of flax, but it has not been seen
since 1939 and is probably extinct. **C. microcarpa** Andrz. ex DC.,
(*C. sylvestris* Wallr.), has not been seen for several decades and
is undoubtedly extinct. **Neslia paniculata** (L.) Desv., (*Vogelia*

Thlaspi arvense L.   Field Penny-cress
Doubtfully native, but widely distributed as a weed of arable and cultivated land, especially cornfields and root-crops. Quite common in the south and east, much less so in the north and west. (207)

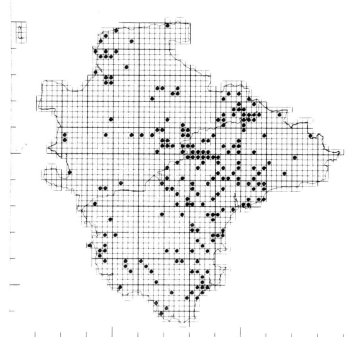

Iberis umbellata L.
Introduced; a native of S. Europe. Recorded occasionally, usually as an escape from gardens, as several forms are cultivated. (2)

Iberis amara L., the Wild Candytuft, was reported from waste ground in 1929 but has not been seen since and is undoubtedly extinct.

Lepidium campestre (L.) R.Br.   Pepperwort, Field Cress
In hedges, on banks and in waste and arable ground. Uncommon and rather local, mostly in the south and east. (43)

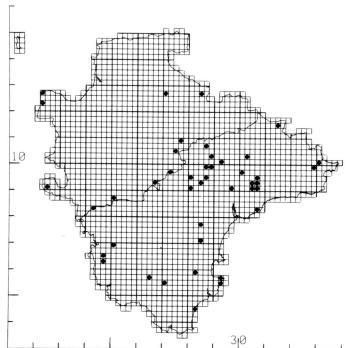

Lepidium heterophyllum Benth.   Smith's Pepperwort
(*L. smithii* Hook.)
Fairly common and generally distributed on roadsides, banks and in waste places and rough pasture; reported to be calcifuge. More frequent in the north than the south. (173)

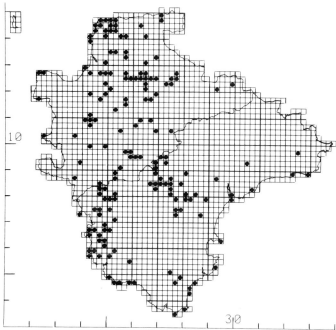

Lepidium ruderale L.   Narrow-leaved Pepperwort
Perhaps native. On roadsides and in waste places, at one time scattered over the county, but recently with only a single record from Fremington Station, in 1965. (1)

Lepidium virginicum L. and **L. densiflorum** Schrad. are N. American species which have both been recorded from Exeter and Newton Abbot in the past, but there are no recent records. **Lepidium perfoliatum** L. is a European species which has not been seen for many years. **Lepidium latifolium** L. is indigenous in salt-marshes in some parts of England, but is only casual in Devon and again, has not been seen for many years. **Lepidium sativum**, L., the Garden Cress is an occasional escape from cultivation which does not persist.

Cardaria draba (L.) Desv.   Hoary Pepperwort
(*Lepidium draba* L.)
Introduced; a native of the Mediterranean region. A weed of arable land and waste places, usually in the vicinity of estuaries, quays and railways. Widely distributed, especially around Exeter. (35)

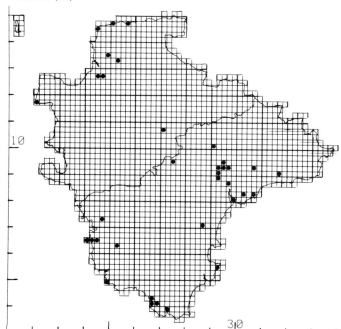

Coronopus squamatus (Forsk.) Aschers.   Swine Cress
(*Carara coronopus* (L.) Medic.)
In waste ground, roadsides, farmyards and gateways. Not uncommon and generally distributed, though most frequent near the coast; perhaps not always distinguished from the next species. (129)

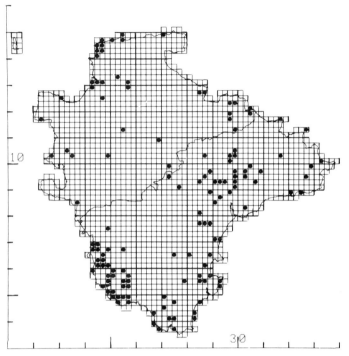

Coronopus didymus (L.) Sm.   Lesser Swine Cress
(*Carara didyma* (L.) Britton)
Introduced; a native of S. America. A very common and widely distributed weed of cultivated and trampled ground. Absent from the higher moors and less frequent in the north-west of the county. (667)

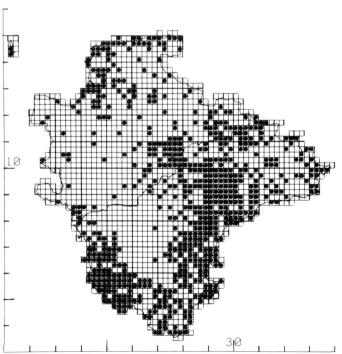

Conringia orientalis (L.) Dum., the Hare's-ear Cabbage, is an introduced weed of arable and waste land which has been reported from several localities in the past, but not seen recently.

Diplotaxis tenuifolia (L.) DC.   Perennial Wall Rocket
Doubtfully native. On old walls, sea cliffs and in waste ground, usually fairly near the sea. Very rare in the north, and only a few scattered records in the south. (9)

Diplotaxis muralis (L.) DC.   Wall Rocket
Introduced; a native of C. Europe. On roadsides and in waste and cultivated land, usually on or near limestone or in base-rich habitats. Not common, but more so than the previous species. (64)

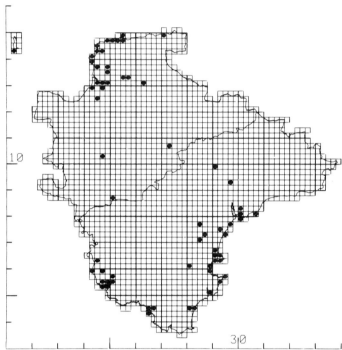

Diplotaxis viminea (L.) DC. has been recorded on one occasion from Torquay, but not seen recently.

Brassica oleracea L.   Wild Cabbage
On sea cliffs, especially where these are steep, limestone and relatively inaccessible; locally frequent around Torquay and Dartmouth, and said to occur at Braunton, though not found recently. All inland records are escapes from cultivation. (16)

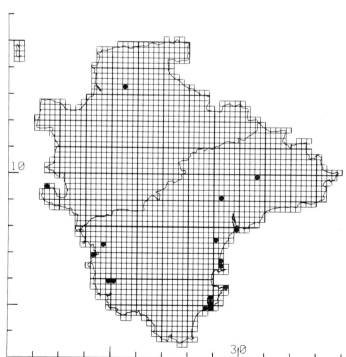

Brassica napus L.   Rape, Swede
Introduced; a native of Europe. An escape from cultivation, found chiefly in the south and east of the county, and rarely persisting. (27)

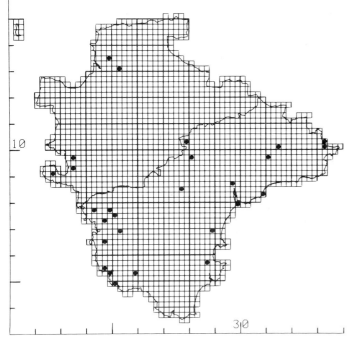

Brassica nigra (L.) Koch   Black Mustard
(*Sinapis nigra* L.)
Abundant in coastal districts around Plymouth and Torbay, and quite frequent elsewhere along the south coast, especially on broken and waste ground around cliffs, as at Dawlish and Branscombe, and in the north around Barnstaple and Ilfracombe. Uncommon inland, usually in the vicinity of rivers. (194)

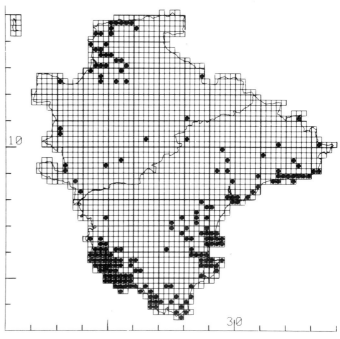

Brassica elongata Ehrh. was reported from Exmouth in 1919; **Brassica juncea** (L.) Czern., (*Sinapis juncea* L.), is sometimes reported as a casual.

Sinapis arvensis L.   Wild Mustard, Charlock
Abundant in cultivated land, waste places and sometimes in hedges. Common throughout the county, though absent from heathland and permanent pasture. (765)

Brassica rapa L.   Turnip
(inc. *B. campestris* L.)
Introduced; a native of Europe. An escape from cultivation which is found in various parts of the county, but rarely persists. (41)

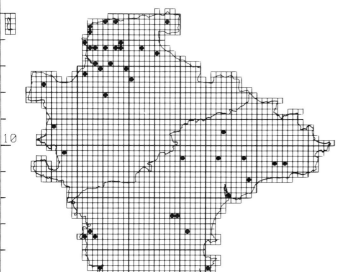
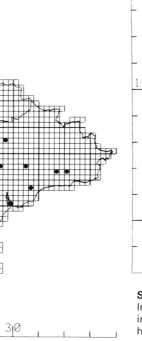

Sinapis alba L.   White Mustard
Introduced; a native of Europe. Scattered throughout the county in waste places and cultivated land, often in more base-rich habitats. (52)

61

Sinapis alba L. White Mustard

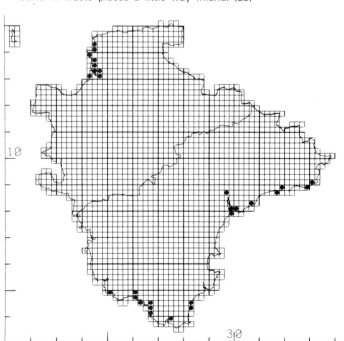

Crambe maritima L. Seakale
On coastal sand and shingle; recorded from Braunton and a few sites in S. Devon, including sea cliffs near Sidmouth, but it is now quite rare. (12)

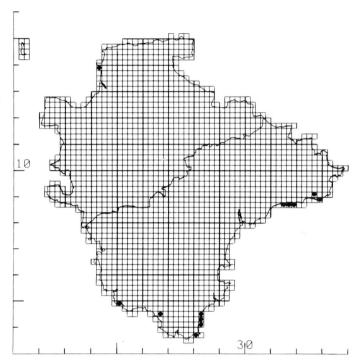

Rhynchosinapis wrightii (O.E.Schulz) Dandy ex Clapham
  Lundy Cabbage
(*Brassicella wrightii* O.E.Schulz)
On sea cliffs and grassy slopes, mostly along the eastern side of Lundy, to which it is endemic. (3)

Rhynchosinapis cheiranthos (Vill.) Dandy ex Clapham, (*Brassicella cheiranthos* Vill.), the Tall Wallflower Cabbage, has been found on occasion on roadsides and waste places in various parts of N. and S. Devon, but none recently and it is probably extinct. **Rhynchosinapis monensis** (L.) Dandy ex Clapham, (*Brassicella monensis* (L.) O.E.Schulz), has been reported from near Torquay, but not seen recently and is probably extinct.

Hirschfeldia incana (L.) Lagrèze-Fossat, (*Brassica incana* (L.) Meigen. non Ten.), the Hoary Mustard, is a native of the Mediterranean region and has been recorded from scattered sites in Devon, but none recently, and it is probably extinct.

Cakile maritima Scop. Sea Rocket
Not uncommon on sandy and shingly shores, especially along the strand-line, on both north and south coasts. Occasionally found in waste places a little way inland. (28)

Raphanus raphanistrum L. White Charlock, Wild Radish
Ssp. **raphanistrum** is widely distributed as a somewhat calcifuge weed of cultivated fields and waste places; local, most frequent in the vicinity of Exeter. (79)

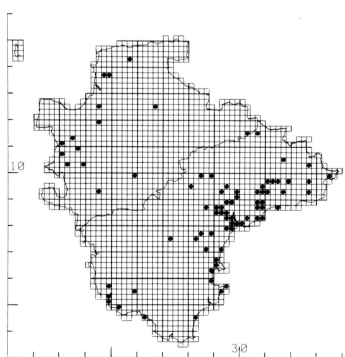

Ssp. **maritimus** (Sm.) Thell., (*R. maritimus* Sm.), the Sea Radish, occurs on sandy shores and sea cliffs, mostly in S. Devon, where it is locally frequent. There are only 2 isolated records from the north coast. (28)

Reseda lutea L. Wild Mignonette
Rather infrequent in sandy and chalky fields and waste places; mainly in the south and east, but with scattered localities elsewhere, some of which may be escapes from cultivation. (25)

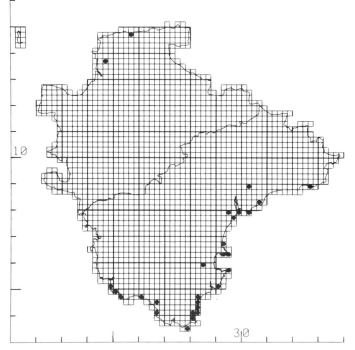

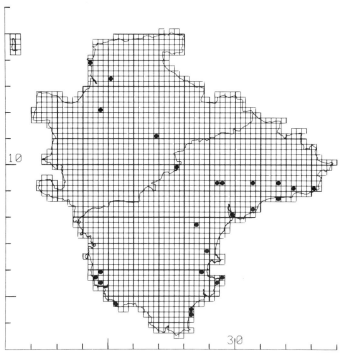

Reseda alba L. Upright Mignonette
Introduced; a native of the Mediterranean region, recorded as a casual in various parts of the county, and perhaps naturalised on Braunton Burrows. (1)

RESEDACEAE

Reseda luteola L. Dyer's Rocket
Locally frequent on waste ground, and also in poor pastures and on cliffs, preferring rather clayey or calcareous habitats, and especially near the sea. Most frequent in the south, and around Braunton Burrows. (119)

DROSERACEAE

Drosera rotundifolia L. Sundew
Widely distributed in *Sphagnum* bogs and wet peaty heathland; throughout the county in suitable habitats. (248)

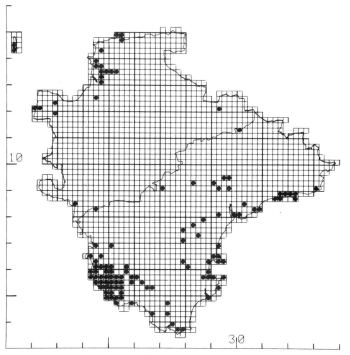

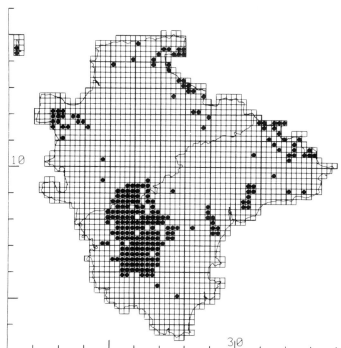

Drosera anglica Huds.   Great Sundew
In similar habitats to the last, but now very rare; there is a single record from Hense Moor, Luppitt. (1)

Drosera x obovata Mert. & Koch
(*D. anglica* x *rotundifolia*)
This hybrid has been recorded from Chardstock; there is a recent record from Hense Moor, Luppitt. (1)

Drosera intermedia Hayne   Long-leaved Sundew
(*D. longifolia* L.)
In damp peaty places on heaths and moors, perhaps preferring rather wetter habitats than *D. rotundifolia,* often in runnels that are wet in winter but dry out in summer. Local in suitable habitats, though sometimes abundant where it occurs. Absent from much of Dartmoor and Exmoor. (27)

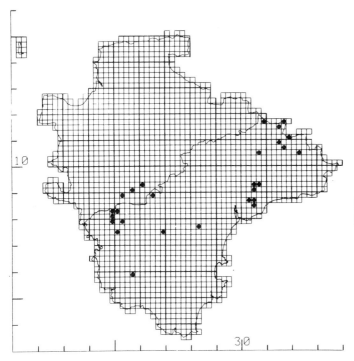

Umbilicus rupestris (Salisb.) Dandy
      Navelwort, Wall Pennywort
(*Cotyledon umbilicus-veneris* L.)
On walls and rocks, sometimes in stony hedgerows, in base-poor habitats. In hedges and on sea cliffs, it may achieve a considerable size. Common and generally distributed. (1386)

Sempervivum tectorum L., the Houseleek, is an introduced species formerly planted on the roofs of houses and at one time common on old thatch. Rarely, if ever, seen in such habitats nowadays, but sometimes cultivated.

Sedum telephium L.   Orpine, Live-long
In hedges and on walls and cliffs, widely distributed but rarely plentiful. Often in situations where it could have escaped from cultivation, but perhaps native in a few. (91)

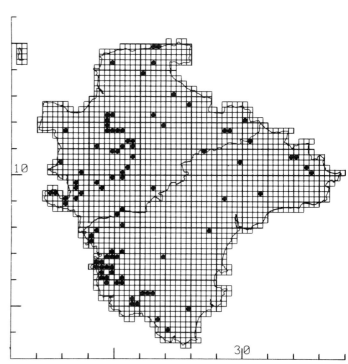

CRASSULACEAE

Crassula tillaea Lester-Garland, (*Tillaea muscosa* L.), the Mossy Tillaea, occurs on bare sand or gravel, usually in or near quarries. It was formerly known from the vicinity of the Rumple slate quarries, in the Plym valley, but has not been seen there for many years.

Ssp. **fabaria** (Koch) Kirsch., (*S. fabaria* Koch), has been found in similar situations but, with no recent records, is probably extinct.

Sedum spurium Bieb.

Introduced; a native of the Caucasus. Sometimes grown in gardens and becoming semi-naturalised on rocks, walls and in dry hedges in the vicinity of habitations. (8)

Sedum reflexum L.   Large Yellow Stonecrop
(*S. rupestre* auct.)

Introduced; a native of Europe. On walls and rocks, occasionally on houses. Commonly cultivated and frequently escaping, and thus usually only in the vicinity of habitations. A white-flowered form has been reported from Torbay. (172)

Sedum acre L.   Wall-pepper

On rocky ledges, sea cliffs and dry dune grassland, less frequently on wall-tops. Most common in coastal districts and preferring base-rich substrata, even if very dry, and even found on cement roofs. Absent from large areas inland. (327)

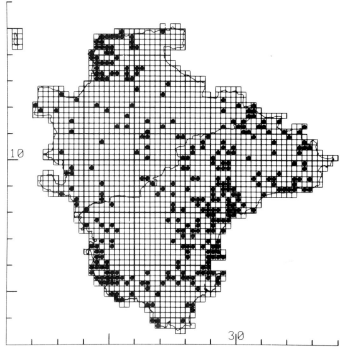

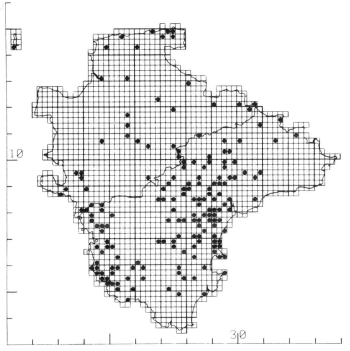

Sedum forsterianum Sm.   Rock Stonecrop
(*S. rupestre* L. p.p.)

A rare species probably confined as native plant to the northern slopes of Exmoor, but also cultivated and escaping into similar situations as the previous species. (29)

Sedum album L.   White Stonecrop

Native at least on the limestones of Berry Head and Bolt Head, but widely grown as a garden plant and frequently escaping, becoming naturalised on walls and similar dry habitats. (163)

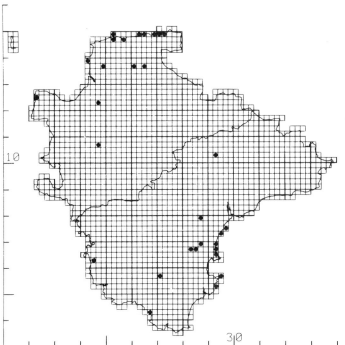

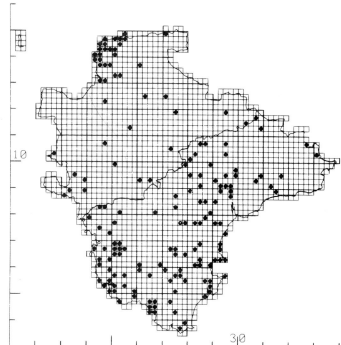

Sedum anglicum Huds.   English Stonecrop
A calcifuge species of rocks, tors, banks and sandy places. Quite common along both coasts and on and near Dartmoor, but rare elsewhere. (426)

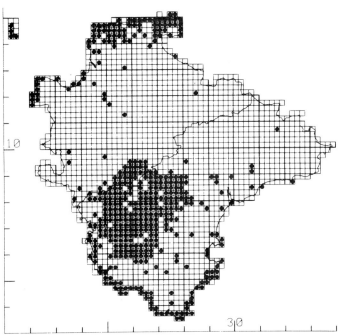

Sedum dasyphyllum L.   Thick-leaved Stonecrop
Introduced; a native of S. Europe. An escape from cultivation found in one or two localities where it has become well established. (1)

Sedum sexangulare L. has been reported as well established on walls at Staverton and Torquay (Fl. Dev.) but it has not been seen recently and it is not known if it survives.

SAXIFRAGACEAE

Saxifraga x urbicum D.A.Webb   London Pride
(*S. spathularis* x *umbrosa*)
Introduced; a hybrid of unknown origin, widely cultivated in gardens and found in the vicinity of habitations or rubbish. Well established for many years at Bittadon, but generally not persisting for any length of time. (15)

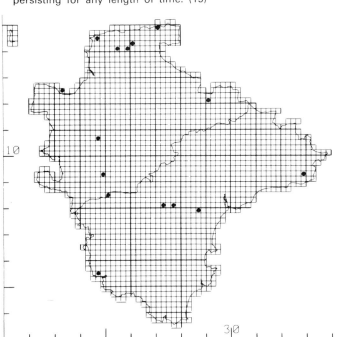

Saxifraga tridactylites L.   Rue-leaved Saxifrage
On the tops of walls, especially with lime mortar, rock ledges and open sandy habitats. Local in calcareous habitats, but widely distributed, mainly in the South Hams, but in scattered localities elsewhere, including Braunton Burrows. (72)

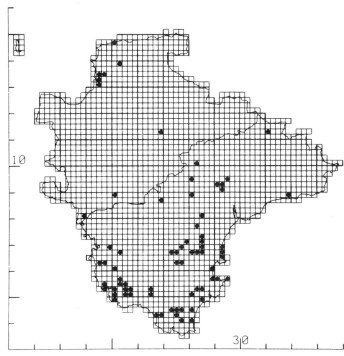

Saxifraga granulata L.   Meadow Saxifrage
Introduced in Devon. A northern species of well-drained neutral to base-rich grassland, reported in Fl. Dev. from several localities, but now to be found only near Barnstaple. (1)

Chrysosplenium alternifolium L.
            Alternate-leaved Golden Saxifrage
By streams, ditches and in damp woods, always in shaded habitats. Rare, with very few and scattered records. (10)

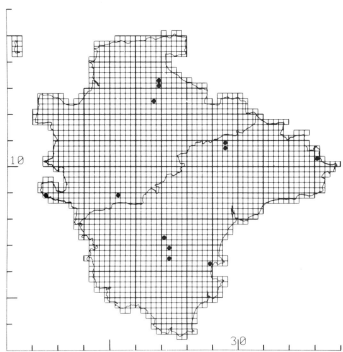

Chrysosplenium oppositifolium L.

Opposite-leaved Golden Saxifrage

In woods, by streams and on wet mud or rocks, in shaded habitats. Common and generally distributed, avoiding the higher moors. (882)

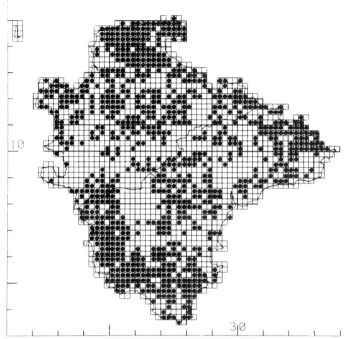

Tellima grandiflora (Pursh) Dougl. ex Lindl. is grown in gardens and has become naturalised in damp places in a few localities. (8)

ESCALLONIACEAE

Escallonia macrantha Hook. & Arnott

Introduced; a native of Chile. Commonly grown in gardens, or as a hedge, especially near the sea, and sometimes naturalised. (3)

GROSSULARIACEAE

Ribes rubrum L.   Red Currant

(*R. sylvestre* (Lam.) Mert. & Koch)

Perhaps introduced; native in Europe. Widely cultivated and occasionally found in woods and hedges throughout the county, often well away from habitations and rather frequent in the Teign valley, though all records probably originate from cultivated plants. (129)

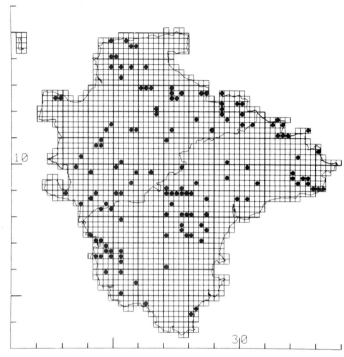

Ribes nigrum L.   Black Currant

Occurs sporadically in woods and hedges, often in damp habitats. Widely scattered throughout the county, usually as single specimens and perhaps always bird-sown from cultivated plants. (75)

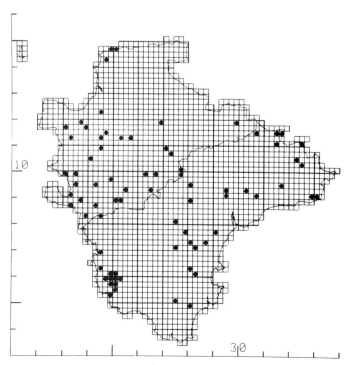

Ribes uva-crispa L.   Gooseberry
(*R. grossularia* L.)
Commonly cultivated and frequently found in woods and
hedges, often as single plants. Perhaps always bird-sown from
cultivated specimens. (264)

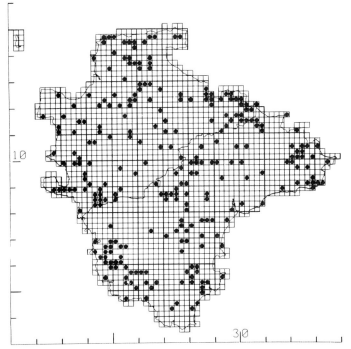

Filipendula vulgaris Moench   Dropwort
(*F. hexapetala* Gilib.)
In dry and usually calcareous habitats, especially grassland and
open scrub. Probably confined to the Torbay limestone and the
chalk in E. Devon, where it is locally frequent. (23)

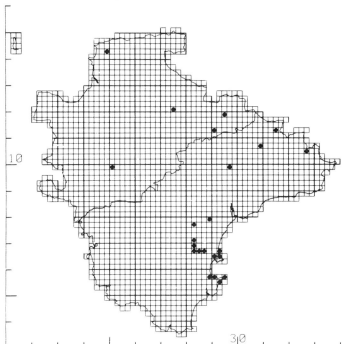

ROSACEAE

Spiraea salicifolia L.   Willow-leaved Spiraea
Introduced. A native of Europe, sometimes planted in hedges
and becoming established in wood margins and scrub, usually
in rather moist habitats. (11)

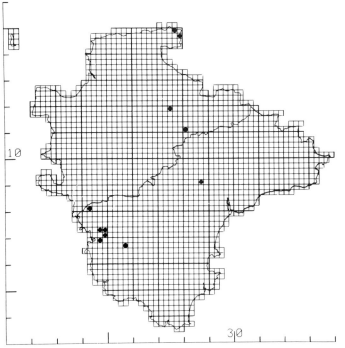

Filipendula ulmaria (L.) Maxim.   Meadow-sweet
In wet meadows, marshes, stream-sides and hedges. Common
and generally distributed, and locally very abundant. (1450)

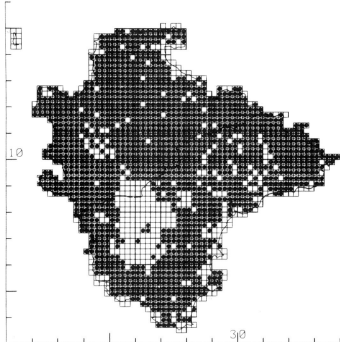

Rubus saxatilis L.   Stone Bramble
A species of woods and heaths in Northern Britain which is
confined to a very small area at Watersmeet, near Lynton. (1)

Rubus idaeus L.   Raspberry
In woods and scrub, usually on fairly well-drained or sandy
soils. Widely distributed though often in small quantities, except
in parts of N. Devon, where it is locally frequent in hedges. (406)

It is not possible to give a detailed treatment of all the
microspecies which have been recorded for Devon. There is
some controversy over the extent to which British microspecies
can be properly assigned to very similar Continental taxa, and a
number of new microspecies have been described recently in
consequence. Readers who are interested in this group will find
a full account in the forthcoming "Flora of Great Britain and
Ireland".

Rubus caesius L.   Dewberry
Common and widely distributed in woods and open habitats
including heathland, and sometimes in damp or wet places on
clay or limestone. It hybridises readily with many of the true
blackberries, and particularly those in Section Triviales, and
there is strong evidence that this section is of hybrid origin with
R. caesius as one of the parents. (181)

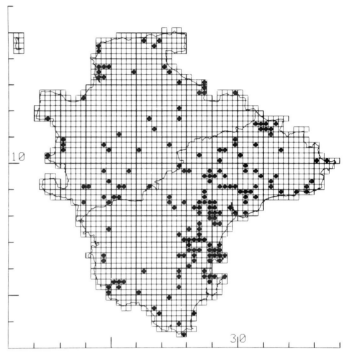

Rubus fruticosus L. agg.   Bramble, Blackberry
Very common throughout the county, in all except the more
extreme habitats; especially frequent in woods, scrub and
hedgerows. (1736)

Rosa arvensis Huds.   Field Rose
Widespread throughout the county, though absent from Dartmoor and Exmoor, in hedges, scrub and waste places. Tends to
be rather rare in the immediate vicinity of the coast. (1145)

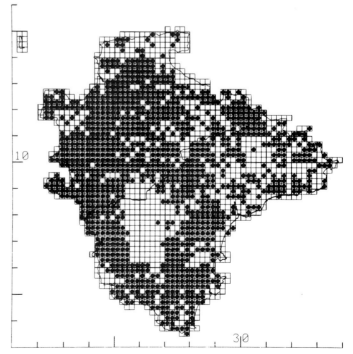

This aggregate contains a large but uncertain number of
apomictic species (microspecies); pollination is required for the
development of the fruit, and the seeds this then contains will
germinate to produce progeny identical to the female parent.
Sexual reproduction takes place only very occasionally, but in
such cases, the progeny will usually differ from both parents.

Rosa pimpinellifolia L.   Burnet Rose
(*R. spinosissima* L. p.p.)
Largely confined to coasts, especially the north coast between Morthoe and Hartland, and on the south coast from Salcombe westwards. All inland records are doubtful, as a rather similar plant is grown in gardens and may escape. (30)

R. x wheldonii W.-Dod, (*R. arvensis* x *canina*, *R. canina* var. *flexilis* (Deseg.) Rouy, *R. canina* var. *schottiana* Ser.) has been reported from the county, but without locality.

Rosa tomentosa Sm.
(*R. villosa* agg.)
In hedges and waste places, mostly in scattered localities in the west and north; probably less common than formerly, but not always easy to recognise. (74)

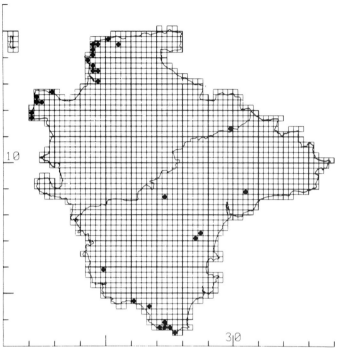

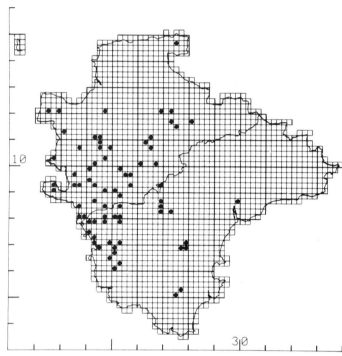

Rosa stylosa Desv.
Recorded by Savery in Fl. Dev. as a frequent species in the lowlands, especially on rich soils, but it now seems far less common than formerly, with records only from Torbay and a few sites elsewhere. (9)

Rosa canina L.   Dog Rose
Very common throughout the county, in hedgerows, scrub and waste places, though absent from the higher moors. Often grows with *R. arvensis,* but is more frequent. Numerous varieties and forms have been described. (1303)

Rosa rubiginosa L.   Sweet Briar
Quite widely distributed but scattered, in hedges and waste places. Probably only truly native on calcareous soils. A rather similar plant is sometimes cultivated, and may escape, and some records may be of this. (51)

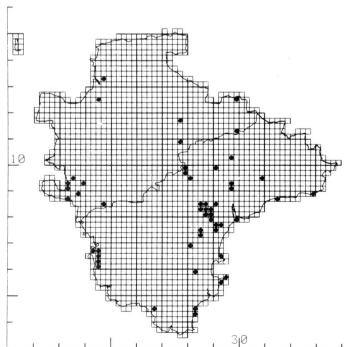

Rosa micrantha Borrer ex Sm.
Very similar to *R. rubiginosa,* with which it is sometimes confused. Rather less confined to calcareous soils, but rare, and found in scattered localities mostly around the periphery of Dartmoor. (11)

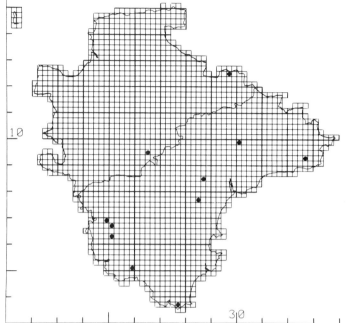

Rosa obtusifolia Desv., (*R. tomentella* Leman), is not readily distinguishable from *R. canina,* but could probably be found in hedges in various parts of the county; there are no specific records. **Rosa corymbifera** Borkh., (*R. dumetorum* Thuill.), is also very similar to *R. canina* and has been reported as common and widespread. The absence of recent records may reflect the difficulties of the taxonomy. **R. sherardii** Davies has been reported from both N. and S. Devon, but it is a species with a northern distribution and its occurrence in the county requires confirmation.
There is much need for further work on the distribution of the *Rosa villosa* aggregate, and of related species, in Devon.

Agrimonia eupatoria L.   Agrimony
Along roadsides, in hedges and the edges of fields; common and generally distributed, but rather local in the north-west. (777)

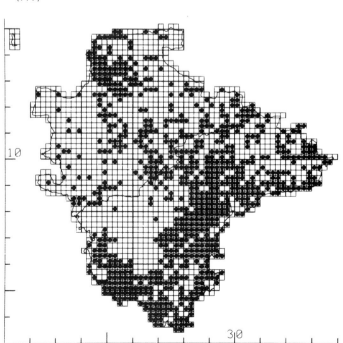

Agrimonia procera Wallr.   Fragrant Agrimony
(*A. odorata* auct.)
In woods, scrub and grassy places, generally calcifuge. Very scattered over the county, locally not uncommon but seemingly absent from considerable areas. (68)

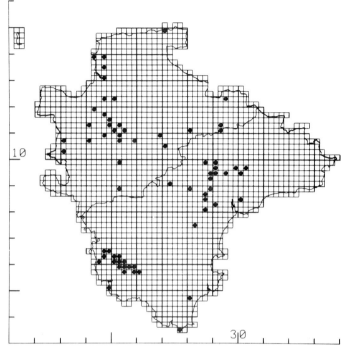

Sanguisorba officinalis L.   Great Burnet
(*Poterium officinale* (L.) A.Gray)
In damp meadows and beside rivers and streams; generally rather local, most frequent in parts of the west and north-west. (53)

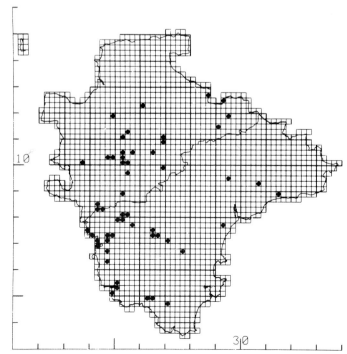

Sanguisorba minor Scop.   Salad Burnet
(*Poterium sanguisorba* L.)
Abundant in calcareous grasslands in E. Devon and around
Torbay, and can also be found in base-rich soils or near the sea,
on cliff-tops, in grassland and rocky places. (124)

Geum urbanum L.   Herb Bennett, Wood Avens
In woods, scrub and hedges; common and generally distributed, usually in rather damp soils. (1540)

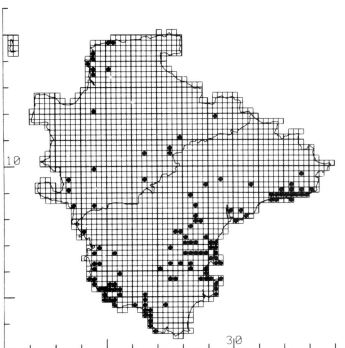

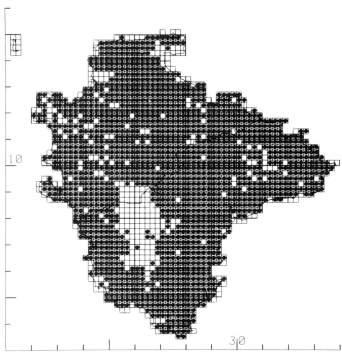

Ssp. **muricata** Briq., (*P. polygamum* Waldst. & Kit.), has been
cultivated as a fodder crop and has been reported as naturalised
in a few localities, but now appears to be extinct.

Acaena novae-zelandiae Kirk
(*A. anserinifolia* auct., non (J.R. & G.Forster) Druce)
Introduced; a native of New Zealand. It was imported with wool
and is now naturalised in scattered localities. It is sometimes
grown in gardens, and may escape. (7)

Geum rivale L.   Water Avens
In moist woods and beside streams and rivers. Rare, only in
scattered localities, and in small quantity, but perhaps more
frequent in the north. (19)

Geum x intermedium Ehrh.
(*G. urbanum* x *rivale*)
This hybrid occurs frequently where the parents grow together,
as in Barton Wood, E. Anstey. It is fertile and forms hybrid
swarms showing a wide range of variation. The very few
records doubtless reflects the rarity of one of its parents. (2)

Potentilla palustris (L.) Scop.   Marsh Cinquefoil
In bogs and marshes; not uncommon in marshes in the
north-west, but very rare elsewhere and absent from Dartmoor.
(59)

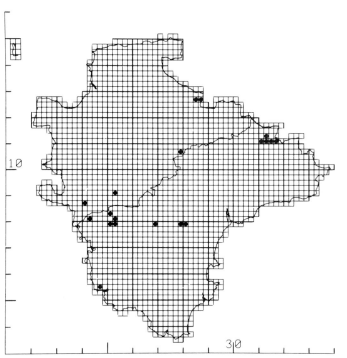

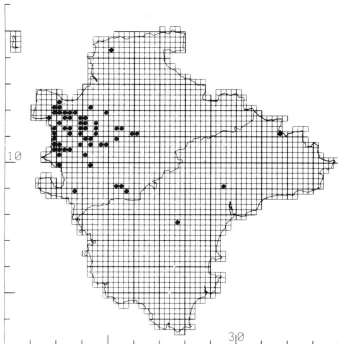

Potentilla anserina L.   Silverweed
In waste places, roadsides, gateways, damp meadows, dune
slacks and on shingle banks. Common and often abundant. It
varies considerably in the silveriness of the leaves. (1520)

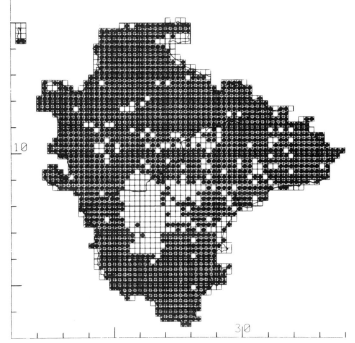

Potentilla argentea L.   Hoary Cinquefoil
In dry, gravelly or sandy grassland. Very rare, with only a single
record from old slate quarries near Ashburton. (1)

Potentilla recta L.
Introduced; a native of Europe. A garden escape which is
well-established on the railway line near Lapford and has been
reported as naturalised in some other localities in the north; the
very few records include one from the south coast. (3)

Potentilla erecta (L.) Raüsch.   Tormentil
In dry pastures and on heaths and moors, avoiding calcareous
habitats. Very common on light acid soils, less frequent on wet
peat, but found over much of Dartmoor, especially in shallow
peat over granite. (1120)

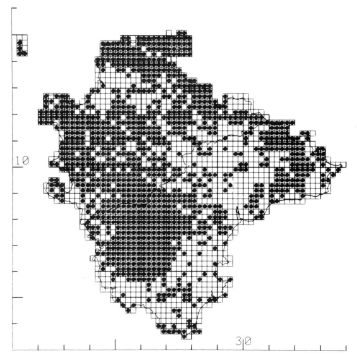

Potentilla anglica Laich.
                          Trailing Tormentil, Creeping Tormentil
(*P. procumbens* Sibth.)
At the edges of woods, in hedges and heathland, in rather
similar situations to *P. erecta,* but much less tolerant of extreme
acidity. Scattered over the county, mostly in the south and west.
(394)

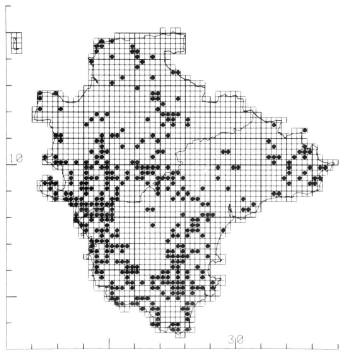

Potentilla x suberecta Zimm., (*P. erecta* x *anglica*), has been
recorded from S. Devon (Fl. Dev.), but it is not known if it
persists.

Potentilla reptans L.   Creeping Cinquefoil
In hedges, waste places and grassland. Common and generally
distributed. (1385)

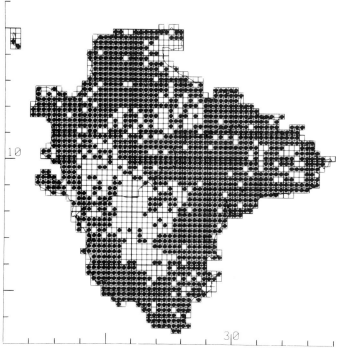

Potentilla x mixta Nolte ex Reichenb., (*P. erecta* x *reptans*, *P. x
italica* Lehm.), has been reported from S. Devon, between
Ermington and Ivybridge, with both its parents, but has not been
seen recently.

Potentilla sterilis (L.) Garcke   Barren Strawberry
In woods and hedgerows, on walls and waste ground. Common
and generally distributed, especially in rather dry habitats.
(1242)

Fragaria x ananassa Duchesne   Garden Strawberry
(*F. chiloensis* x *virginiana*)
Introduced; originated in France. Widely cultivated and frequently escaping to become naturalised on railway banks, in
waste places and near rubbish tips. (27)

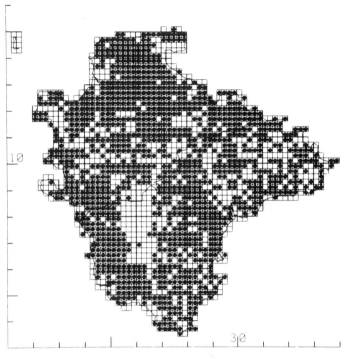

Potentilla norvegica L. is an introduced species which has not
been seen recently and is probably extinct; **P. hirta** L. was once
reported from Chagford, but this, too, has not been seen
recently.

Fragaria moschata Duchesne, the Hautbois Strawberry, is an
introduced species formerly grown for its fruit. It has been
reported on occasion, but perhaps confused with the previous
species. There are no recent records.

Fragaria vesca L.   Wild Strawberry
In woods, hedges and open grassland, preferring well-drained
base-rich or calcareous soils. Common and generally distributed. (1495)

Alchemilla vulgaris L. agg.   Lady's Mantle
In damp grassland and scrub, usually on base-rich or calcareous
soils. Uncommon, and scattered over suitable habitats. (37)

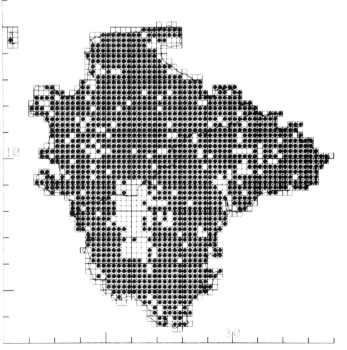

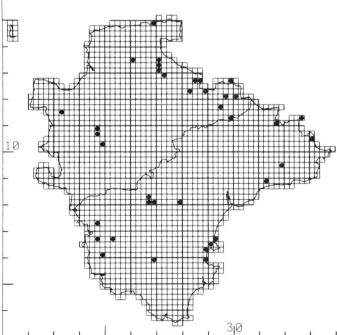

The following species have been recognised in Devon, but not all records of the aggregate species have been appropriately allocated:

Alchemilla xanthochlora Rothm.
In grassland and damp pastures, often beside rivers and streams. Rare and rather scattered. (15)

Aphanes arvensis L.   Parsley Piert
In dry habitats in fields, hillsides, cliffs, gardens and waste places. Fairly common and generally distributed, though not a very prominent plant and perhaps overlooked. (476)

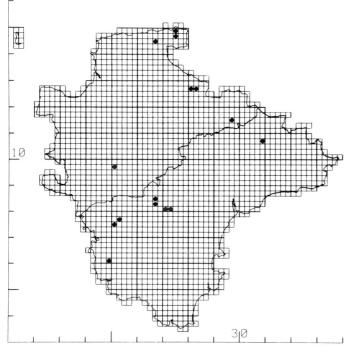

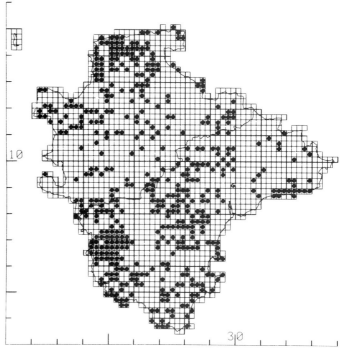

Alchemilla filicaulis Buser
(*A. vulgaris* var. *filicaulis* Buser)
In pastures and grassland by roadsides, usually at low altitudes. Rare and very local. Our plants all belong to ssp. **vestita** (Buser) Bradshaw. (10)

Aphanes microcarpa (Boiss. & Reut.) Rothm.
In similar habitats to the last, but restricted to acid and rather sandy soils. Perhaps less common than *A. arvensis*, but the two species have not always been distinguished. (10)

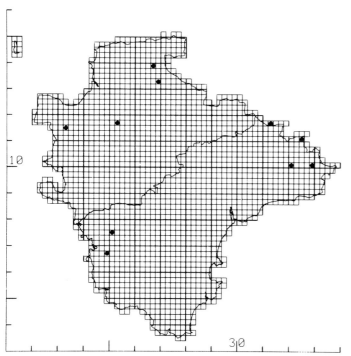

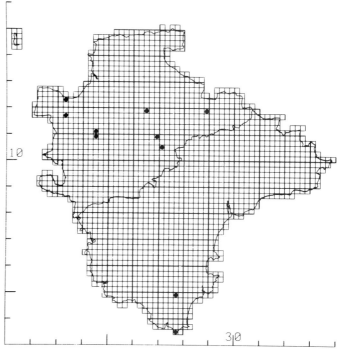

Alchemilla mollis (Buser) Rothm.
Introduced; a native of S.E. Europe. Frequently grown in gardens and sometimes escaping. The single record is from near Yelverton Station, in S.W. Devon. (1)

Pyrus cordata Desv.   Plymouth Pear
Grows in two hedges near Plymouth, where it has been established for over 100 years. This is a listed endangered species, and transplants have been preserved in cultivation. (1)

Pyrus pyraster Burgsd.   Pear
(*P. communis* auct.)
Introduced in Devon. Sometimes found as an escape or as isolated trees in hedges or scrub. Rare, and widely scattered. (8)

Malus sylvestris Mill.   Crab Apple
(*Pyrus malus* L.)
In woods, scrub and hedgerows. Uncommon; a few of the records may apply to *M. domestica* growing in old orchards or escapes from cultivation. (387)

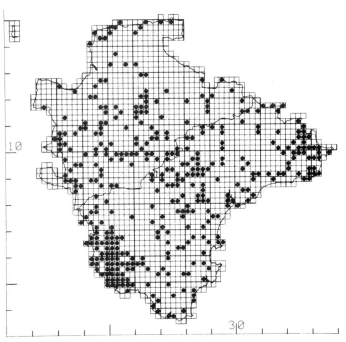

Sorbus torminalis (L.) Crantz   Wild Service Tree
Thinly distributed in woods and scrub, usually over clay or limestone. Occasional around Exeter, and absent from large areas elsewhere. Sometimes regarded as an indicator of ancient woodland. (33)

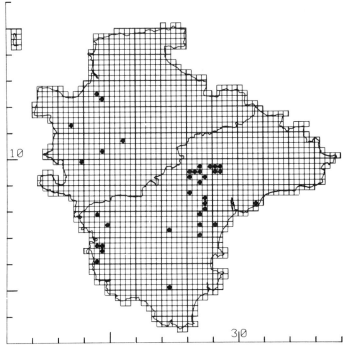

Malus domestica Borkh.   Apple
(*M. sylvestris* ssp. *mitis* (Wallr.) Mansf.)
Introduced; a native of S.W. Asia. Cultivated for its fruit and occasionally escaping, growing from stray pips or in old orchards, but not naturalised. Often not readily distinguishable from *M. sylvestris*. (2)

Sorbus aucuparia L.   Rowan, Mountain Ash
In woods, scrub and hedges, often more prominent at higher altitudes and sometimes the only tree on moorlands and tors. Tending to be absent from clayey and calcareous soils, but otherwise common and generally distributed. (1133)

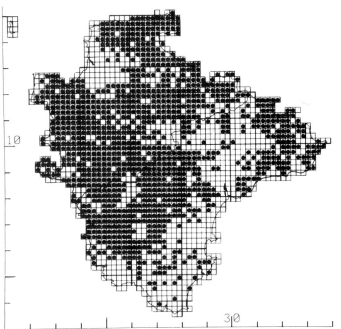

Sorbus aria (L.) Crantz   Whitebeam
Introduced in Devon. Probably invariably planted and not naturalised. Several of the following species are often regarded as belonging to this species in an aggregate sense. (29)

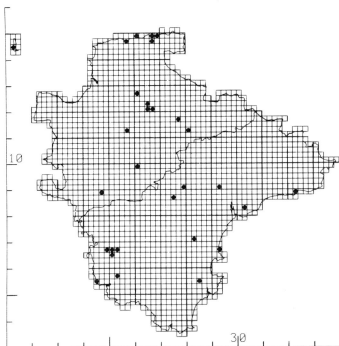

Sorbus vexans E.F.Warb.   Rock Whitebeam

In rocky woods near the north coast. It has been recorded between Lynmouth and Watersmeet, and at Coombe Martin (Herb. EXR, det. Warburg), but there could well be other localities, as access to these woods is very difficult. (3)

Sorbus anglica Hedl.

In rocky woods on limestone. Very rare, with records only from Newton Abbot and Torquay. (2)

Sorbus devoniensis E.F.Warb.   French Hales

In woods and hedges, usually on rather sandy or well-drained soils. Locally frequent, especially in the north-west, and the commonest species of this complex in the county. It is thought to have arisen as an apomictic species derived from the hybrid *S. aria* x *S. torminalis* (*S. x vagensis* Wilmott). (35)

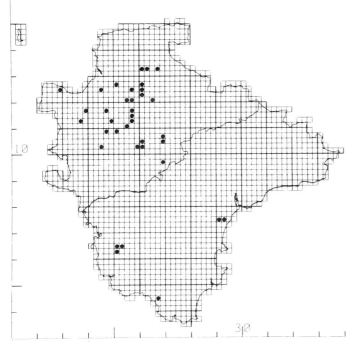

Sorbus subcuneata Wilmott

In rocky woods along the north coast. In similar localities to *S. vexans,* with rather few and usually isolated trees, especially in the Lyn valley and near Watersmeet. It, too, is thought to have been derived from *S. x vagensis.* (3)

Sorbus porrigentiformis E.F.Warb. is reported from S. Devon by Warburg (1957), but without locality or habitat. **Sorbus rupicola** (Syme) Hedl. has been recorded from limestone rocks near the coast at Torquay and Babbacombe. Although there are no recent records, there is no reason to suppose it does not persist.

Cotoneaster simonsii Baker

Introduced; a native of Assam. Frequently cultivated and occasionally naturalised on walls, in hedges and in waste places, especially around Plymouth, more rarely elsewhere, and probably always from bird-sown seed. (56)

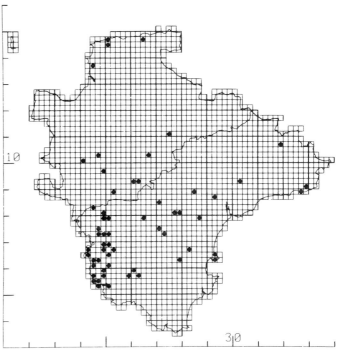

Cotoneaster microphyllus Wall. ex Lindl.

Introduced; a native of the Himalayas and China. Commonly cultivated and naturalised in many places on limestone, usually near the sea, also on walls and rocky places near habitations, and on old mine tips in W. Devon. (52)

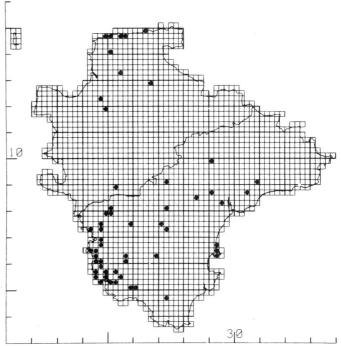

Cotoneaster horizontalis Decaisne

Introduced; a native of China. Quite frequently grown in gardens and sometimes escaping or bird-sown, but scarcely naturalised. (7)

Cotoneaster integerrimus Medic. is an introduced European species, sometimes grown in gardens and sometimes escaping, but scarcely naturalised and there are no recent records.

Mespilus germanica L.   Medlar
Introduced; a native of S.W. Asia. It used to be grown for its fruits and has been reported as naturalised in scrub and hedges, but the only recent record is of one old tree in the Axmouth-Lyme Regis Undercliffs Nature Reserve. (1)

Crataegus laevigata (Poir.) DC.
(*C. oxyacantha* auct., *C. oxyacanthoides* Thuill.)
Introduced in Devon. This species is recorded from time to time, and is planted occasionally, but most reports undoubtedly refer to *C. monogyna.* (1)

Crataegus monogyna Jacq.   Hawthorn, May
In scrub, woods and hedges. Very common and generally distributed, absent only from wet peat on the higher moors, and sometimes scattered on the slopes of tors. Frequently planted in new hedges. (1753)

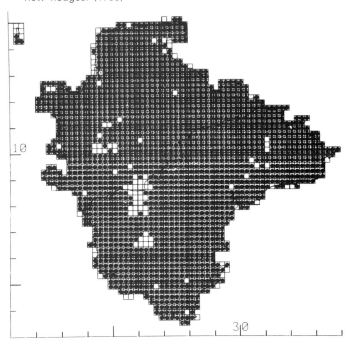

Crataegus crus-galli L. is an introduced tree sometimes grown for ornament in several N. Devon towns, and has become semi-naturalised in a few places.

Prunus spinosa L.   Blackthorn, Sloe
In woods and hedges, and on sea cliffs. Common and generally distributed, but absent from the higher moors. (1667)

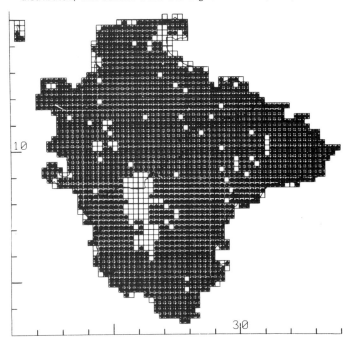

Prunus domestica L.   Plum, Bullace
Introduced; a native of S.W. Asia. In scrub and hedges, widely cultivated and not uncommonly naturalised, especially in the south and west. (132)

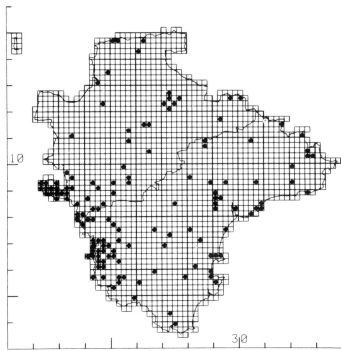

Ssp. **domestica** is very commonly grown for its fruit and is occasionally found naturalised.
Ssp. **insititia** (L.) C.K.Schneid., (*P. insititia* L.), is often regarded as a native plant. It is quite widely distributed, often some distance from habitations.
The hybrid **P. x fruticans** Weihe, (*P. domestica* x *spinosa*), appears to be quite frequent over much of southern England, but has not been specifically recorded from Devon.

Prunus avium (L.) L.   Gean, Wild Cherry
In woods and hedges, usually on fairly base-rich soils. Common and generally distributed, most apparent when it is flowering in spring. (638)

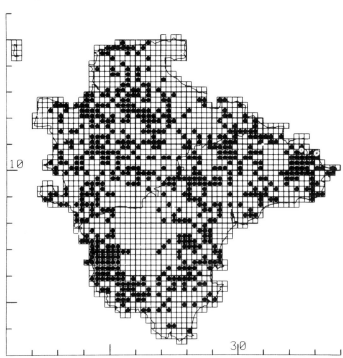

Prunus cerasus L.   Sour Cherry
In woods and hedges. Probably largely, if not always, bird-sown from cultivated plants. Thinly scattered over the county, and rather rare. Modern trimming methods largely seem to prevent it from flowering in hedges. (40)

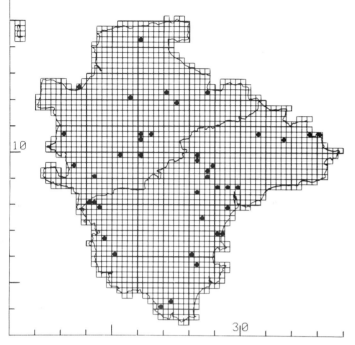

Prunus padus L.   Bird Cherry
Introduced in Devon. In woods and scrub, very local, and probably always planted or bird-sown from cultivated plants. (5)

Prunus cerasifera Ehrh.   Cherry Plum
Introduced; a native of S.W. Asia. Occasionally planted and sometimes escaping but not or scarcely naturalised. (2)

Prunus laurocerasus L.   Cherry Laurel
Introduced; a native of S.W. Asia. Often planted, either for ornament or for pheasant coverts, and sometimes self-sown or naturalised in a few localities. Most records are of planted specimens or escapes from cultivation. (329)

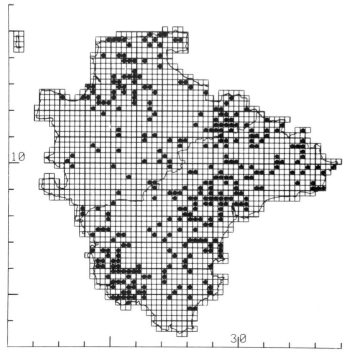

Prunus lusitanica L., the Portuguese Laurel, is an introduced species, occasionally planted as an ornamental shrub, but probably not naturalised.

LEGUMINOSAE

Laburnum anagyroides Medic., the Golden Rain tree, is introduced from Europe and is usually planted or found as an escape from cultivation. It is scarcely naturalised.

Cytisus scoparius (L.) Link   Broom
(*Sarothamnus scoparius* (L.) Wimm. ex Koch)
On heaths, in woods and hedges, on banks and in waste ground, usually markedly calcifuge. Occurs rather sparingly on the moors, in well-drained habitats, and especially along the banks of streams. (528)

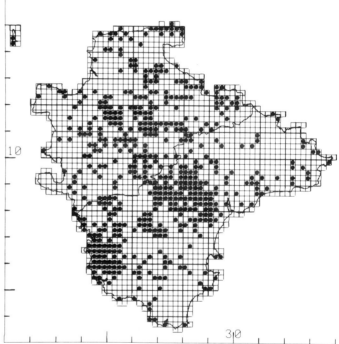

Ssp. **scoparius** is the common erect form.
Ssp. **maritimus** (Rouy) Heywood, (*C. scoparius* var. *prostratus* Bailey), with prostrate branches and silky-hairy leaves, is found on Hartland Quay and on Lundy, where it is locally frequent.

Genista tinctoria L.   Dyer's Greenweed
In rough grassland and road-verges, usually on base-rich soils.
Rare, only to be found locally in the north-west and east of the
county. A prostrate form, sometimes referred to var. *humifusa,*
grows on cliffs at Hartland. (13)

Ulex europaeus L.   Whin, Furze, Gorse
On heaths and commons, in hedges, roadsides and waste
places. Common and generally distributed on well-drained and
usually acid soils. It tends to be absent from moorland except
along the margins of roads and tracks. (1642)

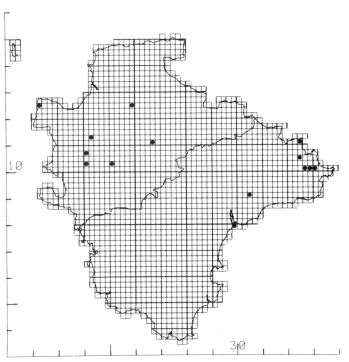

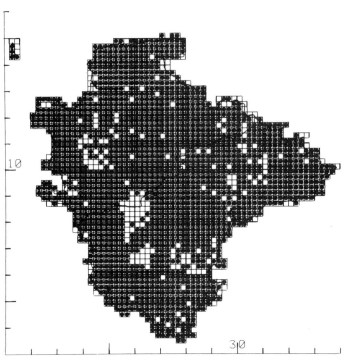

Genista anglica L.   Petty Whin, Needle Furze
On heaths and acid grassland. Scattered over the county, but
mainly in the north-west and absent from Dartmoor and many
lowland heaths. Has suffered from grazing in many localities,
and is now extinct on Roborough Down. (59)

Ulex gallii Planch.   Western Gorse, Dwarf Furze
On heaths, moors and acid grassland. Common in suitable
habitats, and a strict calcifuge. A notable component of the
moorland flora which is found up to 530 m (1740 ft.) on eastern
parts of Dartmoor, though at lower altitudes in the west. (685)

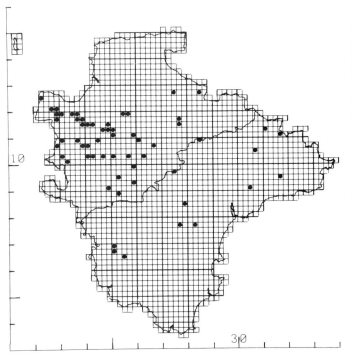

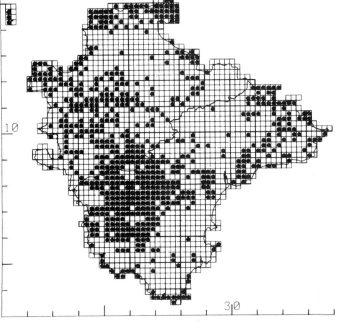

Ulex minor Roth does not occur in Devon.

Lupinus arboreus Sims   Tree Lupin

Introduced; a native of California. Much planted to stabilise sand dunes and china-clay waste tips. It is established on Dawlish Warren, around the north coast between Saunton and Croyde, and in scattered localities elsewhere. It is often damaged or killed by severe frosts, but the seeds germinate readily in sandy soils. (13)

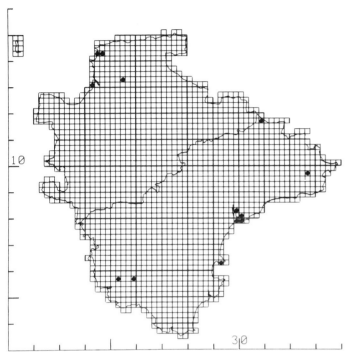

Vicia sylvatica L.   Wood Vetch

In scrub and waste places, usually near the sea. Scattered on cliffs along both coasts, perhaps sometimes cultivated; the few inland records are probably escapes from cultivation. (29)

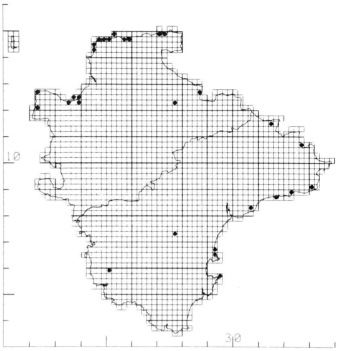

Astragalus glycyphyllos L., the Milk Vetch, no longer occurs in Devon.

Vicia cracca L.   Tufted Vetch

In hedges, scrub and waste places; generally distributed in lowland areas, and fairly common, but easily overlooked before it flowers in mid- to late summer. (1114)

Vicia hirsuta (L.) S.F.Gray   Hairy Tare

Common on hedgebanks and in grassy and waste places. Generally distributed, but absent from the moors. (695)

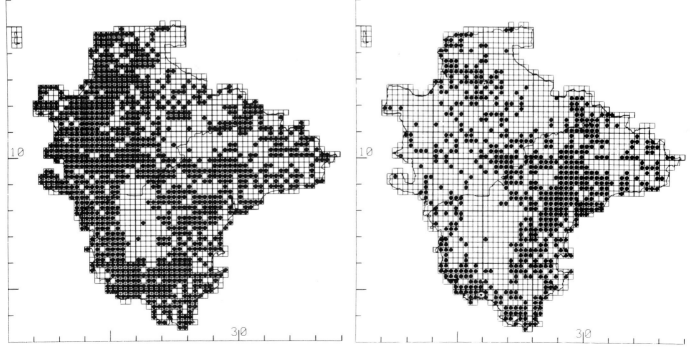

Vicia tenuissima (Bieb.) Schinz & Thell.   Slender Tare
(*V. gracilis* Lois.)
In grassland and waste places. Rare, mostly in the south of the
county, but also along the road between Exeter and Barnstaple.
(9)

Vicia tetrasperma (L.) Schreb.   Smooth Tare
In hedges and grassy waste places. Less common than *V.
hirsuta*, but generally distributed over the county. (229)

Vicia sativa L.   Common Vetch
On roadsides, in hedges and grassy places. Common and
generally distributed.

Ssp. **sativa** is introduced from Europe. It is sometimes cultivated
or appears as a weed and is naturalised in many places. (179)

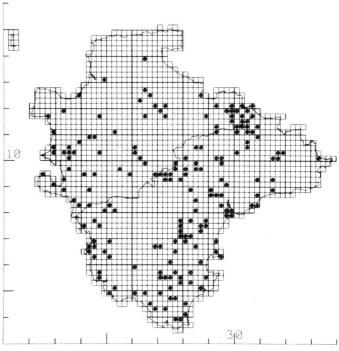

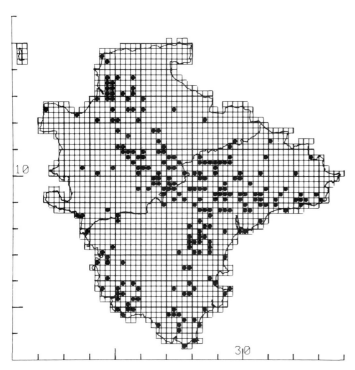

Ssp. **nigra** (L.) Ehrh., (*V. sativa* ssp. *angustifolia* (L.) Gaud., *V.
angustifolia* L.), is very common in hedges, banks and waste
places throughout the county. (1125)

Vicia sepium L.   Bush Vetch
In grassland, hedges and scrub, and base-rich woodland.
Common and generally distributed, though absent from Dart-
moor and rather less frequent in the north-west. (1260)

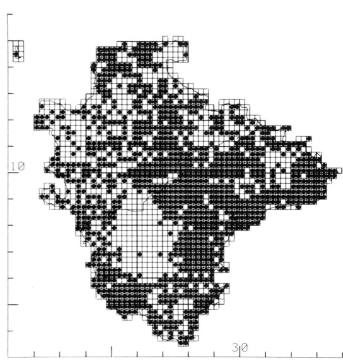

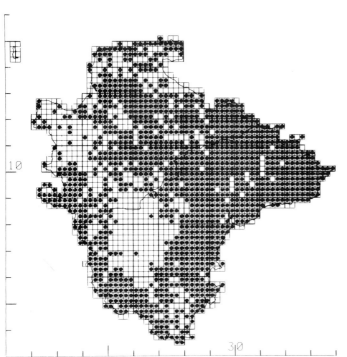

Vicia lutea L.   Yellow Vetch
Very rare; perhaps native at Start Point, but doubtfully elsewhere and the Exeter record is probably an introduction. (2)

Vicia bithynica (L.) L.   Bithynian Vetch
On cliffs and in hedges near the sea. Very rare, now only to be
found in the Exe estuary and on cliffs at Exmouth. (3)

Vicia orobus DC., the Bitter Vetch, has not been seen for many years and is undoubtedly extinct. **Vicia lathyroides** L., the Spring Vetch, may still be found as an introduction, but is probably also extinct. **Vicia pannonica** Crantz has not been seen for more than a century!

Lathyrus japonicus Willd.   Sea Pea
(*L. maritimus* Bigel.)
On shingle beaches; only known with certainty from Slapton Sands, where it is rather rare. Our plant belongs to ssp. **martitimus** (L.) P.W.Ball. (1)

Lathyrus montanus Bernh.   Wood Pea, Bitter Vetch
In woods or scrubby and open heaths and banks, always on acid soils. Quite common, perhaps more frequent in the north-west and around Dartmoor. (630)

Lathyrus sylvestris L.   Narrow-leaved Everlasting Pea
In scrub and waste places, especially in damper habitats on sea cliffs; locally frequent. (67)

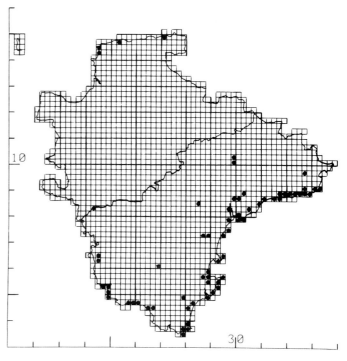

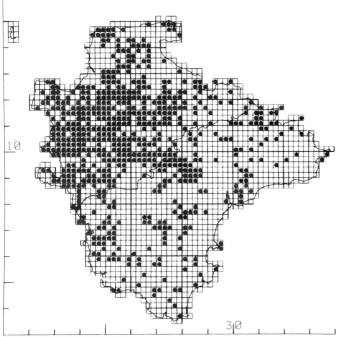

Lathyrus pratensis L.   Meadow Vetchling
In hedges, along roadsides and in grassy places. Common and generally distributed, except on the moors. (1448)

Lathyrus latifolius L.   Everlasting Pea
Introduced; a native of S. Europe. Cultivated in gardens and sometimes escaping. There are scattered records from all over the county, often on railway embankments. (39)

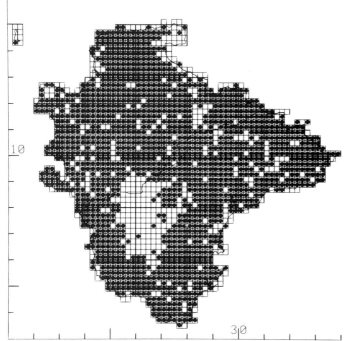

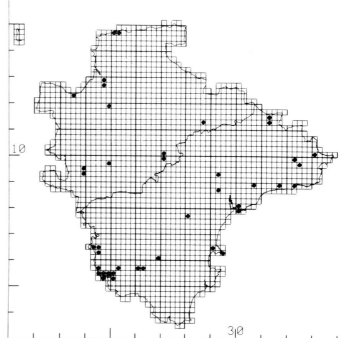

Lathyrus nissolia L.   Grass Vetch, Crimson Vetchling
In grassy waste places, fields and dry banks. A rare plant, from
scattered localities in S. Devon, and one near Instow. (14)

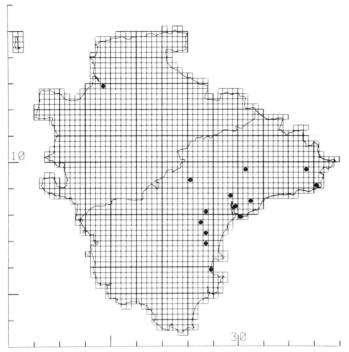

Lathyrus aphaca L.   Yellow Vetchling
In dry grassland, hedges and waste places. Rare and local, with
a few records from S.E. Devon and near Hartland. (8)

Lathyrus hirsutus L., the Hairy Vetchling, was introduced from
S. Europe, and used to occur as a cornfield weed, but is now
probably extinct.

Ononis spinosa L.   Spiny Rest-harrow
Only known to occur in Devon in the extreme east, near
Axminster, where it is found in rough grassland and waste
places, and has persisted for many years. (2)

Ononis repens L.   Rest-harrow
In sandy places, dune grassland and on sea cliffs. Common all
round the coast, but rare and local inland. (200)

Ssp. **repens** is the commonest form, with large flowers and
fairly rampant growth.
Ssp. **maritima** (Gren. & Godr.) Asch. & Graeb. is a smaller plant,
with quite small flowers. It has been recorded from both coasts,
but its distribution is not known with certainty.

Ononis reclinata L.   Small Rest-harrow
In dry walls and grassy places on limestone near the sea. Very
rare, only known from Berry Head, where its numbers vary
considerably from year to year. (1)

Melilotus altissima Thuill.   Tall Melilot
Probably introduced; a native of Europe. In waste places, scrub
and grassland, in fairly dry habitats; scattered throughout the
county, but mostly near the coast. (62)

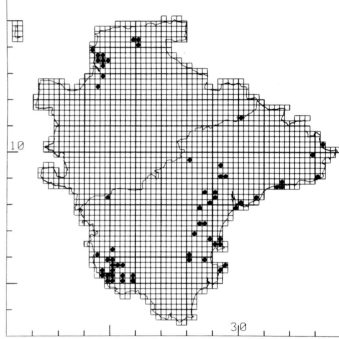

Melilotus alba Medic.   White Melilot
Introduced; a native of Europe. In waste places and fields, with a
rather similar distribution to the previous species, but less
common. (27)

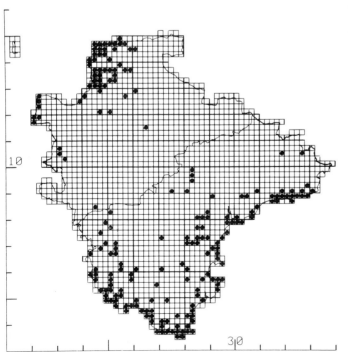

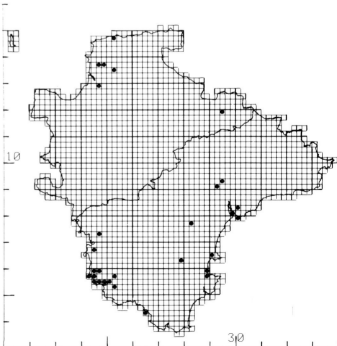

Melilotus officinalis (L.) Pallas   Common Melilot
Introduced; a native of Europe. In waste ground and along
grassy roadsides, usually near ports. Most frequent in the
vicinity of Plymouth, but recorded from several other parts of
the county. (46)

Medicago sativa L.   Alfalfa, Lucerne
Introduced; a native of S. Europe and W. Asia. It occurs
occasionally in S. Devon, as an escape from cultivation, usually
persisting for only a limited time. (28)

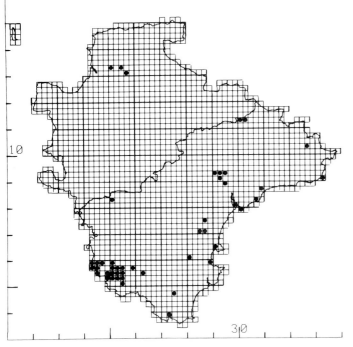

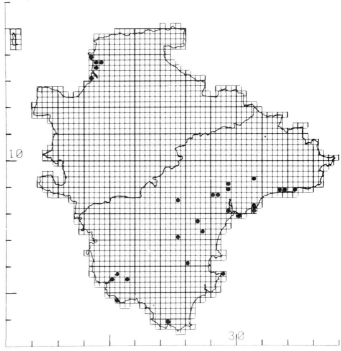

This species is cultivated in many parts of the world for animal
fodder. **M. falcata** L., (*M. sativa* ssp. *falcata* (L.) Arcangeli, has
been recorded in Devon as an introduction, but not seen
recently. A plant which has been referred to **M. x varia** Martyn,
(*M. sativa* x *falcata*, *M. x media* Pers.), is also sometimes
cultivated.

Melilotus indica (L.) All.   Small-flowered Melilot
Introduced; a native of S. Europe. In waste places and rubbish
tips, and along roadsides. Rare, persisting only near Exeter and
Torquay. (3)

Medicago lupulina L.   Black Medick
In fields, dry banks, grassland and waste places. Common and
quite generally distributed in base-rich habitats, perhaps rather
less frequent inland. (790)

Medicago arabica (L.) Huds.   Spotted Medick
In grassy places, hedges, fields and roadsides, especially near
the coast, but also found considerable distances inland. Locally
rather common, but absent from most of the Culm. (203)

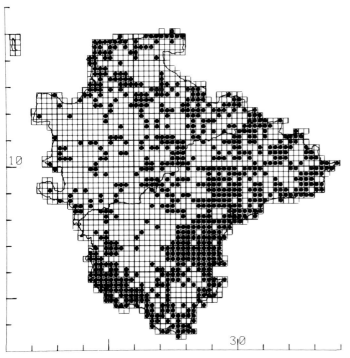

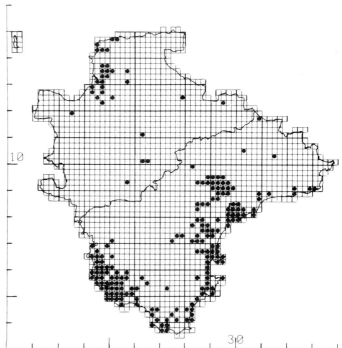

Medicago polymorpha L.   Hairy Medick
(*M. hispida* Gaertn.)
In dry, open sandy and rocky places, usually near the sea; also
found inland in well-drained habitats. (12)

Trifolium repens L.   Dutch Clover, White Clover
In pastures, roadsides and waste places; very common and
almost ubiquitous, especially common on clayey soils, but
absent from the higher moors. Widely cultivated as a forage
crop and a common component of sown leys and grass-seed
mixtures. (1749)

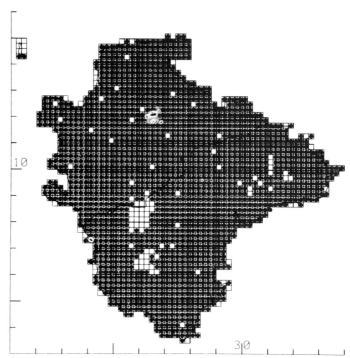

Trifolium occidentale Coombe
In dry sandy soil near the sea. Probably very rare, with only one
recent record from Welcombe Mouth. (1)

Trifolium ornithopodioides L.   Bird's-foot Fenugreek
(*Trigonella ornithopodioides* (L.) DC.)
On gravelly and sandy banks and waste places, mostly near the
sea. Scattered over the county, but rare. (21)

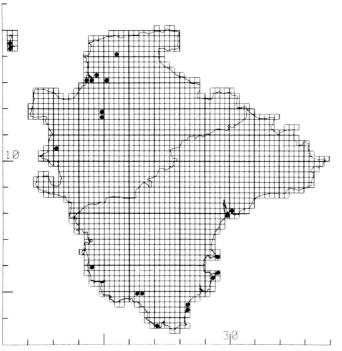

Trifolium hybridum L.   Alsike Clover
Introduced; a native of Europe. Naturalised on roadsides and in
the vicinity of farms and in waste places. Scattered over the
county, but uncommon. (165)

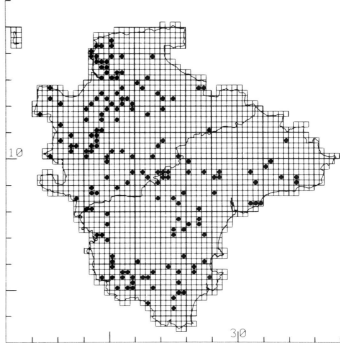

Trifolium glomeratum L. Small Round-headed Clover
In dry sandy and gravelly places near the sea. Rare, and only known from Berry Head, Dawlish Warren, Lobb Quarry, Saunton and near Torrington. (4)

Trifolium suffocatum L. Suffocated Clover
In dry sandy and gravelly places. Rare, and only known from Dawlish Warren and a few localities around Torbay, though it used to be found on the shingle beach at Budleigh Salterton in the 1960's. (6)

Trifolium fragiferum L. Strawberry Clover
In damp grassy places, usually on clay soils and near the sea, rarely inland. Rare, but sometimes locally abundant. (19)

Trifolium dubium Sibth.

Suckling Clover, Lesser Yellow Trefoil
In meadows, pastures, dune grassland and waste places. Very common and generally distributed. (1461)

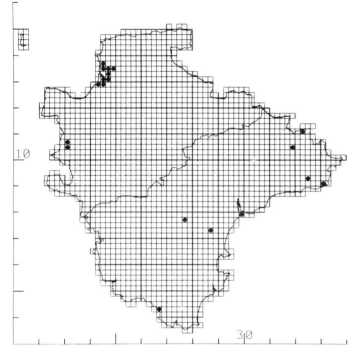

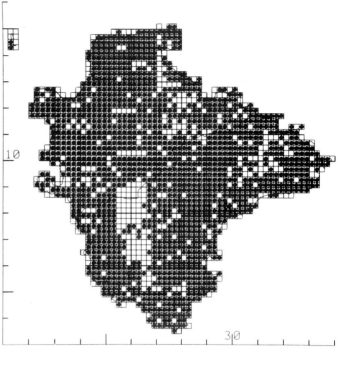

Trifolium campestre Schreb. Hop Trefoil
(*T. procumbens* L., nom. ambig.)
In fields, along roadsides and in waste places. Not uncommon, and quite generally distributed, but much less frequent than *T. dubium*. (406)

Trifolium micranthum Viv. Slender Trefoil
(*T. filiforme* L., nom. ambig.)
In open grassy places on sand and gravel, most frequent near the sea. Not very common, and not always easy to distinguish from depauperate forms of *T. dubium*. (68)

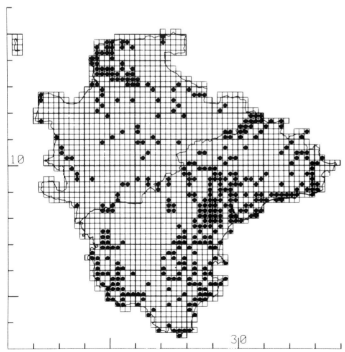

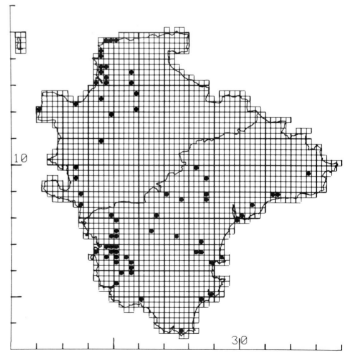

Trifolium striatum L.   Soft Trefoil
In dry pastures and waste places, always in well-drained
habitats. Most frequent near the sea, though sometimes found
inland. (31)

Trifolium scabrum L.   Rough Clover
In dry gravelly or sandy pastures and dry waste places, mostly
near the sea. Locally common, and there is a single inland
record from Broadhempston, near Totnes. (33)

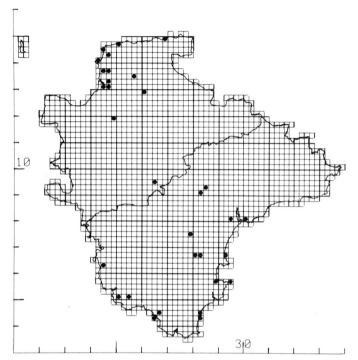 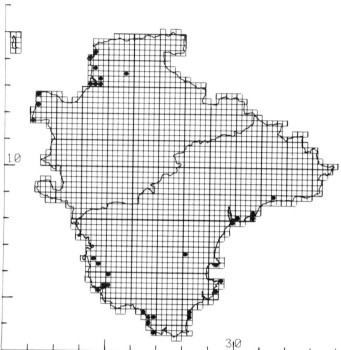

Trifolium incarnatum L.   Crimson Clover
Introduced; a native of the Mediterranean region. A rare species
which used to occur as an escape from cultivation. There are
fairly recent records from Rockbeare and Winkleigh. (2)
ssp. **molinerii** (Balb.) Hook.f., (*T. molinerii* Balb.), was once
found at Budleigh Salterton, but has not been seen since.

Trifolium arvense L.   Hare's-foot Clover
In sandy fields and dunes, occasionally in dry heathland. Most
frequent around the coasts, where it may be quite abundant, but
also occasionally inland. (69)

Trifolium pratense L.   Red Clover
In meadows, along roadsides and in other grassy or waste
places. Very common and generally distributed. Frequently
cultivated, such forms usually being rather larger vegetatively.
(1634)

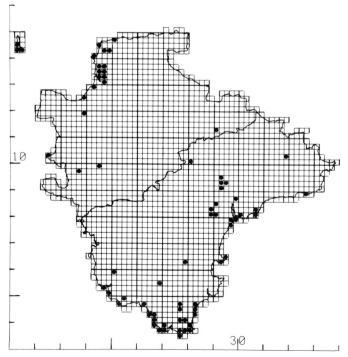 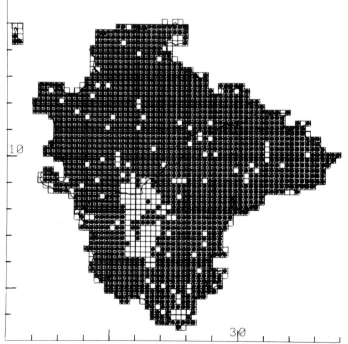

Trifolium medium L.   Zig-zag Clover
In fields, hedges, and damp and grassy waste places. Particularly frequent in the north-west of the county, scattered and very local elsewhere. (225)

Trifolium resupinatum L. was recorded in 1929 on the sands at Slapton, but is undoubtedly extinct. **T. aureum** Poll., (*T. agrarium* L., nom. ambig.), which was formerly recorded as a weed of cultivated land, has also not been seen recently. **T. ochroleucon** Huds. is not known to occur in Devon.

Lotus tenuis Waldst. & Kit. ex Willd.
       Narrow-leaved Bird's-foot Trefoil
In dry pastures and grassy places, especially in rather clayey soils. Not at all common, and very thinly scattered over the county. (17)

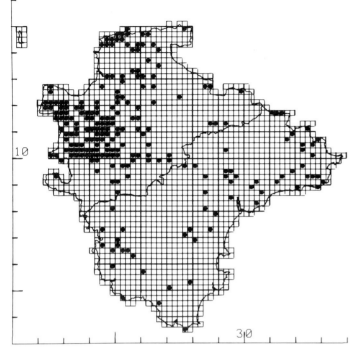

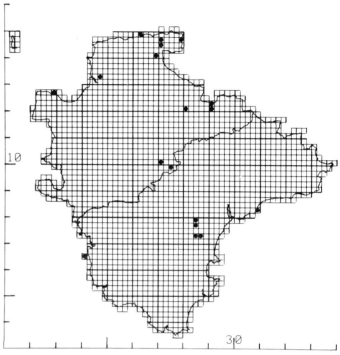

Trifolium squamosum L.   Maritime Clover, Sea Clover
(*T. maritimum* Huds.)
In grassy places near the sea and at the edges of salt-marshes. Rare, and only known from Braunton, Instow and Velator in the north, and from Torquay. (5)

Trifolium subterraneum L.   Dwarf Clover
In sandy and gravelly pastures and sea cliff-tops. Not very common, and mostly around the coast, though occurring some distance inland in the south-east. (30)

Lotus corniculatus L.   Eggs-and-Bacon, Bird's-foot Trefoil
In pastures, dry heaths, roadsides and dunes. Fairly common and generally distributed, though very local on the poorly drained soils on the Culm. (1335)

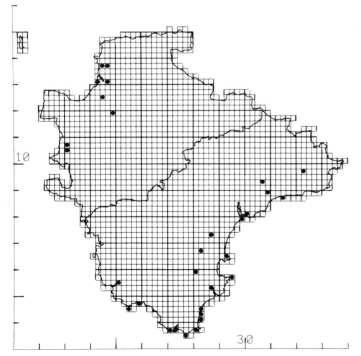

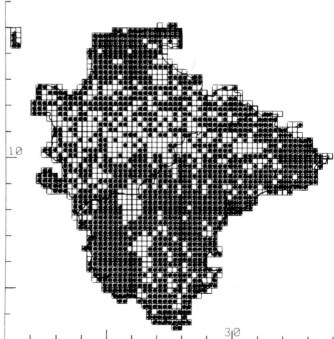

Lotus uliginosus Schkuhr
          Marsh Bird's-foot Trefoil, Large Bird's-foot Trefoil
(*L. pedunculatus* Cav.)
In damp grassy places, marshes and wet heaths. Common and
generally distributed, and locally abundant. (1309)

Lotus x davyae Druce, (*L. angustissimus* x *subbiflorus*), has
been reported by Druce from Start Point, but the specimen in
Herb. Druce (OXF) appears to be typical *L. angustissimus* (Stace,
1975).

Anthyllis vulneraria L.   Kidney Vetch, Lady's Fingers
In pastures, dry banks, cliffs and sandy places near the sea.
Common around both coasts, but also found inland in dry
habitats in heaths. (119)

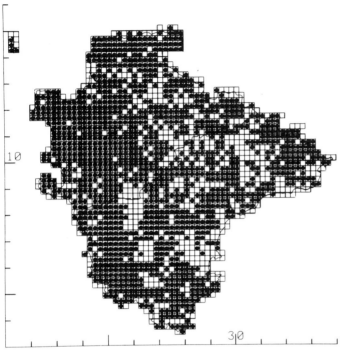

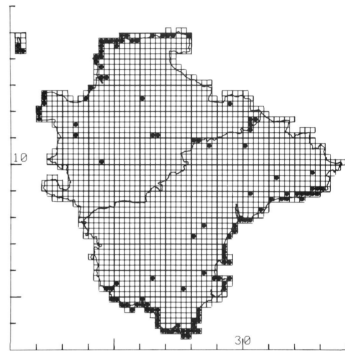

Lotus angustissimus L.   Slender Bird's-foot Trefoil
On dry banks and cliff-tops, and sandy waste places. Very rare,
and known only from one or two sites in N. Devon. Depauperate
forms of *L. corniculatus* have been mistaken for this plant. (2)

Lotus subbiflorus Lag.   Hispid Bird's-foot Trefoil
(*L. hispidus* Desf. ex DC.)
In dry banks and grassy places near the sea. Rare, mostly along
the south coast between Torquay and Plymouth, but also on
cliffs in the vicinity of Saunton. (14)

Ornithopus perpusillus L.   Bird's-foot
In dry sandy places on heaths and roadsides. Local around the
periphery of Dartmoor, and very infrequent elsewhere. (97)

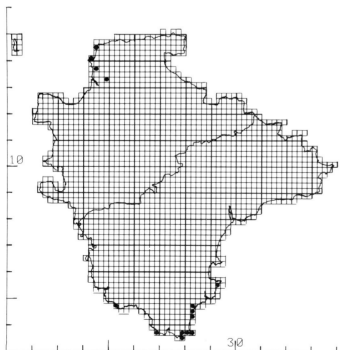

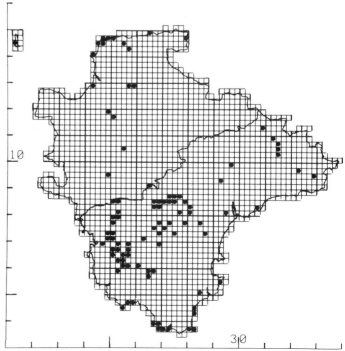

Coronilla varia L.   Crown Vetch
Introduced; a native of Europe. Occasionally recorded in woods, scrub and waste places in the south of the county. (6)

Hippocrepis comosa L.   Horse-shoe Vetch
In limestone and chalky grassland and on sea cliffs. Confined to the south and south-east of the county, most consistently in the immediate vicinity of the coast, but occurring sporadically inland. (10)

Oxalis europaea Jord.   Upright Yellow Sorrel
(*O. stricta* auct. non L.)
Introduced; a native of N. America. Found occasionally in waste places and as a garden weed. (12)

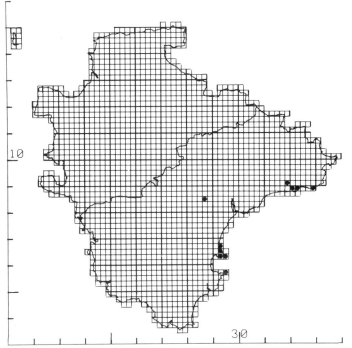

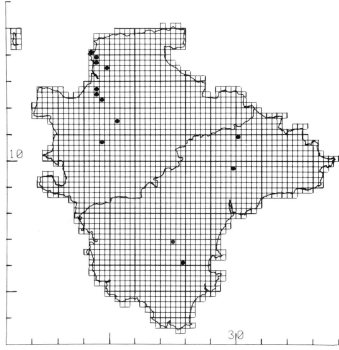

Onobrychis viciifolia Scop., the Sainfoin, could at one time be found as a relic of cultivation, but it is no longer grown as a fodder plant and there are no recent records.

OXALIDACEAE

Oxalis corniculata L.   Procumbent Yellow Sorrel
Introduced; a native of warmer temperate regions. In waste places and as a garden weed; not uncommon and naturalised in a few places. (96)

Oxalis articulata Sav.
(*O. floribunda* Lehm.)
Introduced; a native of S. America. Much grown in gardens and sometimes naturalised on waste ground and in hedges in the vicinity of houses. (33)

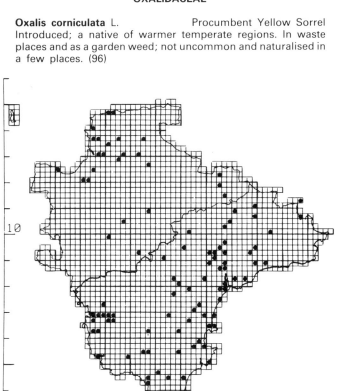

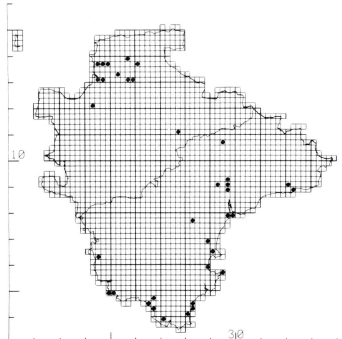

Oxalis acetosella L.   Wood Sorrel
In woods, hedges and under shaded rocks, sometimes growing
in humus, but avoiding very wet or heavy soils. Common and
generally distributed, and reaching about 600 m (2000 ft.) on
Dartmoor tors. (1177)

Geranium macrorrhizum L.
Introduced; a native of S. Europe. It has been reported as a
garden escape on walls in several scattered localities and has
persisted for a long time at Postbridge. (1)

Geranium sanguineum L.   Bloody Crane's-bill
In dry rocky places along the coast, notably at Prawle Point and
Bolt Head, but quite local. Recorded from several inland sites,
probably as a garden escape. (12)

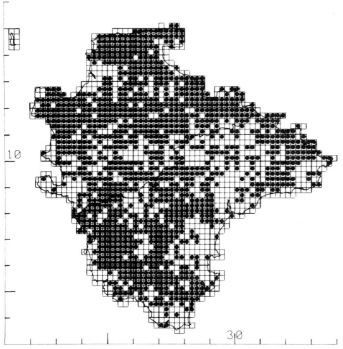

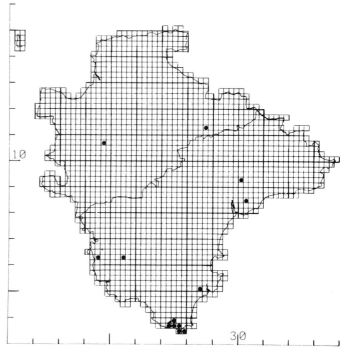

Oxalis corymbosa DC.
Introduced; a native of S. America, and naturalised or as a weed
of cultivation in a few scattered localities in the south. (3)

Oxalis latifolia Kunth
Introduced; a native of S. America, sometimes grown in
gardens and found rarely as a weed or around rubbish tips. (1)

Oxalis incarnata L.
Introduced; a native of S. Africa and naturalised on walls and in
hedges in a few scattered localities; sometimes found as a weed
of cultivation. (5)

Oxalis pes-caprae L.   Bermuda Buttercup
Introduced; a native of S. Africa. A weed of bulb-fields which
has been reported from a number of scattered localities, mostly
in the south, but has only been seen recently at Woolacombe.
(1)

Geranium pratense L.   Meadow Crane's-bill
Introduced in Devon. By roadsides and in waste places, usually
as an escape from cultivation, but apparently naturalised in a
few sites. (74)

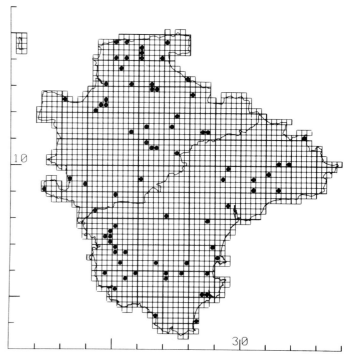

Geranium endressii Gay   French Crane's-bill
Introduced; a native of S. France. It occurs sporadically as a garden escape but is not, or scarcely, naturalised. (10)

Geranium phaeum L.   Dusky Crane's-bill
Introduced; a native of C. and S. Europe. Naturalised in hedges and roadsides in several localities, usually near habitations. (12)

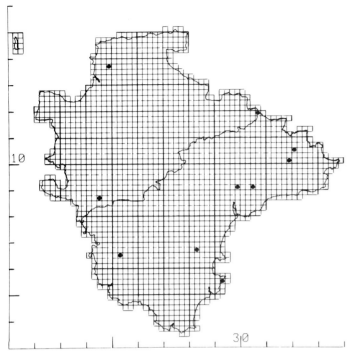

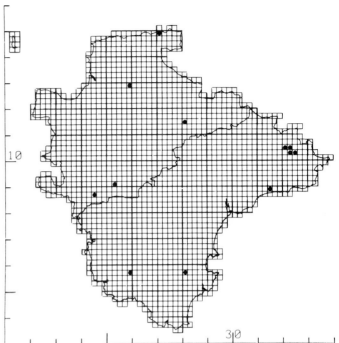

Geranium versicolor L.   Pencilled Crane's-bill
Introduced; a native of S. Europe. It occurs in waste places, along roadsides and in hedges, and is widely scattered over the county, often as a garden escape but persisting briefly in many places. (34)

Geranium pyrenaicum Burm.f.   Mountain Crane's-bill
In hedges and waste places, and along roadsides; not at all common, but scattered over the county, especially in the south. (130)

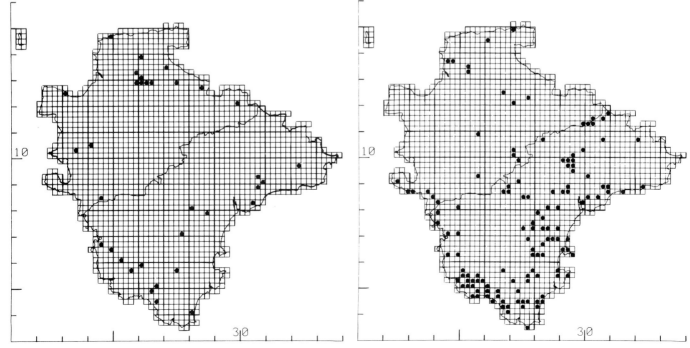

Geranium rotundifolium L.   Round-leaved Crane's-bill
In dry hedges, walls and along roads; particularly frequent around Plymouth, chiefly on limestone, and scattered around the coast of south and south-east Devon. Much rarer in the north, but nowhere common. (118)

Geranium pusillum L.   Small-flowered Crane's-bill
In cultivated ground, hedges and waste places. Rather rare and mostly in the south, and apparently considerably less common than formerly, though perhaps under-recorded. (64)

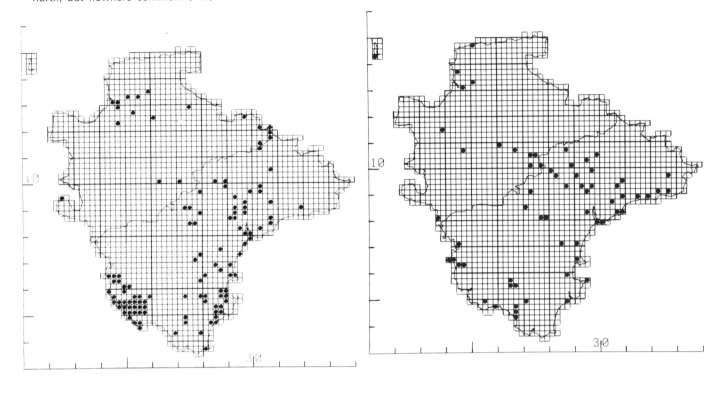

Geranium molle L.   Dove's-foot Crane's-bill
In dry grassland, dunes, fields and waste places. Quite frequent on the lighter soils, but absent from heaths and moors, and to a large extent from the Culm. (659)

Geranium columbinum L.   Long-stalked Crane's-bill
In open grassland, scrub and hedgebanks, usually in base-rich habitats. Local throughout the county, and rarely in any quantity. (340)

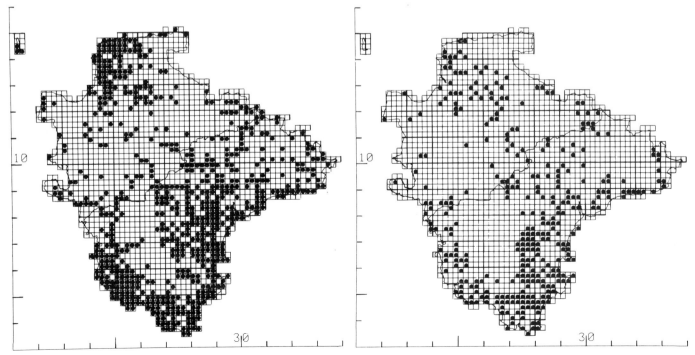

Geranium dissectum L.   Cut-leaved Crane's-bill
In hedges, cultivated ground and roadsides; quite common and generally distributed, though absent from the moors. (1239)

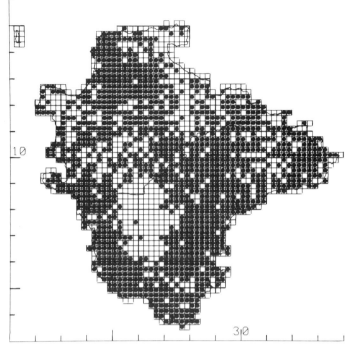

Geranium robertianum L.   Herb Robert
In hedges, woods, walls and waste places. Common and generally distributed, and absent only from the higher moors. (1690)

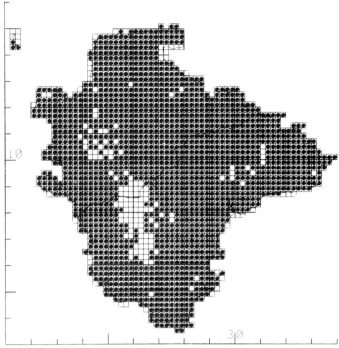

Ssp. **maritimum** (Bab.) H.G.Baker is supposed to grow in shingle and on sea cliffs all round the British Isles, but it has not been reported from Devon and needs looking for.

Geranium purpureum Vill.   Little Robin
On rocks and in hedges, mostly in the vicinity of Torquay and base-rich habitats inland from there; there is also a single record from Braunton. (9)

Geranium sylvaticum L., the Wood Crane's-bill, has been reported from Braunton but is probably an error. **Geranium nodosum** L. has been reported from East Buckland and Teignmouth (Fl. Dev.), but has not been seen recently.

Erodium maritimum (L.) L'Hér.   Sea Stork's-bill
In dry grassland and open habitats, mostly near the sea. Scattered along north and south coasts, though not apparently east of Teignmouth. (48)

Geranium lucidum L.   Shining Crane's-bill
In hedges, rock crevices and old walls, usually in base-rich soils. Locally abundant in the south and east, much rarer in the north and west. (503)

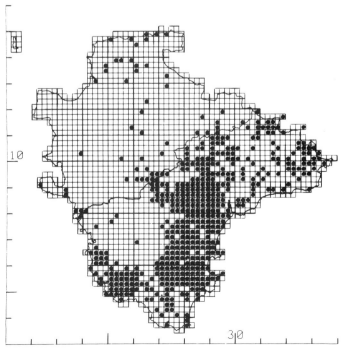

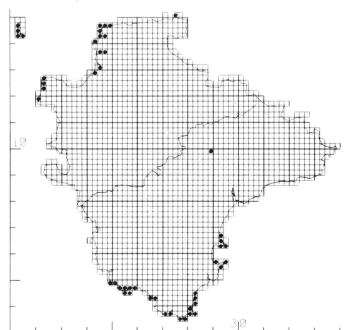

Erodium cicutarium (L.) L'Hér.   Stork's-bill
In dry grassy and sandy places; quite common near the sea but
also inland in suitable habitats. (125)
Most of our plants fall within ssp. **cicutarium**.

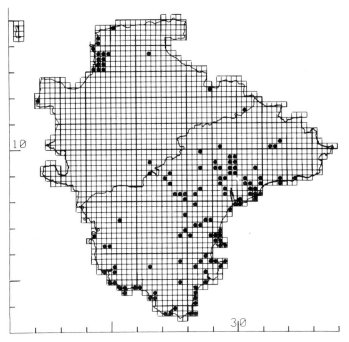

Ssp. **dunense** Andreas, (incl. *E. lebelii* Jord., *E. neglectum* Baker
& Salmon), is sometimes separated as a form intermediate
between ssp. *cicutarium* and ssp. *bipinnatum* Tourlet; it can be
found rather uncommonly on maritime sands.

Erodium moschatum (L.) L'Hér.   Musky Stork's-bill
In waste places in sandy habitats. Rare, mostly around the south
coast, but also recorded from Braunton, Baggy Point and
Torrington. (17)

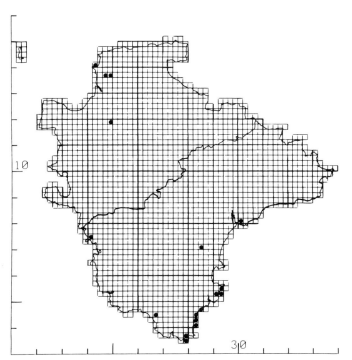

Erodium glutinosum Dum.   Sticky Stork's-bill
On dunes and in sandy places near the sea. Very rare, and only
known from Braunton Burrows. (2)

A number of other species, including **Erodium dentatum** Baker
& Salmon, **E. chium** (L.) Willd. and **E. malacoides** (L.) L'Hér.,
have been reported as casuals, but none have been seen
recently.

Linum bienne Mill.   Pale Flax, Branding Flax
In dry grassland, banks and pastures; widely distributed but
local, and most frequent near the coast. (95)

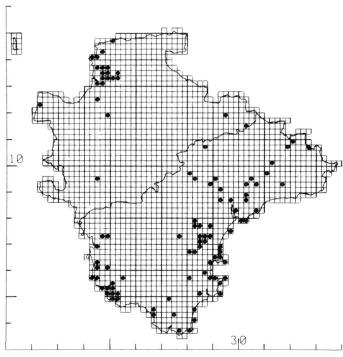

Linum catharticum L.   Purging Flax
In dry grassland and dunes, and occasionally on dry heaths and
moors; preferably calcicole but also found in fairly base-rich
habitats. Generally but patchily distributed, and often quite
common where it occurs. (162)

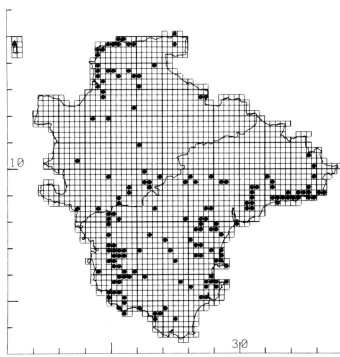

Linum usitatissumum L., the Flax, is an introduced species
which occurs occasionally as an escape from cultivation, and is
now very rare.

Radiola linoides Roth　　　　　　　　　　All-seed
In seasonally damp sandy and peaty habitats in grassland and
heaths. Scattered over central and western parts of the county,
but rather easily overlooked; locally frequent. (16)

Mercurialis perennis L.　　　　　　　Dog's Mercury
In woods, hedges and scrub, usually in well-drained habitats in
the shade. Very common and generally distributed. (1371)

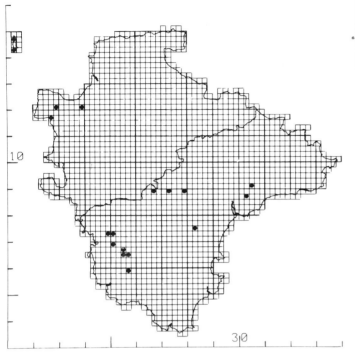

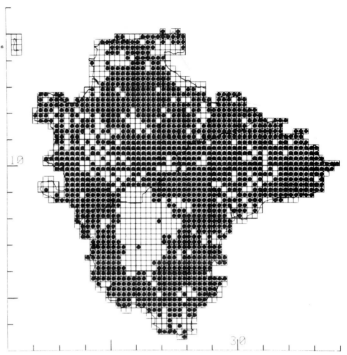

EUPHORBIACEAE

Mercurialis annua L.　　　　Annual Dog's Mercury
Introduced in Devon. A weed of cultivated ground and waste
places which is now quite rare. (17)

Euphorbia hyberna L.　　　　　　　Irish Spurge
In shaded woods. Only in a small region to the north of Exmoor,
where it has been known for many years. (4)

Euphorbia helioscopia L.　　　　　　Sun Spurge
In cultivated ground, fields, gardens and waste places. Quite
common and generally distributed. (391)

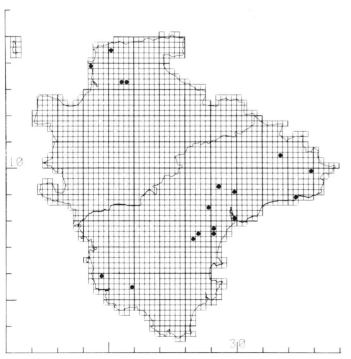

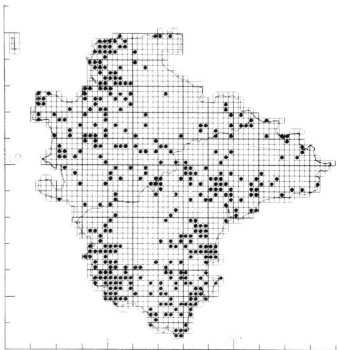

Euphorbia lathyrus L.   Caper Spurge
Introduced; a native of S. Europe. In cultivated ground and
waste places; probably always an escape from cultivation, and
often occurring as only a single specimen. (37)

Euphorbia peplus L.   Petty Spurge
In cultivated fields, gardens, roadsides and waste places. Quite
common and generally distributed. Quite frequent as a weed,
but absent from considerable areas predominantly under
grassland. (494)

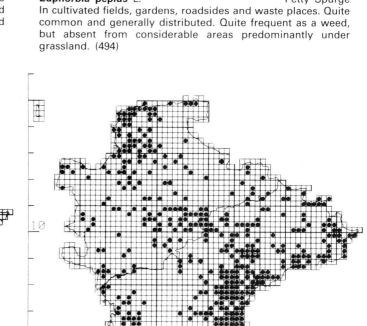

Euphorbia exigua L.   Dwarf Spurge
Occurs locally in arable fields, gardens and waste ground.
Scattered over the county and probably considerably less
common than formerly. (34)

Euphorbia portlandica L.   Portland Spurge
On cliffs, dunes and sandy places, always near the coast. Rather
frequent in suitable habitats. (54)

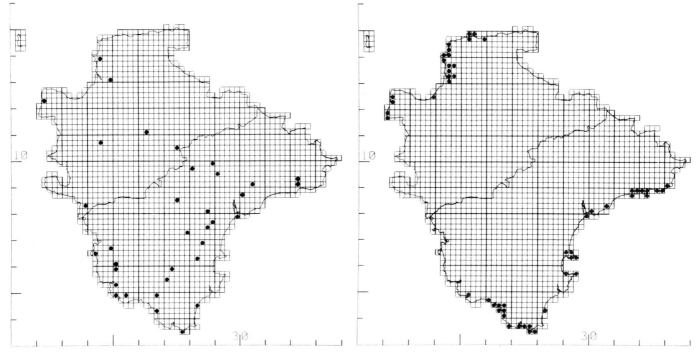

Euphorbia paralias L.   Sea Spurge
On sandy shores and dunes. More restricted in distribution than
E. portlandica, but often more abundant where it occurs,
especially on Braunton Burrows and Slapton Sands. (21)

Euphorbia peplis L., the Purple Spurge, used to occur in some
quantity on a few sandy beaches, and was found at Slapton in
1951, but has not been seen for many years and is almost
certainly extinct. **Euphorbia platyphyllos** L., the Broad Spurge,
has been reported as an escape from cultivation, but can no
longer be found. **Euphorbia dulcis** has been reported from two
localities, but is unlikely to have been correctly identified.

POLYGALACEAE

Polygala vulgaris L.   Common Milkwort
(inc. *P. dubia* Bellynck, *P. oxyptera* Reichenb.)
In grassland and dunes, usually on calcareous or base-rich soils.
Fairly common in suitable habitats. (235)
The flowers show a wide range of colours, including white, pink,
blue and purple.

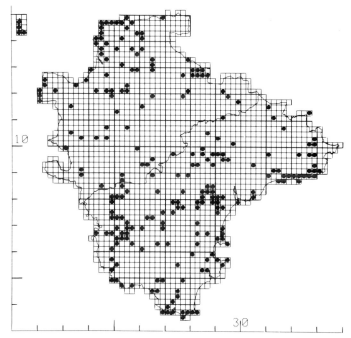

Euphorbia esula L.   Leafy Spurge
Introduced; a native of Europe. It has been reported from a few
sites, and ssp. **esula** still occurs at Exeter. (1)
Ssp. **tommasiniana** (Bertol.) Nyman, (*E. virgata* Waldst. & Kit.),
has also been reported on a few occasions, but there are no
recent records for this.

Euphorbia cyparissias L.   Cypress Spurge
Introduced; a native of Europe. Recorded as a garden escape
from time to time, but it appears to be naturalised near
Braunton. (1)

Euphorbia amygdaloides L.   Wood Spurge
In woods, scrub, hedgerows and waste places; locally common,
especially on the more base-rich soils, but absent from a large
area around and to the west of Dartmoor. (475)

Polygala serpyllifolia Hose
              Thyme-leaved Milkwort, Heath Milkwort
In grassland, heaths and moors, often in relatively dry or sandy
habitats, and always calcifuge. Quite common and fairly
generally distributed. The flowers are usually blue. (367)

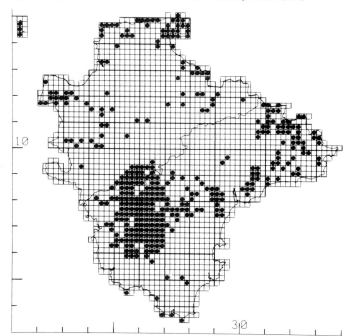

ACERACEAE

Acer platanoides L.   Norway Maple
Introduced; a native of Europe. Occasionally planted and fairly
readily becoming naturalised. (12)

Acer pseudoplatanus L.   Sycamore
Introduced; a native of Europe. Common in woods, hedges and
scrub in moist and often base-rich soils. Extensively naturalised
throughout the county and very tolerant of a wide range of
conditions on the moors, around the coast and on farms. (1566)

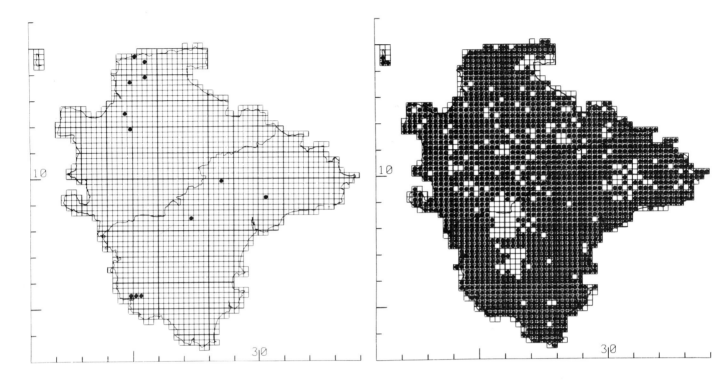

HIPPOCASTANACEAE

Aesculus hippocastanum L.   Horse Chestnut
Introduced; a native of the Balkans. Extensively planted;
although seedlings and young trees can be found quite
frequently, it is not clear that it is truly naturalised. (432)

Acer campestre L.   Maple
In woods, hedges and scrub, usually on well-drained, base-rich
soils. Fairly generally but patchily distributed in the lowlands,
perhaps reflecting some planting in the past. (785)

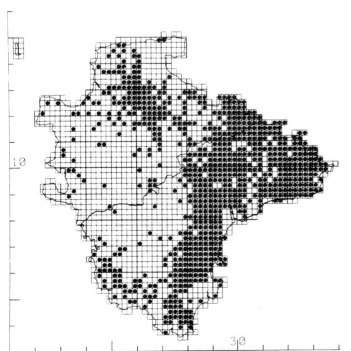

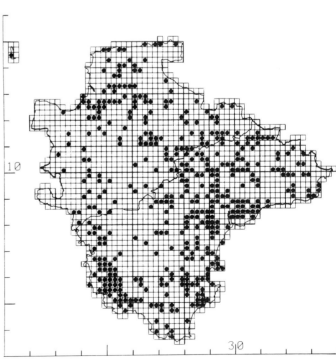

Aesculus carnea Hayne, with pink or red flowers, is an
allopolyploid of garden origin which is fairly frequently planted.

BALSAMINACEAE

Impatiens capensis Meerb.   Orange Balsam
Introduced; a native of N. America. It has become naturalised along rivers and canals and is locally common along the banks of the R. Otter in E. Devon, and near Barnstaple. (7)

Impatiens parviflora DC.   Small Balsam
Introduced; a native of E. Europe. There is a single record from east of Launceston, probably of garden origin. (1)

Impatiens glandulifera Royle
       Indian Balsam, Policeman's Helmet
Introduced; a native of the Himalayas, now extensively naturalised along the margins of rivers, streams and ditches, and in damp waste places. Common in suitable habitats and apparently spreading quite rapidly. (250)

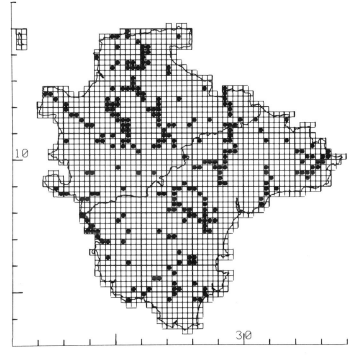

Impatiens noli-tangere L., the Yellow Balsam or Touch-me-not, has been recorded as a casual on one occasion, but has not been seen recently.

AQUIFOLIACEAE

Ilex aquifolium L.   Holly
In woods, scrub and hedges. Common and generally distributed; rather sparse on the moors, though occurring in Wistman's Wood, and it can be found on tors up to 500 m (1700 ft.). It is perhaps rather uncommon in the immediate vicinity of the coast. (1614)

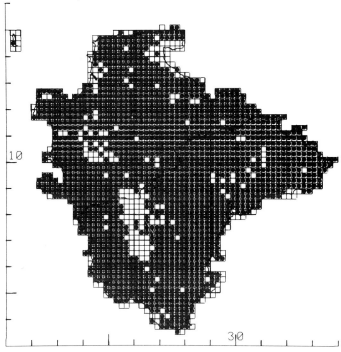

CELASTRACEAE

Euonymus europaeus L.   Spindle Tree
In woods, scrub and hedges, usually on base-rich and especially on calcareous soils, but also on the Culm and New Red rocks west of Exeter. Moderately common, but rather local, except on chalk or limestone. (678)

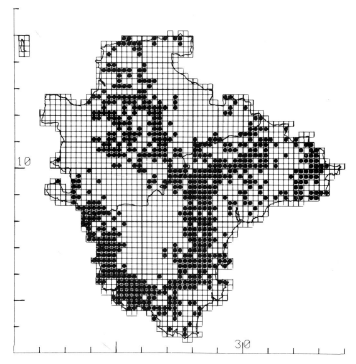

BUXACEAE

Buxus sempervirens L.   Box
Introduced in Devon. Quite frequently cultivated as a hedge or
an edging plant, and it can be found as an escape in hedgerows,
but usually only near habitations. (48)

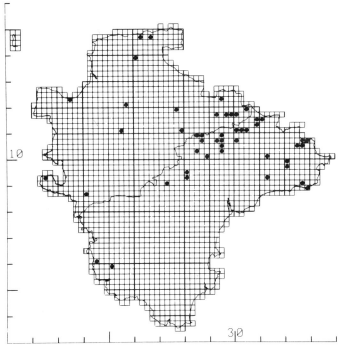

TILIACEAE

Tilia cordata Mill.   Small-leaved Lime
In woods, usually over limestone or in base-rich soils, though
also on the Culm at Holne Chase. Uncommon, mostly in the
south of the county, but it seems to be rather more frequent
than formerly. (24)

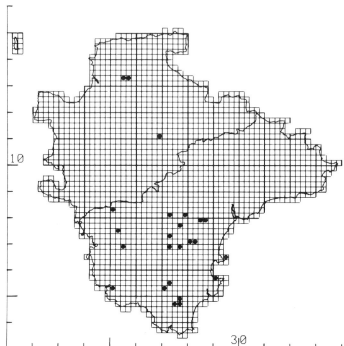

RHAMNACEAE

Rhamnus catharticus L.   Buckthorn
In scrub on calcareous soil. Very rare, with only a single record
from the chalk in E. Devon. (1)

Frangula alnus Mill.   Alder Buckthorn
(*Rhamnus frangula* L.)
On moist heaths and commons, in hedges and around bogs.
Not uncommon and scattered over the county, and least
frequent in agricultural areas. (277)

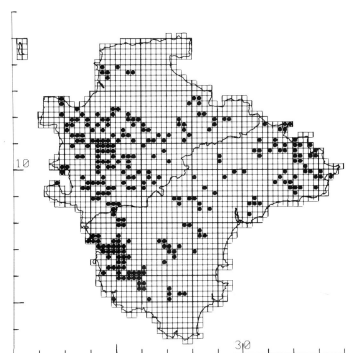

Tilia x vulgaris Hayne   Lime
(*T. cordata* x *platyphyllos, T. x europaea* L. p.p.)
Introduced; a naturally-occurring hybrid in Europe, but in Devon
is always planted. It occurs not infrequently all over the county.
(233)

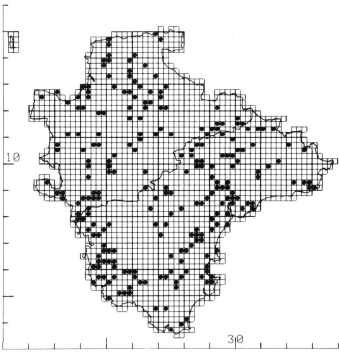

Tilia platyphyllos Scop., the Large-leaved or Broad-leaved Lime,
has been reported on occasion, but is probably always planted
and there are no recent records.

102

MALVACEAE

Malva moschata L.   Musk Mallow
In dry hedgebanks, roadsides and waste places. Quite common and generally distributed. A variable plant, especially in the extent to which the leaves are divided. (410)

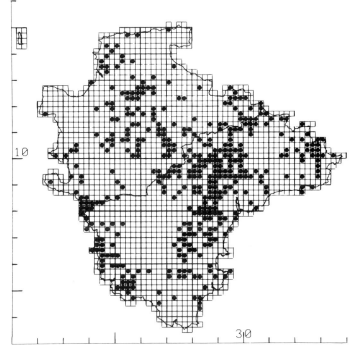

Malva pusilla Sm.   Small Mallow
Introduced; a native of N. and C. Europe. It has been reported from several localities as a casual, but the only recent record is one from near Newton Abbot. (1)

Malva neglecta Wallr.   Dwarf Mallow
In waste places and along roads and hedges. Rare, with a very scattered distribution, mostly in the south-east and near coasts. (59)

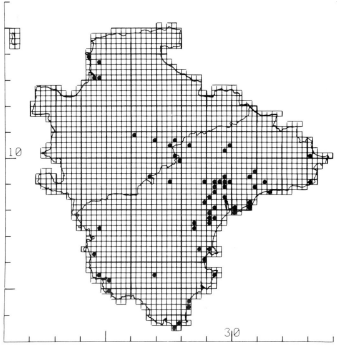

Malva parviflora L. is an introduced species which has been reported on occasion, but probably in error for *M. neglecta*.

Lavatera arborea L.   Tree Mallow
On maritime rocks, cliffs and banks, especially associated with bird-cliffs, and often on limestone. Fairly frequent around both coasts, but also cultivated in gardens and all inland records are escapes from cultivation. (57)

Malva sylvestris L.   Common Mallow
Along roadsides, on banks and in waste places. Especially frequent in the south-east, and also prominent around both coasts. (436)

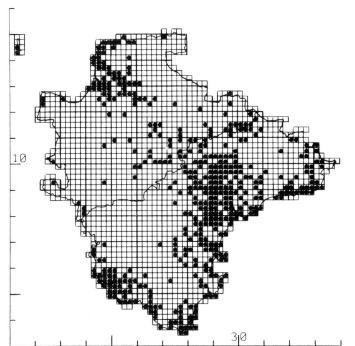

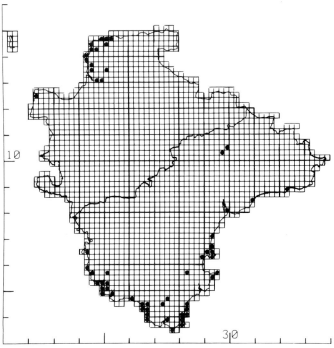

Lavatera trimestris L. has been recorded from Torquay as a casual, but there are no recent records.

103

Althaea hirsuta L.   Hairy Mallow
Introduced; a native of Europe. Recorded as a casual, but perhaps always an escape from cultivation. (2)

Althaea officinalis L., the Marsh Mallow, has been reported from salt-marshes near Ilfracombe, Totnes and Slapton, and at the head of the Tavy estuary. In some places the habitat has disappeared. There are no recent records and it is probably extinct.

THYMELAEACEAE

Daphne laureola L.   Spurge Laurel
In woods and scrub, occasionally in hedges, usually on base-rich or calcareous soils. Uncommon, but scattered over much of the county. Some records could be garden escapes, but it is seldom cultivated. (41)

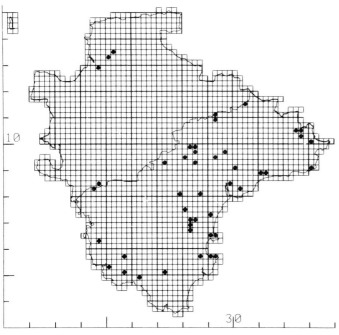

HYPERICACEAE

Hypericum calycinum L.   Rose of Sharon
Introduced; a native of S.E. Europe. It is frequently grown in gardens and readily becomes naturalised from portions of its extensive rhizome system. Not uncommon, but usually near habitations. (115)

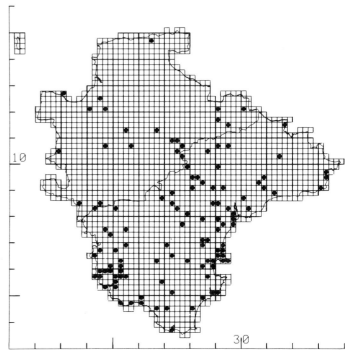

ELEAGNACEAE

Hippophae rhamnoides L.   Sea Buckthorn
Introduced in Devon. On yellow and grey dunes. Originally planted on Braunton Burrows, where it is now fully naturalised and flourishing. Rarely on other dune systems. (10)

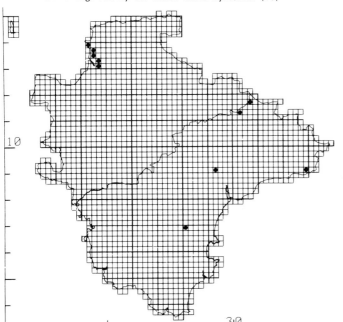

Hypericum androsaemum L.   Tutsan
In damp woods and hedges, sometimes on sea cliffs, usually on base-rich or calcareous soils. Scattered over much of the county, but rarely more than a few plants together. (684)

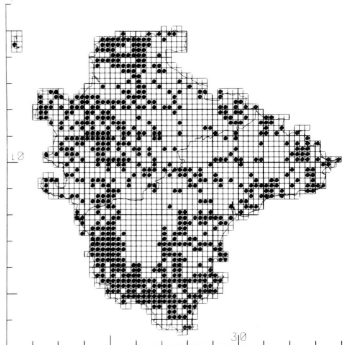

Hypericum hirsutum L.   Hairy St. John's-wort
In woods, hedges and damp grassland on calcareous or base-rich soils. Quite frequent around Torbay, rare elsewhere. (51)

Hypericum montanum L.   Mountain St. John's-wort
In scrub or rough grassland on calcareous or base-rich soils. Almost confined to the chalk and limestone, in the coastal regions around Torquay and the landslips in E. Devon. (35)

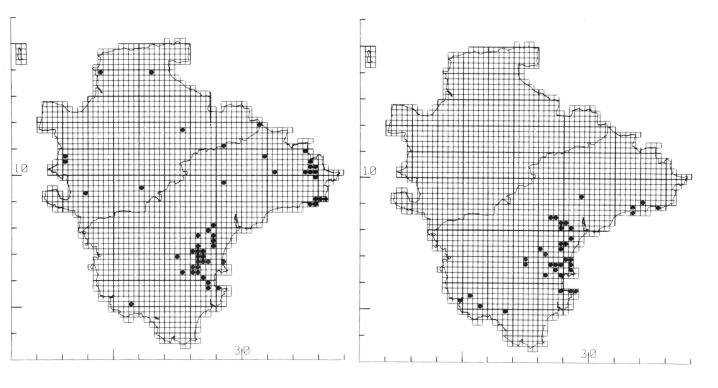

Hypericum pulchrum L.   Slender St. John's-wort
In dry woods, hedges, rough grassland and heaths, on dry and acid soils. Generally distributed in suitable habitats and locally common, especially in heathy hedgebanks. (1096)

Hypericum elodes L.   Marsh St. John's-wort
In bogs, runnels and standing water on the moors, and in clay ponds and acid streams and pools elsewhere. Quite common, though perhaps less so than formerly as a result of drainage. (194)

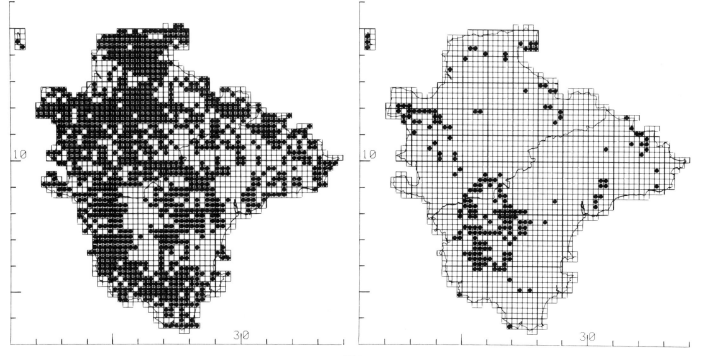

Hypericum linarifolium Vahl   Flax-leaved St. John's-wort
On steep, dry rocky banks facing about south-west, in open vegetation on acid soils. Very rare, with only two localities in the Teign valley where it can be found consistently and in any quantity. (3)

Hypericum humifusum L.   Creeping St. John's-wort
In gravelly and dry heathy habitats on moors and commons. Local, though generally distributed, but rarely occurring in any quantity. (393)

Hypericum undulatum Schousb. ex Willd.
    Wavy St. John's-wort
In damp heaths, rough pasture and bogs, confined to the north-west of the county, where it is locally frequent in acid or base-poor habitats, and also in the Warleigh Nature Reserve, near Plymouth. (66)

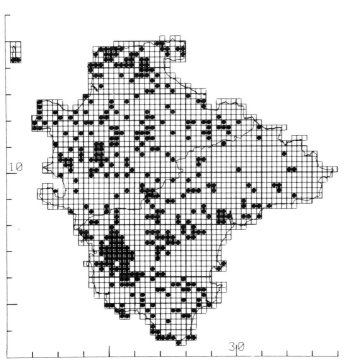

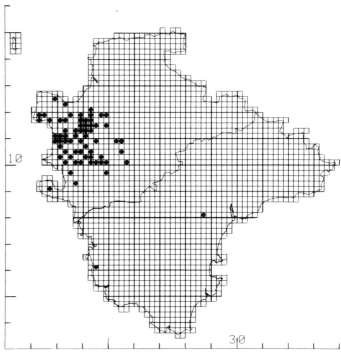

Hypericum maculatum Crantz   Imperforate St. John's-wort
(*H. quadrangulum* auct., non L.)
In damp places at the margins of woods, on stream banks, hedges and waste ground. Rare, and only recorded from scattered localities. (37)

Hypericum tetrapterum Fries
    Square-stemmed St. John's-wort
(*H. quadrangulum* L. nom.ambig., *H. acutum* Moench)
In damp marshy ground by ditches and rivers, and in marshes. Common and quite generally distributed. (648)

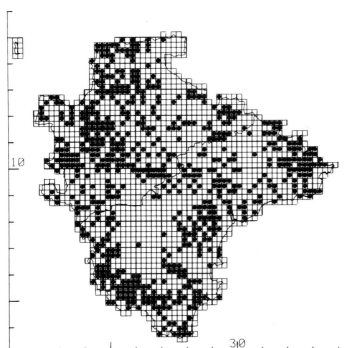

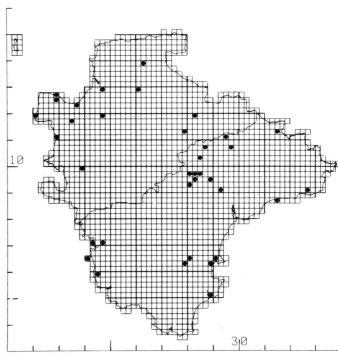

Our plants probably belong to ssp. **obtusiusculum** (Tourlet) Hayek, but they have not always been distinguished from ssp. **maculatum**.

Hypericum perforatum L.   Common St. John's-wort
In hedges and roadside banks, usually in dry habitats and particularly common on chalk and limestone. Generally distributed though absent from moorland areas. (765)

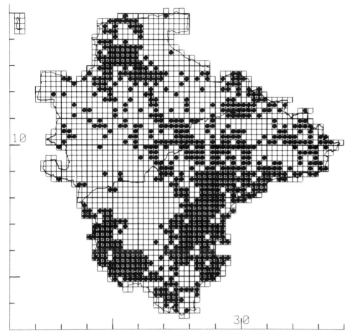

Hypericum hircinum L., the Stinking St. John's-wort, is a native of Europe occasionally grown in gardens and there have been a few records of escapes from cultivation around Torquay and Plymouth, but none recently. **Hypericum x inodorum** Mill., (*H. androsaemum* x *hircinum, H. elatum* Ait.), the Tall Tutsan, has been reported on occasion as a casual but there are no recent records and it is probably extinct. **Hypericum x desetangsii** Lamotte, (*H. maculatum* ssp. *obtusiusculum* x *perforatum*), was reported as a single specimen from Lamerton in 1916. Although the parents rarely grow together, it should, perhaps, be looked for.

VIOLACEAE

Viola odorata L.   Sweet Violet
In hedges, scrub and open woodland, usually on base-rich soils. Quite common and fairly generally distributed. It is found in both white and violet-flowered forms, is not infrequently cultivated, and may be naturalised in some localities. (356)

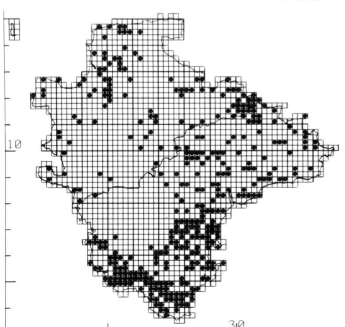

Viola hirta L.   Hairy Violet
In hedges, grassland and scrub, often by the sea and largely confined to the limestone or other calcareous or base-rich habitats. Local. (55)

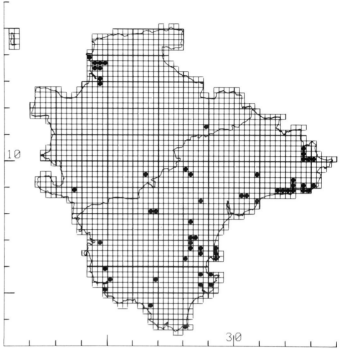

Ssp. **hirta** is by far the more common form.
Ssp. **calcarea** (Bab.) E.F.Warb., (*V. hirta* var. *calcarea* Bab.), is much less frequent, but occurs on the Torbay limestone and on Braunton Burrows.

Viola x permixta Jord.
(*V. hirta* x *odorata*)
Occurs not infrequently with the parents and is intermediate between them. It is usually in more open habitats on base-rich soils and has been recorded from Braunton Burrows.

Viola reichenbachiana Jord. ex Bor.   Wood Violet
(*V. sylvestris* Lam. p.p.)
In woods, hedges and banks, usually on base-rich soils. A characteristic woodland species, and quite common in suitable habitats, but absent from heaths and moors. (319)

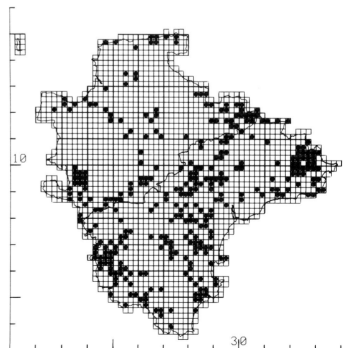

Viola riviniana Reichenb.   Common Violet
In hedges, woods, heaths and rock crevices. Common and
generally distributed in a wide range of habitats. (1601)

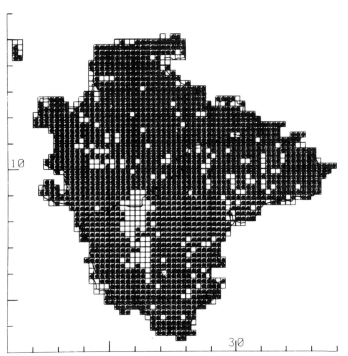

Viola x intermedia Reichenb. non Krock
(*V. reichenbachiana* x *riviniana*)
Intermediate between the parents and occurring frequently
where their populations overlap. Recorded from both vice-
counties.

Viola canina L.   Heath Violet, Dog Violet
On heaths, moors and sand-dunes, usually where there is rather
little humus but adequate calcium. Uncommon on dry heathland and local elsewhere; absent from limestone areas. (163)

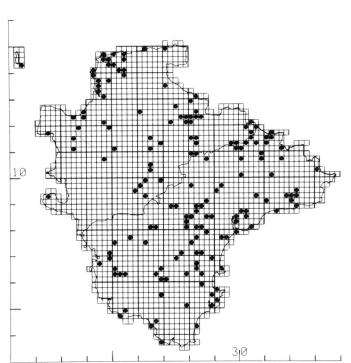

Viola x berkleyi Druce n.n.
(*V. canina* x *riviniana*)
The parents may meet on dunes and in dry heaths; the hybrid
has been recorded from both vice-counties, but seems to be
quite rare.

Viola lactea Sm.   Pale Heath Violet
On dry heaths and moors, in rather comparable habitats to *V.
canina*, but preferring rather more humus and less calcium.
Local, but often quite common where it occurs. (27)

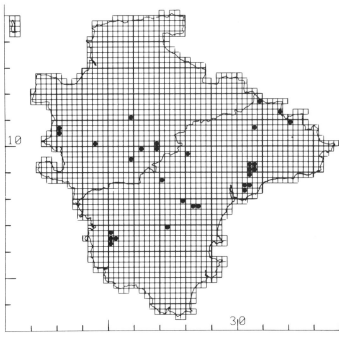

Viola x curnowii Druce n.n.
(*V. lactea* x *riviniana*)
The parents have a wide ecological overlap on heaths; this
hybrid has been reported on several occasions throughout the
county and is probably rather frequent.

Viola x militaris, (*V. lactea* x *canina*), has been recorded rather
rarely from dry heathland, where the ranges of the parents
overlap.

Viola palustris L.   Bog Violet
In bogs on the moors, in wet heaths and wet acid woodland.
Often abundant in suitable habitats, but absent from large areas
including all base-rich communities. (458)

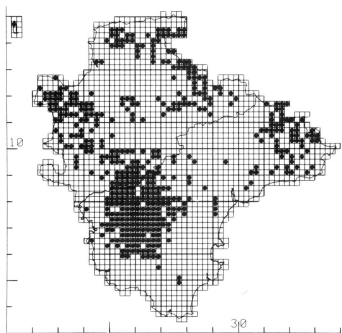

The common form is ssp. **palustris.**
Ssp. **juressii** (Nevers) P.Cout., (*V. epipsila* auct. angl. non
Ledeb.), has been recorded on a few occasions, mostly around
Dartmoor, but it is unclear whether it is truly distinct from ssp.
palustris.

Viola tricolor L.   Wild Pansy
(inc. *V. lepida* auct., *V. variata* auct. p.p., *V. lloydii* auct., *V. lejeunei* auct. p.p.)
In cultivated and waste ground. A complex group which was split by Hall (in Fl. Dev.) into a number of species which are not now normally recognised. (48)

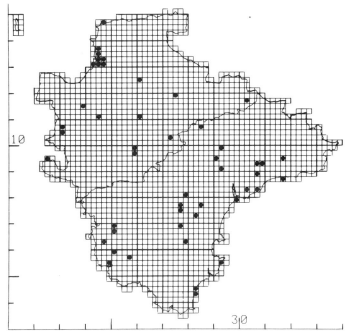

Ssp. **tricolor** includes inland forms and probably a number of escapes from cultivation.
Ssp. **curtisii** (Forst.) Syme, (*V. lactea* Huds. forma *curtisii* (Forst.) Drabble), is common on semi-fixed dune grassland, especially on Braunton Burrows.

Viola arvensis Murr.   Field Pansy
(inc. *V. contempta* auct., *V. agrestis* auct., *V. segetalis* auct., *V. latifolia* Drabble, *V. deseglisei* auct., *V. ruralis* auct., *V. anglica* Drabble, *V. arvatica* auct., *V. derelicta* auct., p.p.)
In cultivated and waste ground, usually on base-rich soils. Quite common and fairly generally distributed. (271)

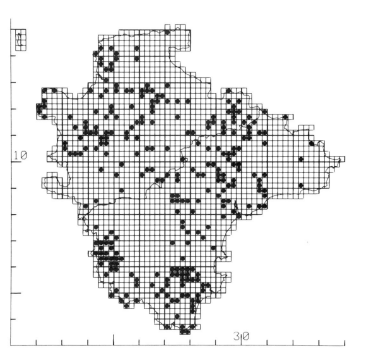

Viola cornuta L. has been reported from the banks of the R. Otter but has not been found this century and is doubtless extinct.

CISTACEAE

Helianthemum nummularium (L.) Mill.   Common Rock-rose
(*H. chamaecistus* Mill.)
In chalk and limestone grassland and open scrub, where it is quite common; occasionally in base-rich gravelly or sandy habitats elsewhere, which may be escapes from cultivation. Absent from N. Devon. (20)

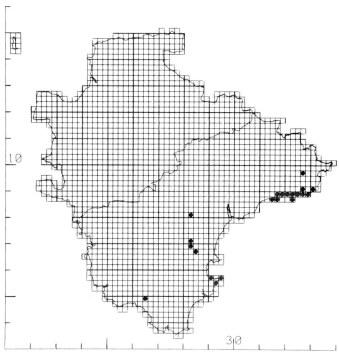

Helianthemum apenninum (L.) Mill.   White Rock-rose
(*H. polifolium* Mill.)
On dry limestone cliffs and cliff grassland near Torbay, where it is very locally abundant. (3)

Helianthemum x sulphureum Willd.
(*H. apenninum* x *nummularium*)
This hybrid is intermediate between its parents in many characters, especially flower colour. It has been recorded from Brixham and occurs quite frequently where the parent ranges overlap.

TAMARICACEAE

Tamarix gallica L.   Tamarisk
(*T. anglica* Webb)
Introduced; a native of S.W. Europe. Often planted in coastal districts for shelter or ornament, as it withstands sea spray well, and it is sometimes naturalised. (31)

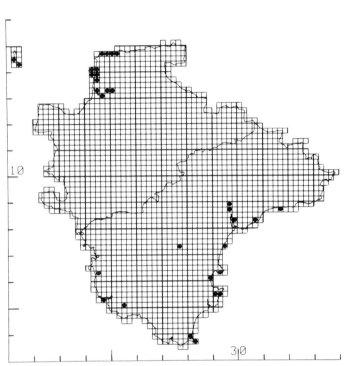

Other species, such as **T. tetrandra** Pallas and **T. pentandra** Pallas, are planted in coastal districts and may appear naturalised.

ELATINACEAE

Elatine hexandra (Lapierre) DC.   Waterwort
In ponds and on wet mud around their margins. Rare, with very few and scattered records, though it is quite abundant in Fernworthy and Tottiford reservoirs. Perhaps a recent arrival, as it is not recorded in Fl. Dev., but an insignificant plant. (4)

CUCURBITACEAE

Bryonia dioica Jacq.   White Bryony, Red Bryony
Recorded from time to time, but often in error for *Tamus communis,* because of the similarity in English names. There is no evidence that it occurs in Devon as a native plant. It has been suggested that it may have been introduced into the south-east and around Exeter, but it is not known to persist there.

LYTHRACEAE

Lythrum salicaria L.   Purple Loosestrife
By the sides of rivers and streams, and in wet fens and marshes. Quite common and generally distributed, especially in the north-west, and in many river valleys. (342)

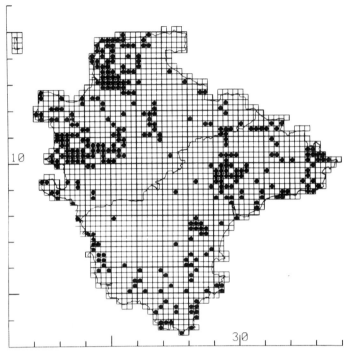

Lythrum portula (L.) D.A.Webb   Water Purslane
(*Peplis portula* L.)
In wet heathy and boggy habitats, ditches and wet roadsides. A calcifuge species quite frequent around Dartmoor and to the north and west, but occasional elsewhere. (199)

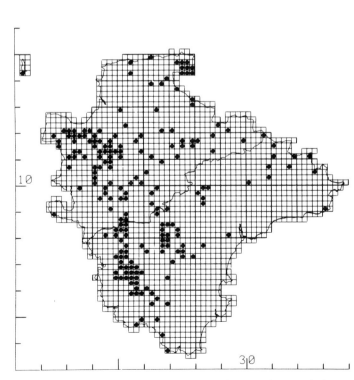

Lythrum junceum Banks & Solander, (*L. graefferi* Ten.), has been reported from Bovey Heath, but probably as an escape and it no longer occurs there. **Lythrum hyssopifolia** L. has been recorded on two occasions as an introduction, but there are no recent records and it is undoubtedly extinct.

ONAGRACEAE

Fuchsia magellanica Lam. Fuchsia
(*F. riccartonii* auct.)
Introduced; a native of S. America. Widely planted in hedges, occasionally naturalised (more readily so in Cornwall), and found mostly along the north coast, in the vicinity of Ilfracombe. (9)
Our plant belongs to var. **macrostema** (Ruiz & Pav.) Munz.

Circaea lutetiana L. Enchanter's Nightshade
In woods, scrub and damp shaded places, usually on base-rich soils. Common and generally distributed. (1177)

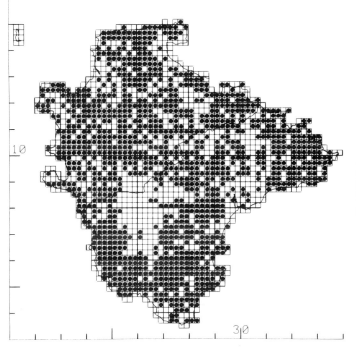

Oenothera biennis L. Lesser Evening Primrose
Introduced; a native of N. America. On dunes, roadsides, railway banks and in waste places; scattered over the county, but very local. (23)

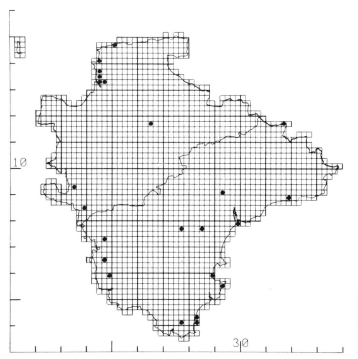

Oenothera erythrosepala Borbás
Large-flowered Evening Primrose
Introduced; of unknown origin. On roadsides, banks, waste places and in dune grassland. Widely distributed and considerably more common than *O. biennis.* (67)

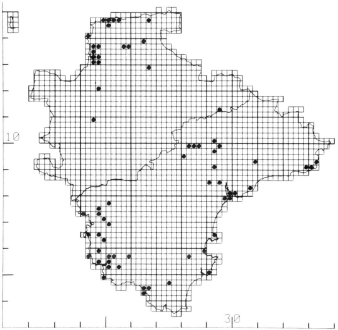

Oenothera cambrica Rost. Small-flowered Evening Primrose
(*O. parviflora* auct., non L.)
Introduced; a native of N. America. Occurs in small quantities on the dunes on Braunton Burrows. (1)

Oenothera stricta Ledeb. ex Link
Fragrant Evening Primrose
Introduced; a native of Chile. It occurs in small quantities on the dunes at Dawlish and on Braunton Burrows. (2)

Oenothera victorini Gates & Catches. has been reported from Cofton, S. Devon (McClintock, 1978). **Oenothera perangusta** Gates was recorded from Saunton in 1972 (McClintock, 1978).

Chamerion angustifolium (L.) J.Holub
Rose-bay Willow-herb, Fire-weed
(*Chamaenerion angustifolium* (L.) Scop., *Epilobium angustifolium* L.)
In open woods, wood margins, disturbed ground and roadsides. Common and often abundant, especially in cleared woodland and waste ground where there have been fires. (1288)

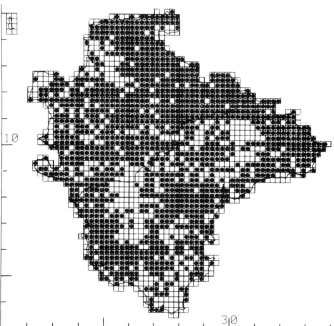

Epilobium hirsutum L.

Great Hairy Willow-herb, Codlins-and-Cream
In moist or damp places beside rivers, streams and ponds. Common over most of the county, but avoiding the moors and less frequent in base-poor habitats. (853)

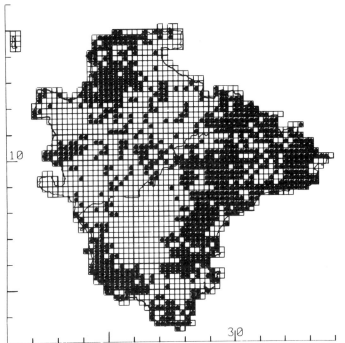

Epilobium montanum L.

Smooth-leaved Willow-herb, Broad-leaved Willow-herb
On shaded banks, hedges and walls, in woods, and as a persistent garden weed. Very common and generally distributed. (1396)

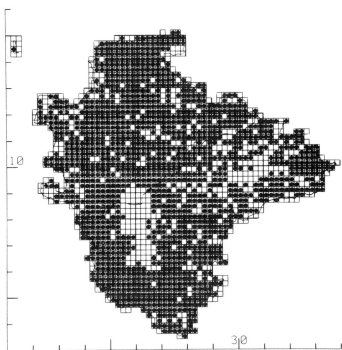

Epilobium parviflorum Schreb.   Downy Willow-herb
Beside streams and ditches, in wet meadows and in marshes. Reasonably common and quite generally distributed though rather local. (592)

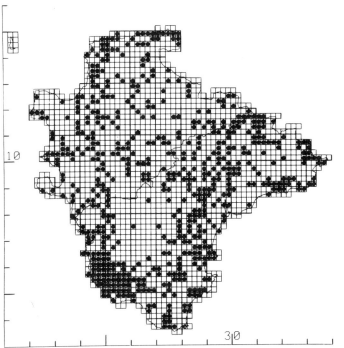

Epilobium lanceolatum Leb. & Mauri

Spear-leaved Willow-herb
Along roadsides, on banks and walls, and in dry waste places. Quite common in the south, especially around Plymouth, much less frequent in the north. (244)

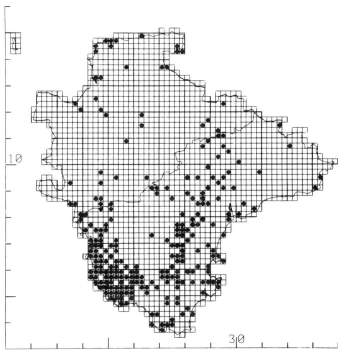

Epilobium tetragonum L.　　　Square-stemmed Willow-herb
In damp woods and hedges, and beside streams and ditches.
Scattered over the county, but of rather uncertain distribution
owing to confusion with other species. (217)

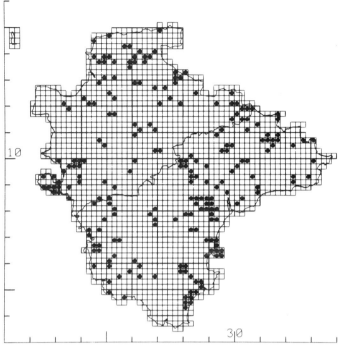

Epilobium roseum Schreb.　　　Small-flowered Willow-herb
In damp places in woods and scrub, and on banks; sometimes
as a garden weed. Scattered over the county, but rather rare.
(117)

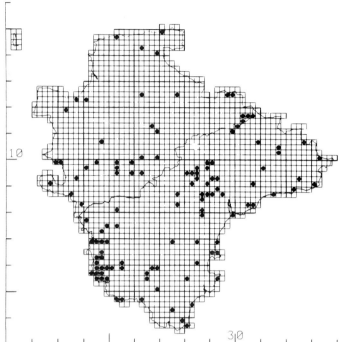

Ssp. **tetragonum** is the more common form.
Ssp. **lamyi** (F.W.Schultz) Nyman, (*E. lamyi* F.W.Schultz), has
been reported from a few sites in the county in the past, but
there are no recent records and it could be extinct.

Epilobium obscurum Schreb.　　　Dull-leaved Willow-herb
In damp places beside streams and in ditches. Generally
distributed though rather uncommon, particularly in the east,
though perhaps under-recorded. (774)

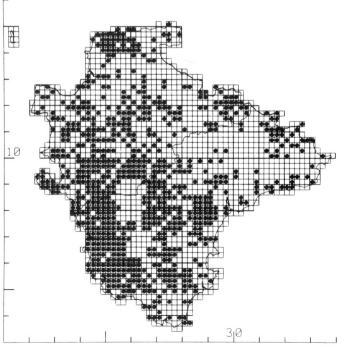

Epilobium palustre L.　　　Marsh Willow-herb
In bogs and marshes, with a marked calcifuge tendency. Not
uncommon in the north-west and around the moors, but local
and rather rare elsewhere. (411)

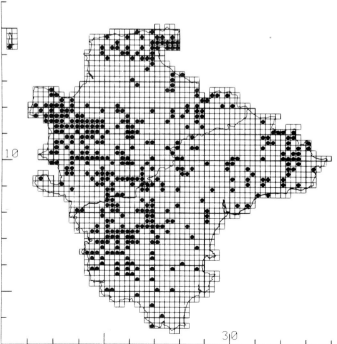

Epilobium ciliatum Rafin.   American Willow-herb
(*E. adenocaulon* Hausskn.)
Introduced; a native of America, now spreading rapidly over the county, and becoming one of the commoner species in damp scrub and hedges, on walls and in waste places, sometimes also as a garden weed. (865)

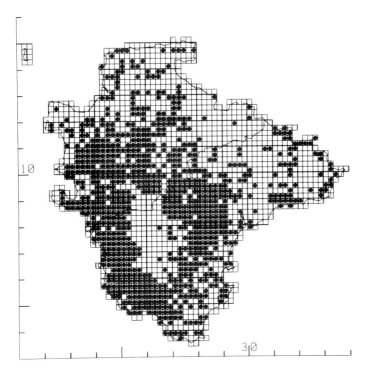

Epilobium *Hybrids*
Interspecific hybrids are readily formed in *Epilobium,* and a considerable number have been reported from the county, often without detailed localities or habitat information. The status of the following have not been re-investigated:
a. From both vice-counties:
E. x limosum Schur, (*E. montanum* x *parviflorum*); *E. x neogradense* Borbás, (*E. montanum* x *lanceolatum*); *E. x aggregatum* Čelak, (*E. montanum* x *obscurum*); *E. x dacicum* Borbás, (*E. obscurum* x *parviflorum*).
b. From S. Devon only:
E. x intermedium Ruhmer non Mérat, (*E. hirsutum* x *parviflorum*); *E. x erroneum* Hausskn., (*E. hirsutum* x *montanum*); *E. x weissemburgense* F.W.Schultz, (*E. parviflorum* x *tetragonum*); *E. x lamotteanum* Hausskn., (*E. lanceolatum* x *obscurum*); *E. x semiobscurum* Borbás, (*E. tetragonum* ssp. *lamyi* x *obscurum*); *E. x aschersonianum* Hausskn., (*E. lanceolatum* x *parviflorum*), which has a very old record from Plymouth; *E. x mutabile* Boiss. & Reut., (*E. montanum* x *roseum*); *E. x waterfallii* E.S.Marshall, (*E. hirsutum* x *palustre*).
c. From N. Devon only:
E. x thuringiacum Hausskn., (*E. obscurum* x *tetragonum*); *E. x schmidtianum* Rostk., (*E. obscurum* x *palustre*); *E. x rivulare* Wahlenb., (*E. palustre* x *parviflorum*).

HALORAGACEAE

Epilobium brunnescens (Cock.) Raven & Engel.
(*E. nerterioides* auct.)
Introduced; a native of New Zealand. Not uncommon in moist peaty or gravelly ground, tracks in plantations and beside streams on Dartmoor, and in similar habitats in a few other localities. (40)

Myriophyllum spicatum L.   Spiked Water-milfoil
In ponds, slow-flowing streams and canals, usually in base-rich water. Rare, though sometimes abundant where it occurs, and especially in the east of the county. (19)

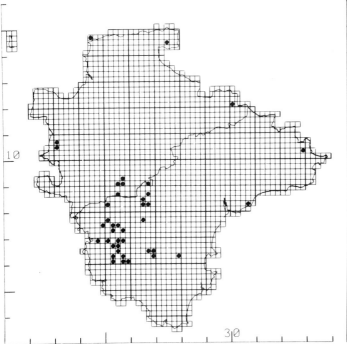

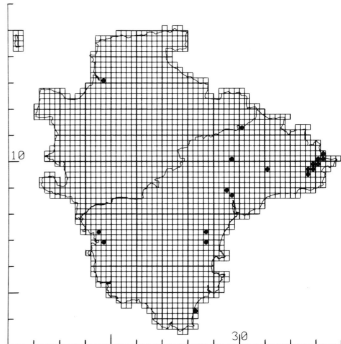

Myriophyllum alterniflorum DC.

Alternate-flowered Water-milfoil

In ponds, streams, canals and ditches, usually in base-poor or peaty water. Local, mostly around Dartmoor and in the north-west of the county. (32)

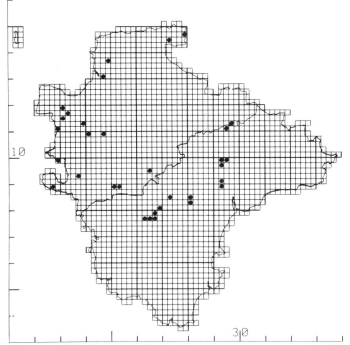

CORNACEAE

Cornus sanguinea L. Dogwood

(*Thelycrania sanguinea* (L.) Fourr.)

In woods, scrub and hedges. Common on the chalk and in limestone districts, and also found in base-rich habitats over the more calcareous rocks. (412)

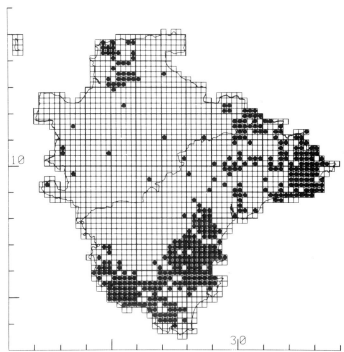

Myriophyllum brasiliense Camb. Parrot's Feather

Introduced; a native of Brazil. Sometimes grown in garden ponds and abundant in the pools at Paignton Zoo and the grounds of Exeter University. Rarely naturalised in ponds and streams in warmer parts of the county, as at Magpie Bridge, Horrabridge, but often barely surviving cold winters. (1)

ARALIACEAE

Hedera helix L. Ivy

In woodlands and hedges, and climbing on and over walls and buildings, and sparsely on numerous tors. Very common and abundant throughout the county. Various forms are cultivated and may sometimes be found as escapes. (1736)

HIPPURIDACEAE

Hippuris vulgaris L. Mare's-tail

This species has been reported recently from the Tiverton Canal, though the record has not been confirmed. It has been believed extinct in Devon for many years, though it is local in parts of Somerset.

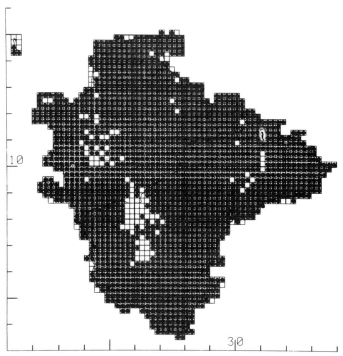

UMBELLIFERAE

Hydrocotyle vulgaris L.   Marsh Pennywort
In bogs and marshes, usually on rather acid soils, but also in dune-slacks on Braunton Burrows. Fairly common and quite generally distributed, and often abundant where it occurs. (413)

Eryngium maritimum L.   Sea Holly
On sandy shores and shingle. Quite frequent on the seaward side of Northam and Braunton Burrows, and in scattered localities along the south coast, but seemingly much less common than formerly. (16)

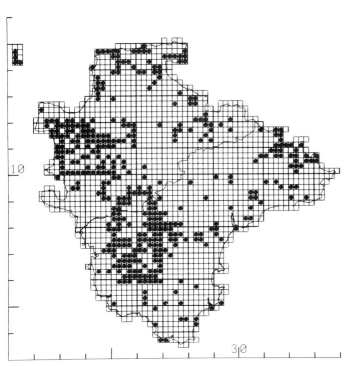

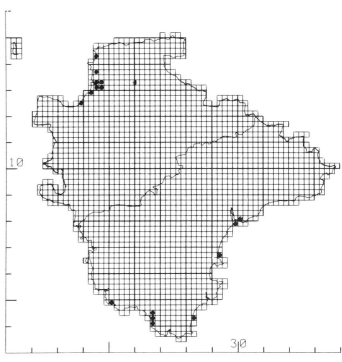

Eryngium campestre L.   Field Eryngo
In dry grassy habitats near the sea. It has been established for a very long time near Plymouth, and has been found recently at Scabbacombe, near Brixham. (3)

Sanicula europaea L.   Sanicle
In woods and scrub, usually in moist and moderately base-rich or clayey soils. Common and generally distributed. (646)

Chaerophyllum temulentum L.   Rough Chervil
In hedges, along roadsides and in rough grassland. Very common and generally distributed. It flowers rather later than *Anthriscus sylvestris.* (1346)

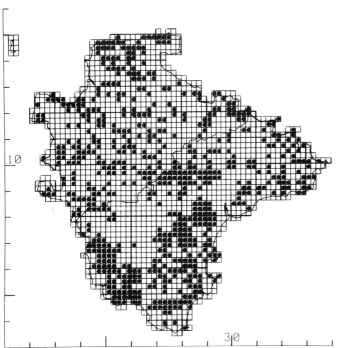

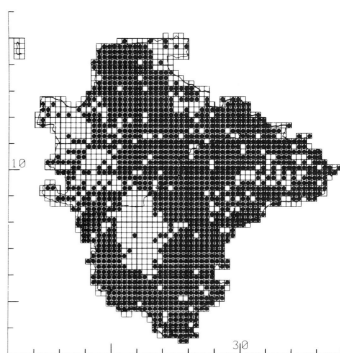

Astrantia major L. has been introduced from Europe and may be found occasionally as a garden escape, but there are no recent records.

116

Anthriscus sylvestris (L.) Hoffm.   Cow Parsley, Keck
In hedges and banks, and the edges of meadows and roadsides. Very common and generally distributed, though absent from the moors. (1299)

Myrrhis odorata L.   Sweet Cicely
Introduced in Devon. Only known from a few localities in pastures and cultivated land near Braunton, where it is probably an escape from cultivation. (3)

Coriandrum sativum L., the Coriander, has been reported from time to time as an adventive, but there are no recent records.

Smyrnium olusatrum L.   Alexanders
Introduced; a native of the Mediterranean region. Extensively naturalised in hedges, along roads and on sea cliffs. Very common near the coast, becoming rare inland. It was formerly cultivated as a pot-herb. (399)

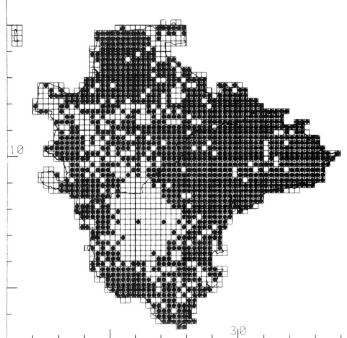

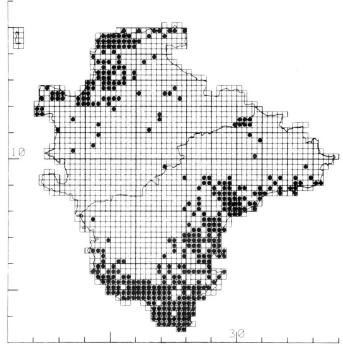

Anthriscus cerefolium (L.) Hoffm.   Chervil
Introduced from Europe. Only known from near Exeter, where it grows on roadsides and is probably an escape from cultivation. (2)

Anthriscus caucalis Bieb.   Bur Chervil
(*A. vulgaris* Bernh.)
In hedges, waste places and in sandy ground near the sea. Most common near the coast, occasionally inland, but generally rare. (23)

Conopodium majus (Gouan) Loret   Pig-nut, Earth-nut
In woods, damp hedgebanks and fields. Common and fairly generally distributed. (1127)

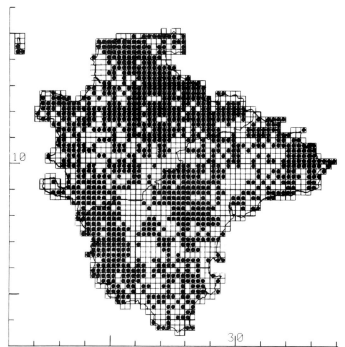

Scandix pecten-veneris L.   Shepherd's Needle
In arable land, as a weed of cultivation. Now very rare, and only known from a very few and scattered localities. (6)

Pimpinella major (L.) Huds. Great Burnet Saxifrage
On hedgebanks, in scrub and at the edges of woods. Quite common in the vicinity of Plymouth, extending north to Tavistock and into the South Hams, but rare or absent elsewhere. (115)

Aegopodium podagraria L. Goutweed, Ground Elder
Probably introduced; a native of Europe which was originally cultivated as a pot-herb, but now well naturalised in waste places and a persistent garden weed in many parts of the county. (974)

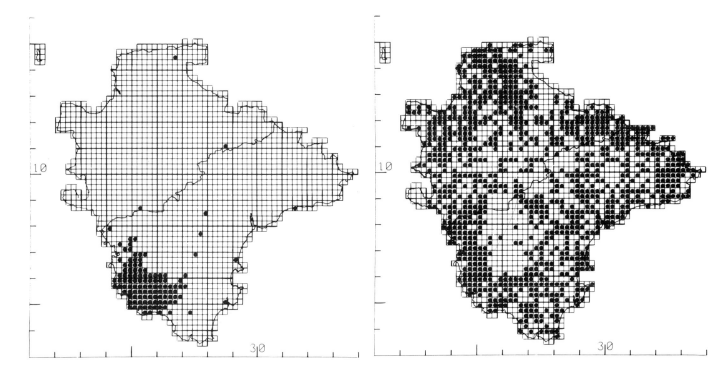

Pimpinella saxifraga L. Burnet Saxifrage
In dry grassland, banks and on hill-sides. Fairly common, especially in base-rich habitats, but absent from considerable areas. (285)

Berula erecta (Huds.) Coville Water Parsnip
(*Sium erectum* Huds.)
Along the margins of ditches, streams and rivers, occasionally in marshes. Mostly in the north of the county, where it is local; rare elsewhere. (27)

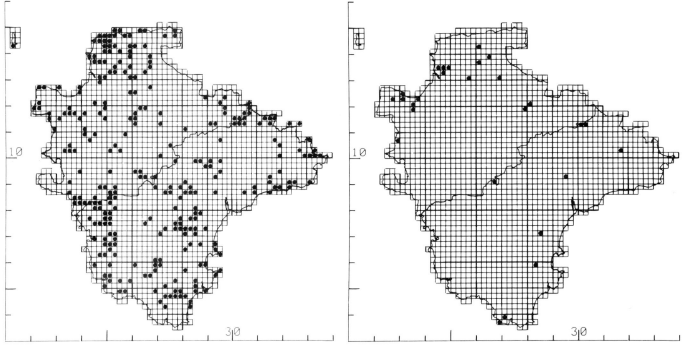

118

Sium latifolium L. is not known to occur in Devon.

Crithmum maritimum L.   Rock Samphire
On cliffs and rocks near the sea, and on walls around estuaries.
Common on both coasts, rarely inland and only along tidal
rivers. (129)

Oenanthe lachenalii C.C. Gmelin   Parsley Water Dropwort
In brackish and salt-marshes, and in tidal estuaries. Rare, with
generally scattered records, except at the southern end of
Braunton Burrows and dune pastures on Northam Burrows,
where it is locally frequent. (22)

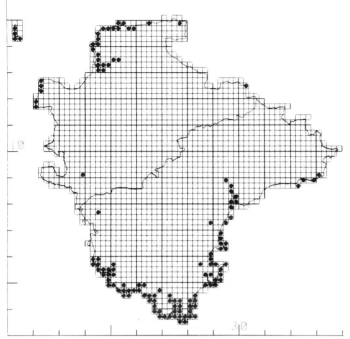

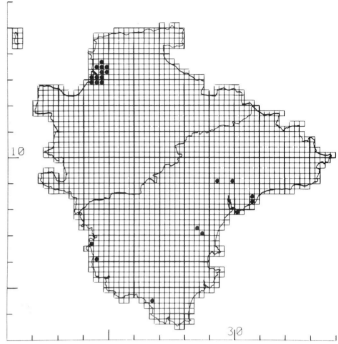

Oenanthe fistulosa L.   Water Dropwort
In marshes and shallow water. Now very rare, with very
scattered records. (4)

Oenanthe pimpinelloides L.   Pimpernal Water Dropwort
In damp grassland, often on alluvial soils. Locally frequent in
S.E. Devon, but very rare elsewhere; perhaps sometimes
confused with the next species (133)

Oenanthe crocata L.   Hemlock Water Dropwort
In wet meadows, beside streams and ditches and in damp waste
places. Very common and generally distributed. A persistent
and noxious weed on many farms, and its tuberous roots are
poisonous to cattle. (1380)

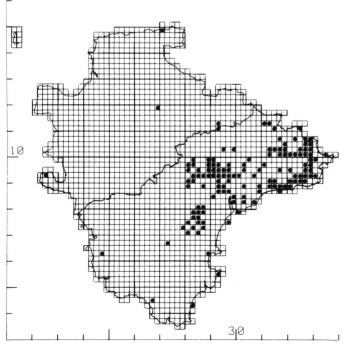

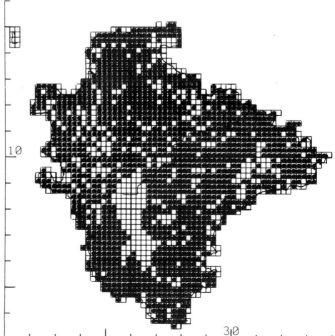

Aethusa cynapium L.   Fool's Parsley
In waste places, fields and gardens, and as a weed of cultivated
land. Generally distributed though rather local, and absent from
considerable areas. (273)

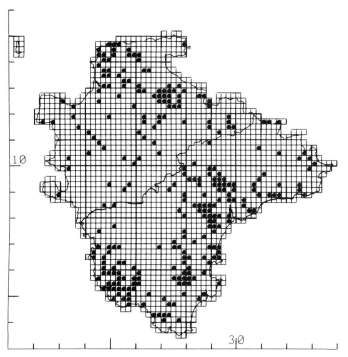

Silaum silaus (L.) Schinz & Thell.   Pepper Saxifrage
In meadows and grassy waste places. Rare, and occurring
almost entirely in E. Devon. (17)

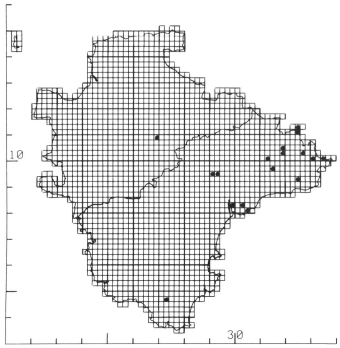

Physospermum cornubiense (L.) DC., (*Danaa cornubiense* (L.)
Burnat), the Bladder-seed, has been reported from woods and
scrub near the R. Tamar, but has not been seen for many years
and is probably extinct, though it still occurs nearby in Cornwall.

Conium maculatum L.   Hemlock
In hedgerows, damp waste places and by streams. Common
and fairly generally distributed, less frequent in the north and
west and absent from the moors. A very poisonous plant. (634)

Foeniculum vulgare Mill.   Fennel
Frequent near the sea, in hedges and grassland and on cliffs,
especially on base-rich soils. Adventive inland, and probably
always an escape from cultivation. (81)

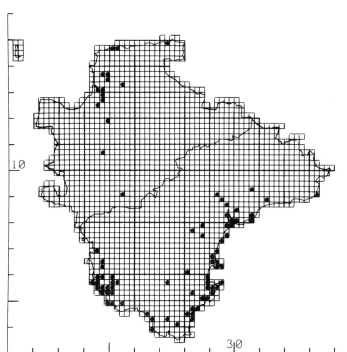

Bupleurum rotundifolium L.   Hare's-ear, Thorow-wax
Introduced; a native of S. Europe. It occurs in arable fields, but is
now very rare and only found in the south of the county. (3)

Bupleurum subovatum Link ex Spreng.
(*B. lancifolium* auct.)
Introduced; a native of S. Europe. It has been recorded on a few
occasions on waste ground in W. Devon. (2)

Bupleurum baldense Turra   Narrow-leaved Hare's-ear
(*B. opacum* (Ces.) Lange)
On dry banks and rocky limestone grassland. Only known from Torbay, at Wall's Hill and Berry Head, where it sometimes occurs in some quantity. (2)

Bupleurum fruticosum L.
Introduced; a native of S. Europe. The single record is from waste ground near Exeter, and is doubtless a garden escape. (1)

Trinia glauca (L.) Dum.   Honewort
In dry limestone grassland. Only known from Berry Head, where it is locally frequent in shallow soils. (1)

Apium graveolens L.   Celery
Moderately common in damp waste places and ditches near the sea or estuaries, and also found on sea cliffs and the upper fringes of salt-marshes. All inland stations are probably escapes from cultivation, though some may be incorrect identifications, as it is easily confused with the poisonous *Oenanthe crocata*. (66)

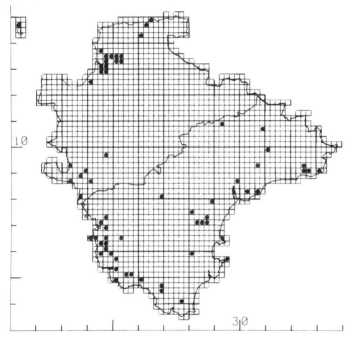

Apium nodiflorum (L.) Lag.
     Common Marshwort, Fool's Watercress
In ditches, shallow streams and wet places in meadows. Common and generally distributed in lowland habitats. (981)

Apium inundatum (L.) Reichenb.   Water Honewort
In ponds, ditches and streams. Apparently now very rare, and only to be found in S.E. Devon. (3)

Petroselinum crispum (Mill.) A.W. Hill   Parsley
(*P. hortense* auct.)
Introduced; a native of S. Europe. Naturalised in a few localities along the coast on rocky banks and in dry grassland, especially near Plymouth and Torbay; inland, an escape from cultivation. (9)

Petroselinum segetum (L.) Koch
     Corn Parsley, Corn Caraway
In hedgerows and waste places, often not far from the sea. Thinly scattered over the county, and quite rare. (11)

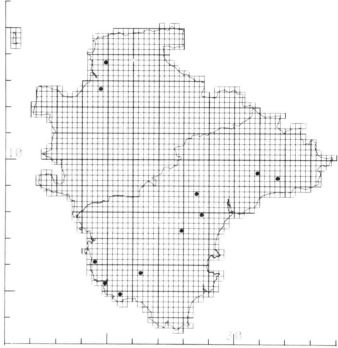

Sison amomum L.   Stone Parsley
In grassland and hedges and along roadsides. Not uncommon in S. and E. Devon, especially in clayey or base-rich habitats, and also to be found around Barnstaple, but very rare or absent elsewhere. (156)

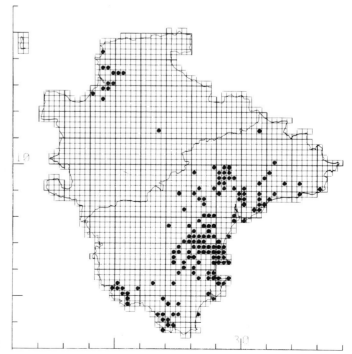

121

Ammi majus L.   Bullwort
Introduced; a native of the Mediterranean region. A rare casual, only known from waste ground near Haldon, Exeter. (1)

Ammi visnaga (L.) Lam. is an introduced species which was found at Churston Ferrers on one occasion, but has not been seen recently.

Falcaria vulgaris Bernh.   Long-leaf
Introduced from Europe. Only known as an alien on the sea-cliffs near Exmouth. (1)

Carum verticillatum (L.) Koch   Whorled Caraway
In marshy meadows and moorland. Confined to N.W. Devon, where it is locally abundant in damp acid habitats. (28)

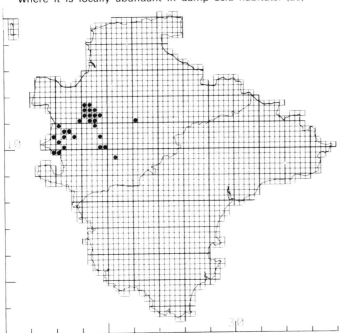

Pastinaca sativa L.   Wild Parsnip
(*Peucedanum sativum* (L.) Benth. ex Hook.f.)
Along roadsides and in dry grassy places, particularly characteristic of calcareous or base-rich habitats. Quite common around Plymouth and in some other localities in the south; rare in the north, except on Braunton Burrows. (69)

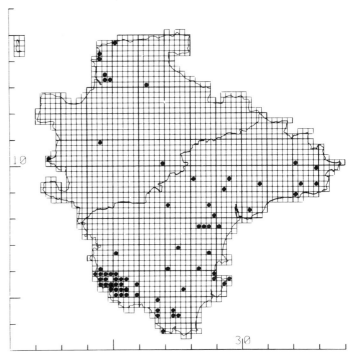

Carum carvi L.   Caraway
Introduced; a native of Europe. Reported on occasion from waste places and roadsides, probably as an escape from cultivation. There is a single record from Bratton Clovelly. (1)

Angelica sylvestris L.   Wild Angelica
In damp woods, hedgerows and in wet places along roadsides. Common and generally distributed. (1431)

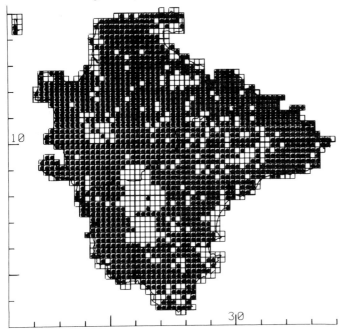

Angelica archangelica L.
Introduced; a native of Europe. The only record of this species is from Lundy, where it has been established for many years. (1)

Heracleum sphondylium L.   Cow Parsnip, Hogweed
In woods, hedges, pastures and along roadsides. Very common and generally distributed. (1687)

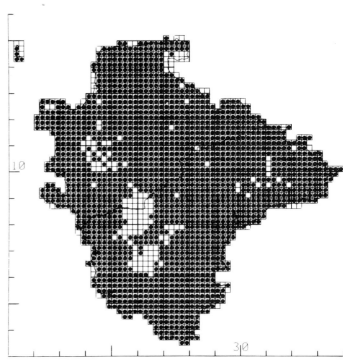

Heracleum mantegazzianum Somm. & Lev. Giant Hogweed
Introduced; a native of S.E. Europe and the Caucasus, sometimes grown in gardens and escaping, but now naturalised in
several widely separated localities and probably on the increase. (28)

Torilis arvensis (Huds.) Link   Spreading Hedge Parsley
Introduced in Devon. Now a very rare plant of arable fields on
chalk or limestone. A record from near Lapford should be
treated with some reserve. (2)

Torilis japonica (Houtt.) DC.   Upright Hedge Parsley
(*Caucalis anthriscus* Huds.)
In fields and hedges and along roadsides. Common and
generally distributed. (752)

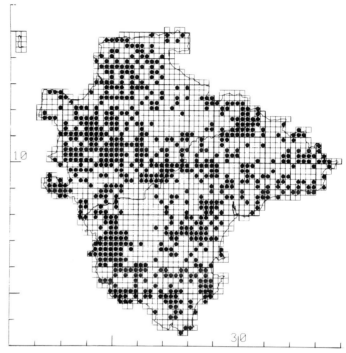

Daucus carota L.   Wild Carrot
On dry banks, in fields and grassy waste places, most common
near the sea and in base-rich or chalky soils. (304)

Torilis nodosa (L.) Gaertn.   Knotted Hedge Parsley
(*Caucalis nodosa* (L.) Crantz)
In fields and on dry exposed banks. Scattered over the county,
most frequent in calcareous or base-rich habitats, and usually
near the sea; rather rare inland. (50)

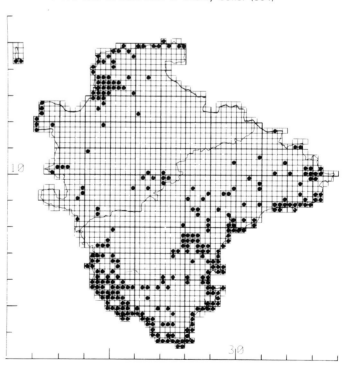

Ssp. **carota** is common in all these habitats; it has an umbel
which is markedly concave in fruit.
Ssp. **gummifer** Hook.f., (*D. gummifer* Lam. non All.), has a
nearly flat umbel and is found on sea cliffs and in dunes.
The cultivated carrot, which sometimes escapes, is placed in
ssp. **sativus** (Hoffm.) Arcang.

PYROLACEAE

Pyrola rotundifolia L.　　　　　　Larger Wintergreen
A species which has become established in dune slacks on
Braunton Burrows, and has spread quite rapidly so that it it now
locally abundant there. (2)

There is no evidence for the occurrence of **Pyrola minor** L., the
Common Wintergreen, in Devon. It used to occur at Burlescombe until 1967, when the site was destroyed for road
improvements.

Monotropa hypopitys L.　　　　　　Yellow Bird's-nest
In woods, usually of beech. Was found in the early 1960's in the
Axmouth-Lyme Regis landslip, under beech, but has not been
seen since. (1)

ERICACEAE

Erica ciliaris L.　　　　　　Dorset Heath
Introduced in Devon. On heaths and moors, and confined to one
locality on Dartmoor, where it has been established for many
years, though it also used to occur in Yarner Wood. It was first
introduced into a forestry plantation clearing at 400m (1250 ft.),
where the site is bisected by a tetrad boundary! (3)

Erica tetralix L.　　　　Cross-leaved Heath, Bog Heather
On wet heaths and moors, in damper habitats than *E. cinerea*.
Very common in suitable habitats on Dartmoor, Exmoor and
elsewhere. (445)

Erica cinerea L.　　　　　　Bell Heather
On the drier parts of heaths and moorland, in hedgerows and on
some roadsides in acid or peaty soils. Common and generally
distributed in suitable habitats. (598)

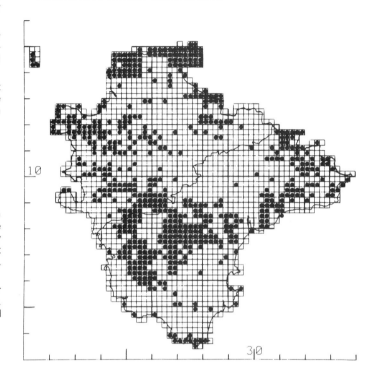

Erica vagans L.　　　　　　Cornish Heath
Introduced in Devon. It has been reported from two localities,
probably planted or escapes from cultivation, but is only
recorded from the cliffs at Baggy, where it was planted many
years ago and is still plentiful. (1)

Calluna vulgaris (L.) Hull　　　　　　Heath, Ling
On heaths and moors, and in woods on acid soils. Common and
often abundant in suitable habitats. (726)

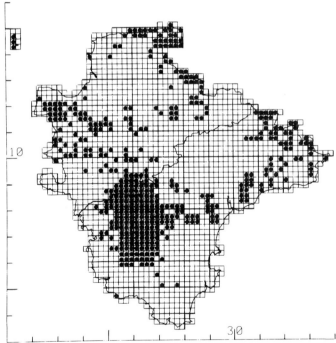

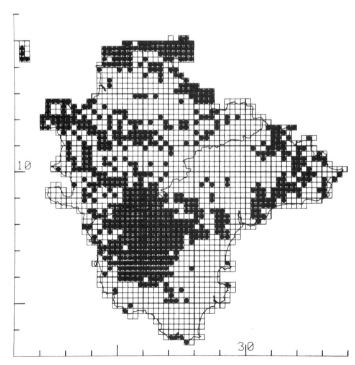

Rhododendron ponticum L.   Rhododendron
Introduced; a native of S. Europe. Commonly cultivated or planted in woods and scrub, and naturalised in many places, usually on acid, sandy or peaty soils. Generally distributed over much of the county, and regarded by some as a woodland weed. (424)

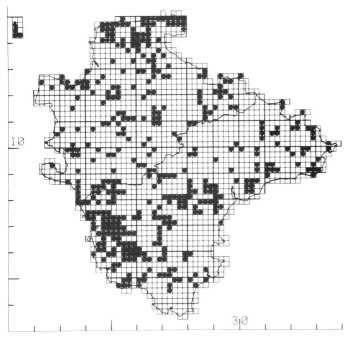

Vaccinium myrtillus L.   Bilberry, Whortleberry
On heaths and moors, and in open woods on acid or peaty soils, with a preference for drier or better drained habitats. Common and often abundant in suitable habitats throughout the county. (640)

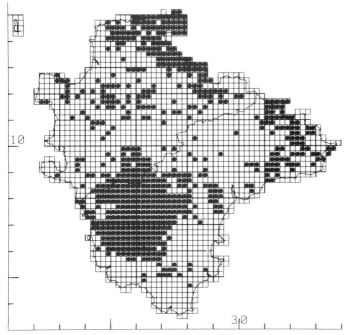

Vaccinium oxycoccus L., (*Oxycoccus quadripetalus* Br.-Bl.), the Cranberry, has been reported from three stations in wet peat bogs, but has not been seen for many years and is probably extinct. **Vaccinium vitis-idaea** L., the Cowberry, has not been seen at either of its two stations near Lydford for a long time and is also probably extinct. **Vaccinium macrocarpon** Ait., the American Cranberry, was reported as established for many years in a road cutting near Tavistock, but is not known to be persisting there.

Arbutus unedo L.   Strawberry Tree
Introduced in Devon. Occasionally planted and sometimes found as an escape, but scarcely naturalised, except perhaps in the Axmouth-Lyme Regis landslip. (4)

EMPETRACEAE

Empetrum nigrum L.   Crowberry
This used to occur in the vicinity of several tors on Dartmoor, but is now only known from Okement Hill, where it is has persisted for many years. It is steadily decreasing in quantity and is now very rare. (1)

PRIMULACEAE

Primula vulgaris Huds.   Primrose
In woods and hedges, especially on damp clayey soils, with a preference for S-facing banks and hedges. Absent from the moors and lighter or sandy habitats. Fairly frequent, but perhaps less common than formerly due to collecting; quite generally distributed. (1488)

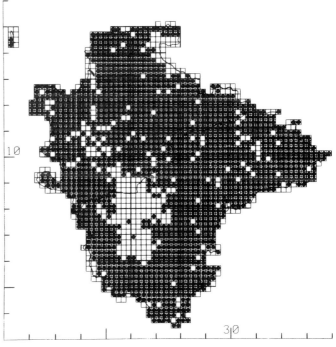

125

Primula veris L. Cowslip

In meadows and pastures, usually on base-rich soils or fairly near the sea. Widely distributed and rather frequent in E. Devon, quite uncommon elsewhere and much affected by the grazing regime. (69)

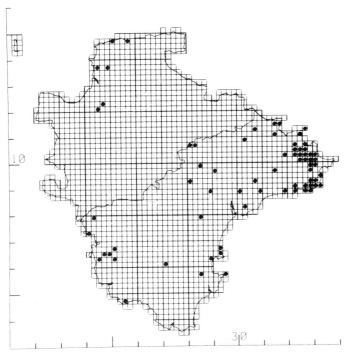

Cyclamen hederifolium Ait. Cyclamen, Sowbread

Introduced; a native of S. Europe. Naturalised in a few localities, especially around Torbay, but always originally either planted or a garden escape. (14)

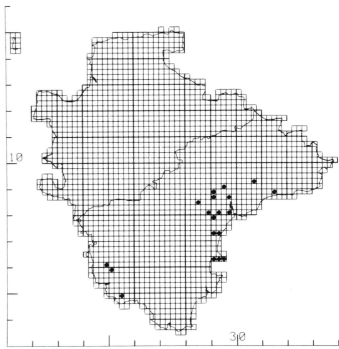

Primula x tommasinii Gren. & Godr. False Oxlip

(*P. veris* x *vulgaris*)

A vigorous hybrid, intermediate between the parents and often growing with *P. veris,* though preferring wetter or more shaded sites. Not uncommon in E. Devon, where the cowslip is quite frequent, but very rare elsewhere. (11)

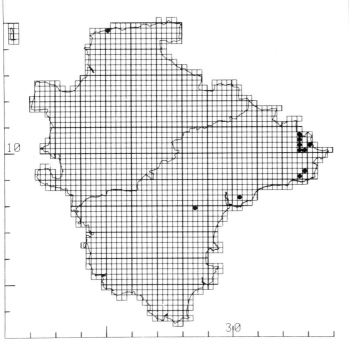

Lysimachia nemorum L. Yellow Pimpernel

In damp woods and shaded hedges. Common and generally distributed, especially in woods on clayey soils. (885)

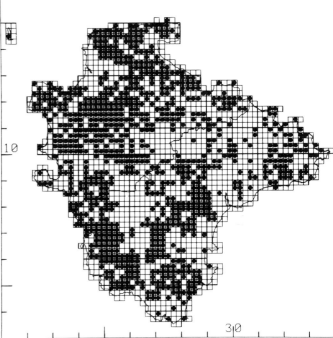

126

Lysimachia vulgaris L.   Yellow Loosestrife
Along river and canal banks, less often in marshes. Very local,
though not uncommon in some habitats. Some records may
reflect confusion with the commonly cultivated *L. punctata,*
which sometimes escapes, but is not naturalised. (45)

Glaux maritima L.   Sea Milkwort
In damp maritime sands, salt-marshes and along estuaries,
sometimes occurring inland on exposed coasts. Quite common
in suitable habitats. (64)

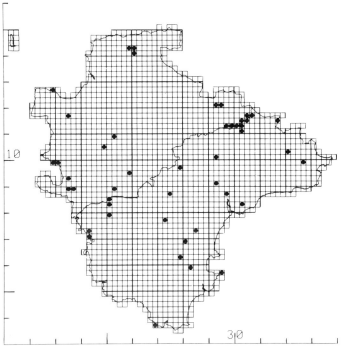

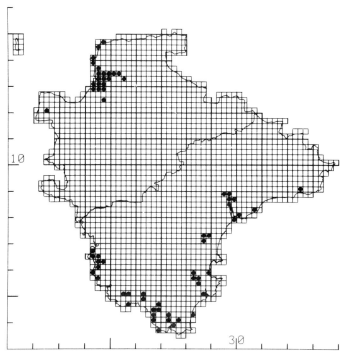

Anagallis minima (L.) E.H.L.Krause   Chaffweed
(*Centunculus minimus* L.)
In damp open sandy or peaty habitats on heaths or near the sea,
often where the ground is disturbed. Scattered over the county
and rather rare, but inconspicuous and perhaps overlooked. (9)

Anagallis tenella (L.) L.   Bog Pimpernel
In damp peaty or grassy habitats on moors or in marshes, in
dune slacks and in seepages and wet places at the base of
calcareous cliffs. Locally common and sometimes abundant in
suitable habitats. (316)

Lysimachia nummularia L.   Moneywort, Creeping Jenny
In shaded or woody places, moist hedges and lanes, often near
houses. Scattered over the county, but perhaps always an
escape from cultivation. (72)

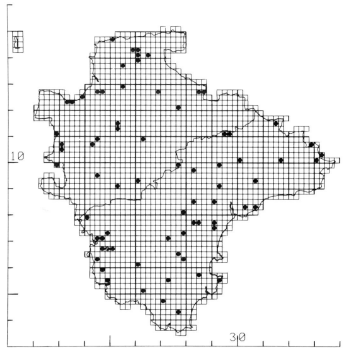

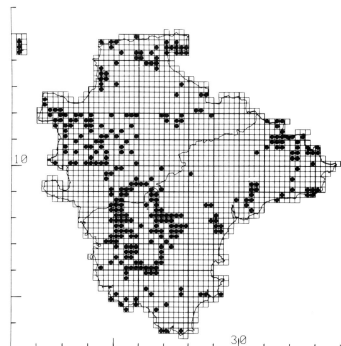

127

Anagallis arvensis L.   Scarlet Pimpernel
In cultivated land, waste places, roadsides and in open dune vegetation. Common and generally distributed. (1140)

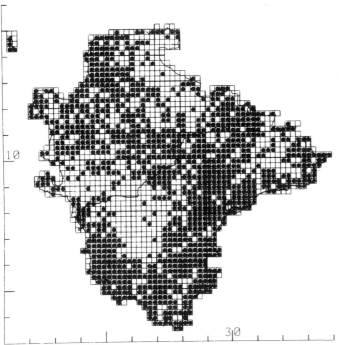

Our plant should be referred to ssp. **phoenicea** (Scop.) Schinz & Keller.
Ssp. **foemina** (Mill.) Schinz & Keller, the Blue Pimpernel, has been reported from arable fields in various parts of the county, but there have been no recent records. It seems unlikely that it still occurs in the county, as it is a spectacular plant. Care must always be taken to distinguish it from blue-flowered forms of *A. arvensis*.

Samolus valerandi L.   Brookweed
On wet cliffs, damp muddy sand and in estuaries. Scattered around both coasts, and generally not uncommon in suitable habitats. Rare inland, and probably only imported with sand, and unlikely to persist away from the sea. (50)

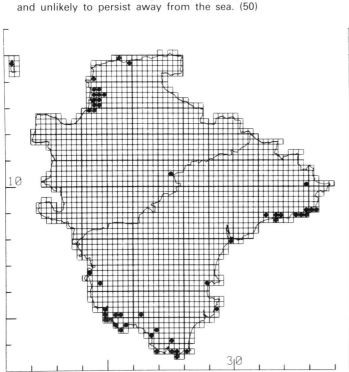

Armeria maritima (Mill.) Willd.   Sea Pink, Thrift
On maritime rocks and cliffs, salt-marshes and in grassland near the sea. Occasionally inland, but always in habitats affected by wind-borne spray. Common and often abundant around the coast. (164)

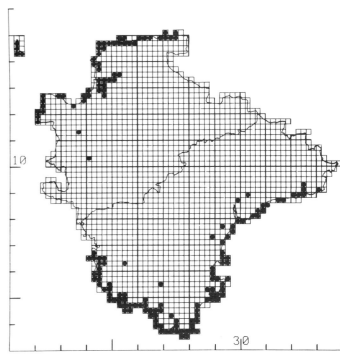

Limonium vulgare Mill.   Sea Lavender
In tidal estuaries and salt-marshes. Scattered around both coasts, but nowhere common. (18)

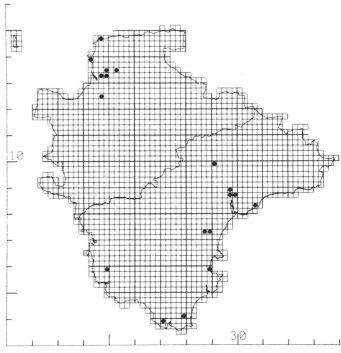

Limonium binervosum (G.E.Sm.) Salmon
Rock Sea Lavender
On dry rocky cliffs and gravel near the sea, more rarely a little way inland. Local around both coasts, and rarely plentiful. (30)

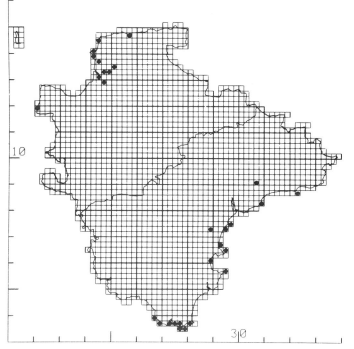

Syringa vulgaris L.
Lilac
Introduced; a native of S.E. Europe. Much planted in gardens and often naturalised in hedges and scrub, especially in the immediate vicinity of habitations. Generally distributed. (69)

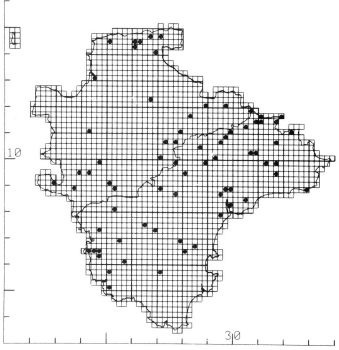

OLEACEAE

Fraxinus excelsior L.
Ash
In woods and hedges, usually on the damper and more base-rich soils, but common and quite generally distributed except on the moors. (1658)

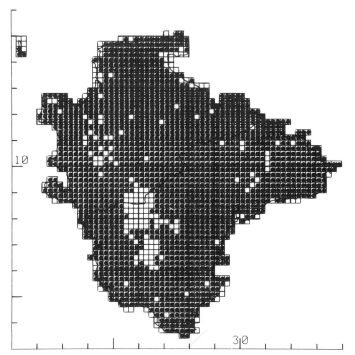

Ligustrum vulgare L.
Privet
In hedges and scrub; common on calcareous soils, over marly clays and in fixed dune grassland. Sometimes cultivated as a hedge and naturalised near habitations. (799)

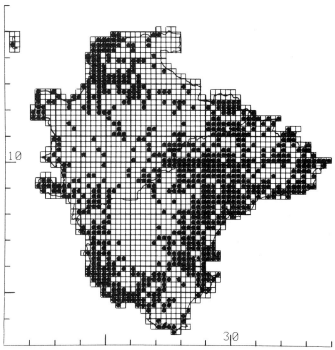

Ligustrum ovalifolium Hassk., the Garden Privet, a native of Japan, is now more generally cultivated as a hedge, and is the commoner species near habitations. The number of records includes both species.

129

GENTIANACEAE

Cicendia filiformis (L.) Del.
In damp sandy and peaty places near the coast in N. Devon. Very rare, with only a single record in recent years. (1)

Blackstonia perfoliata (L.) Huds.   Yellow-wort
In calcareous or base-rich grassland and hedges, on calcareous sea-cliffs and also in sand-dunes. Local, but abundant in some localities. (39)

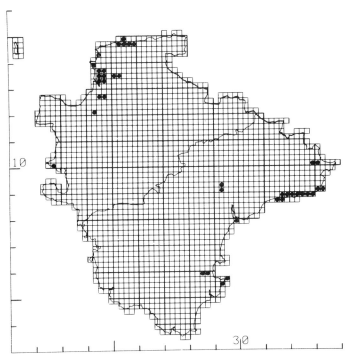

Centaurium erythraea Rafn   Centaury
(*C. umbellatum* Gilib., inc. *C. capitatum* (Willd.) Borbás)
In dry heaths, grassland and banks, sometimes near the sea. Common and fairly generally distributed, but avoiding damper habitats. (541)

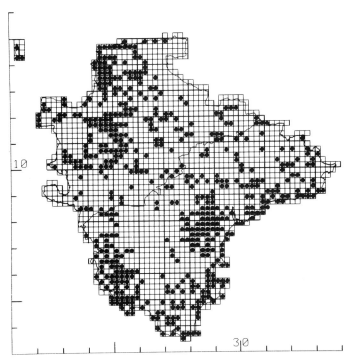

C. capitatum, with the stamens inserted at the base of the floral tube, is now considered to be distinct at the varietal level, as var. *capitatum* (Willd.) Meld.

Centaurium pulchellum (Swartz) Druce   Slender Centaury
In sandy or open places in pastures on clayey soils; most usually near the sea, but rarely inland. (23)

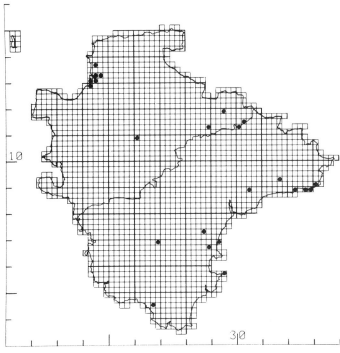

Gentianella amarella (L.) Borner   Felwort
In calcareous grassland and on dunes. Only known from Braunton and Northam Burrows, where it is not infrequent, and in the Axmouth-Lyme Regis Undercliffs. (14)

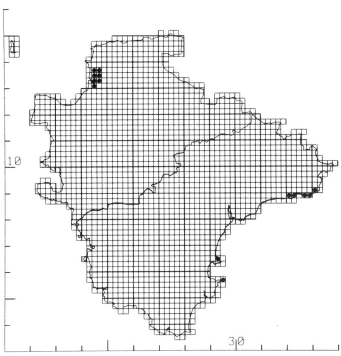

Gentianella campestris L.   Field Gentian
This has been reported from neutral or slightly acid pastures around the north coast and on Exmoor and Dartmoor, but the only recent record is from a small area on Roborough Down, where it is very rare. (1)

Gentianella anglica (Pugsl.) E.F.Warb.
In calcareous grassland and dunes. In similar localities to *G. amarella*, but much less common. (6)

130

MENYANTHACEAE

Menyanthes trifoliata L.   Bog-bean
In very wet bogs and marshes. Local on Dartmoor, but very
frequent in the bogs in the nort-west of the county. (121)

Vinca major L.   Greater Periwinkle
Introduced; a native of Europe. In similar habitats to the last, but
perhaps rather less common, though it is widely cultivated and
often naturalised. (268)

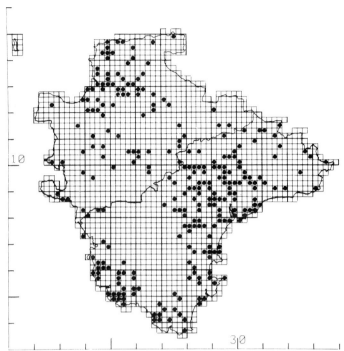

Nymphoides peltata (S.G.Gmelin) O.Kuntze
                    Fringed Water Lily
In ponds and slow-flowing rivers. Only known from a few
scattered localities in E. Devon, where it is either planted or an
escape from gardens. It has increased rapidly in the Exeter canal
in recent years. (5)

CONVOLVULACEAE

APOCYNACEAE

Vinca minor L.   Lesser Periwinkle
Introduced; a native of Europe. In woods, scrub, hedges and
around walls, widespread and often naturalised, though usually
in the vicinity of habitations. (475)

Cuscuta epithymum (L.) L.   Dodder
(inc. *C. trifolii* Bab.)
Parasitic on species of *Calluna*, *Ulex* and *Trifolium*, sometimes
on *Erica cinerea* and *Agrostis curtisii*, more rarely on other
shrubs or herbs. Scattered over the county, but rather rare on
the moors, and seemingly most common near the coast. (117)

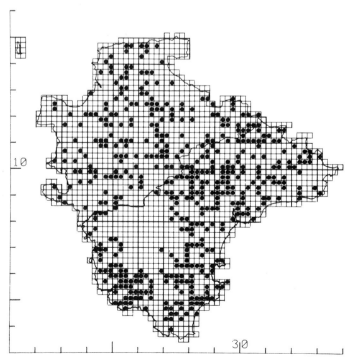

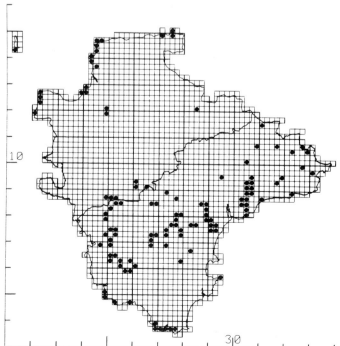

Cuscuta epilinum Weihe, which is parasitic on Flax, *Linum usitatissimum,* no longer occurs in the county.

Calystegia soldanella (L.) R.Br.   Sea Bindweed
On sand and shingle on the shore above high water mark, and at the edges of dunes on loose sand. Local, but rather common where it occurs. (10)

Ssp. **silvatica** (Kit.) Maire (*C. silvatica* (Kit.) Griseb.) is introduced and has become widely naturalised in scrub and waste places. (196)

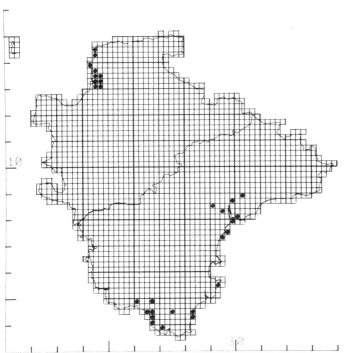

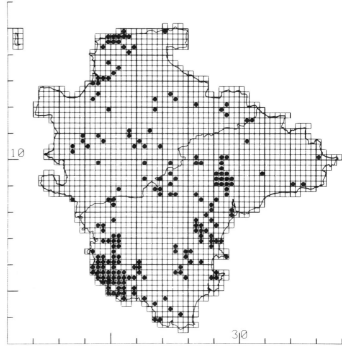

Ssp. **pulchra** (Brummitt & Heywood) Tutin (*C. pulchra* Brummitt & Heywood) has become naturalised in a few scattered localities near habitations. It is said to be rather frequent on fences around lorry parks. (4)

Calystegia sepium (L.) R.Br.   Greater Bindweed
Ssp. **sepium** occurs in hedges, scrub and waste places. It is common, generally distributed, and locally very abundant. (1072)

Convolvulus arvensis L.   Bindweed
In cultivated land and waste places, on roadsides and near the sea, especially in the south and east of the county. Frequently a noxious weed of gardens. (801)

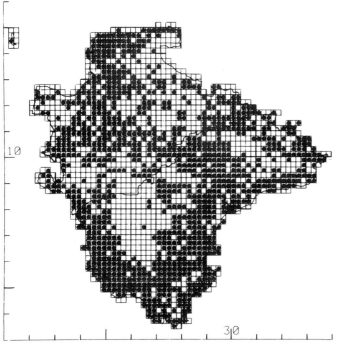

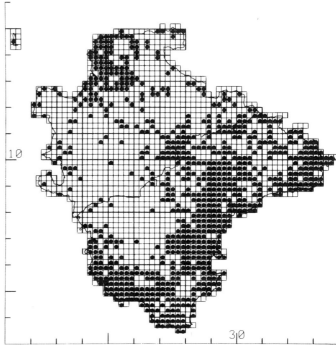

BORAGINACEAE

Lithospermum officinale L.   Gromwell
On banks, sea cliffs and in the edges of fields, usually on calcareous soils. Scattered and rather local, mostly in the east of the county. (40)

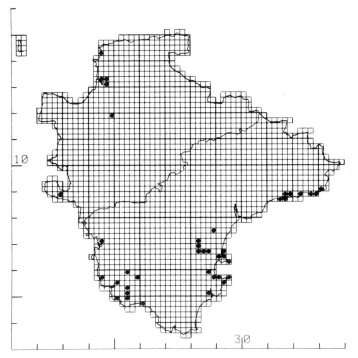

Lithospermum purpureo-caeruleum L.   Blue Gromwell
On chalky soil in scrub and the edges of woodland. Largely confined to the landslips near Branscombe, but the record in an old hedge at Dartington is of a plant not known to have been introduced. (7)

Lithospermum arvense L.   Corn Gromwell
In arable fields, usually with cereals or clover. Rare, scattered around the coast, usually in sandy soils. (10)

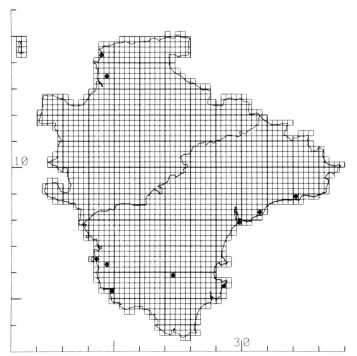

Echium vulgare L.   Viper's Bugloss
In grassy places and waste ground, usually on chalky or sandy soils. Most frequent near the sea, and it may be locally abundant on fixed dunes. (56)

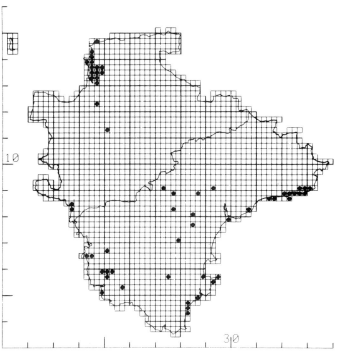

Echium plantagineum L.   Purple Viper's Bugloss
(*E. lycopsis* L. p.p.)
Probably introduced in Devon. Is grown occasionally in gardens and has been known to escape and become naturalised. (1)

Pulmonaria officinalis L.   Lung-wort
Introduced; a native of Europe. In woods, scrub and hedges; scattered over the county, but probably always as an escape from cultivation. (17)

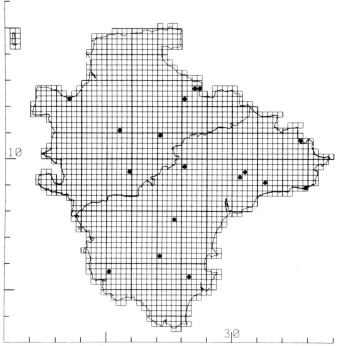

Pulmonaria longifolia (Bast.) Bor.
Introduced in Devon. In woodlands and scrub, usually on base-rich clayey soils. Rare, with only a single record. (1)

133

Symphytum officinale L.   Comfrey
On the banks of rivers and streams, by ditches and in damp
meadows. Generally distributed and locally common. (257)

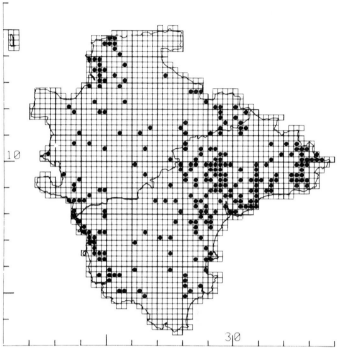

Symphytum tuberosum L.   Tuberous Comfrey
Introduced in Devon. Occasionally found in gardens and
sometimes escaping, but rare and local. (4)

Symphytum orientale L.
Introduced; a native of Turkey. In hedges and waste places,
mostly in the vicinity of Barnstaple and Bideford, but with
scattered records elsewhere. (10)

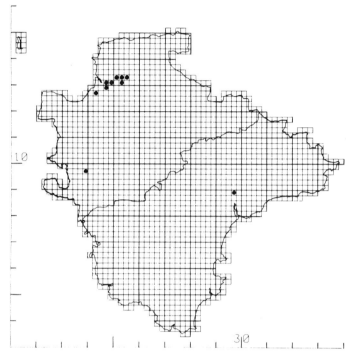

Symphytum asperum Lepech.   Rough Comfrey
Introduced; a native of Iran and the Caucasus. Has been
cultivated or grown as a fodder plant, and still persists in a few
scattered localities. (4)

Symphytum x uplandicum Nyman
                    Russian Comfrey, Blue Comfrey
(*S. asperum x officinale*)
Along roadsides and in hedges and woodland. It has probably
originated spontaneously, though has also been grown for
fodder and is scattered over much of the county, mainly in the
south. (90)

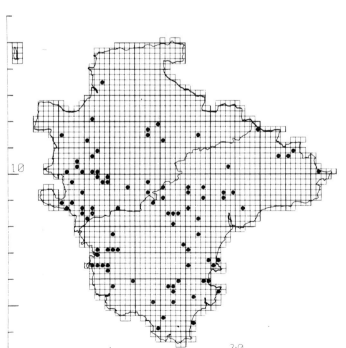

Anchusa arvensis (L.) Bieb.   Small Bugloss
(*Lycopsis arvensis* L.)
On sandy and other base-rich soils, often near the sea, and
absent from clays on the Culm. Generally rather uncommon.
(58)

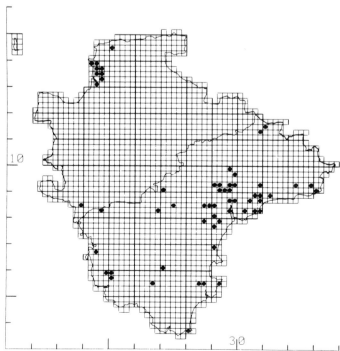

Anchusa officinalis L., **A. myosotidiflora** Lehm. and **A. azurea**
Mill. have been recorded in the past, probably all as garden
escapes; there are no recent records.

Pentaglottis sempervirens (L.) Tausch ex L.H.Bailey Alkanet
(*Anchusa sempervirens* L.)
Perhaps native. In hedges, on banks and in waste places, often near houses. It frequently has the appearance of a native plant, and is quite frequent in some parts of the county, though often only in small quantities at any one site. (460)

Myosotis arvensis (L.) Hill   Common Forget-me-not
In hedges, woods and at the edges of arable fields. Very common and generally distributed. (1035)

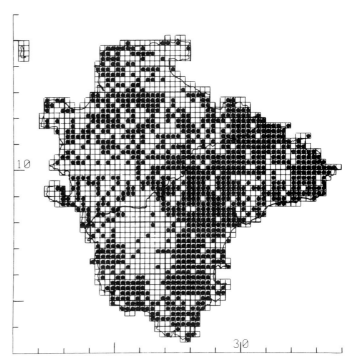

Borago officinalis L.   Borage
Introduced; a native of S. & C. Europe. In hedges and waste ground, usually near houses. It has been cultivated in the past as a source of nectar. (19)

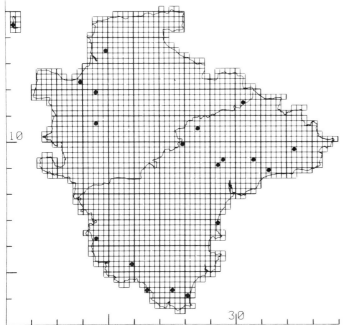

Myosotis ramosissima Rochel   Early Forget-me-not
(*M. collina* auct., *M. hispida* Schlecht.)
On dry sandy soils on heaths and dunes, sometimes on walls and paths. Most common near the sea, but also found inland on heaths. (53)

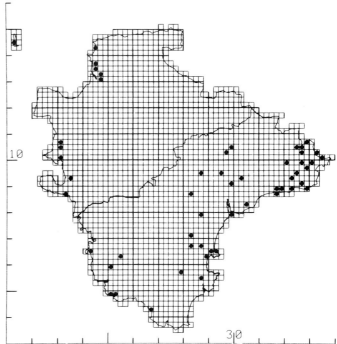

Trachystemon orientalis (L.) D.Don has been recorded from damp woods on base-rich soils near Torquay and Babbacombe, but there are no recent records. **Omphalodes verna** Moench was at one time quite widely distributed, as was **Lappula squarrosa** (Retz) Dum. (*L. echinata* Fritsch), but there are no recent records. **Amsinkia hispida** (Ruiz & Pav.) I.M.Schurt, **A. intermedia** Fischer & C.A.Meyer and **A. menziesii** (Lehm.) Nels. & Macbr. have all been recorded in the past as casuals, but not seen recently.

Myosotis discolor Pers.　　Yellow and Blue Forget-me-not
On dry banks, pastures and waste places. Fairly common and
generally distributed. This species is incorrectly referred to as
M. lutea in Fl. Dev. (354)

Myosotis secunda A.Murr.　　Water Forget-me-not
(*M. repens* Don ex Reichb.)
Along ditches and in the margins of streams and ponds;
confined to acid soils. Common and fairly generally distributed,
especially around Dartmoor and in the bogs in the north-west.
(492)

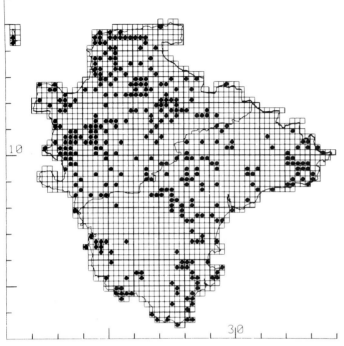

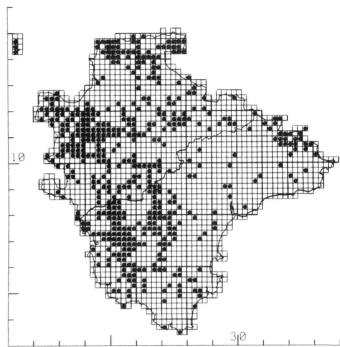

Myosotis sylvatica Hoffm.　　Wood Forget-me-not
In woods and scrub on damp and often clayey soils; scattered
over the southern half of the county, but not at all common. (35)

Myosotis laxa Lehm.　　Water Forget-me-not
(*M. caespitosa* C.F.Schultz)
In marshes and damp meadows; generally distributed but not
very common, or perhaps not always distinguished from *M.
scorpioides*. Our plants belong to ssp. **caespitosa** (C.F.Schultz)
Hyl. & Nordh. (146)

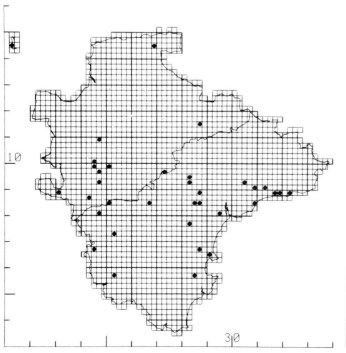

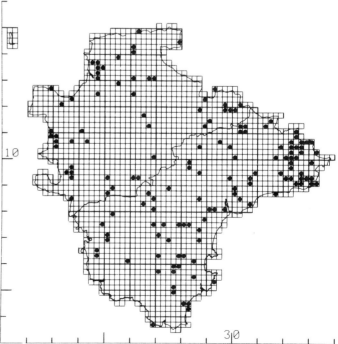

136

Myosotis scorpioides L.   Water Forget-me-not
(*M. palustris* (L.) Hill)
In ditches and beside streams, rivers and ponds. Common and
generally distributed. (369)

Verbena officinalis L.   Vervain
In dry waste places and along roadsides; most common fairly
near the sea, but not confined to such localities. (90)

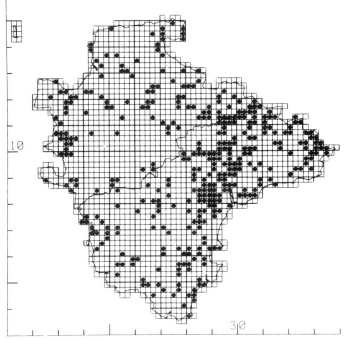

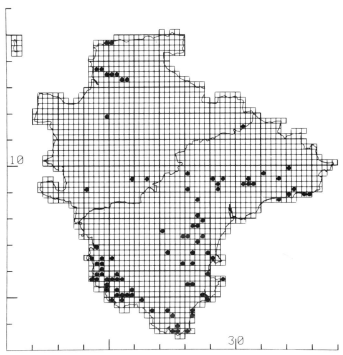

CALLITRICHACEAE

Species in the genus **Callitriche** are extremely difficult to identify
with certainty, as their morphology is much affected by the
environment. Records for the following species undoubtedly
reflect this.

Callitriche truncata Guss.   Short-leaved Water-starwort
In pools and ditches. Recorded only from the extreme east of the
county, where it seems to be locally frequent. (5)

Callitriche stagnalis Scop.   Common Water-starwort
In ponds and ditches. Rather common and generally distributed.
(641)

Cynoglossum officinale L.   Hound's-tongue
In dry soils on sand-dunes and in fields, usually on base-rich
soils and near the sea. Common on Braunton Burrows, and with
scattered records elsewhere. (18)

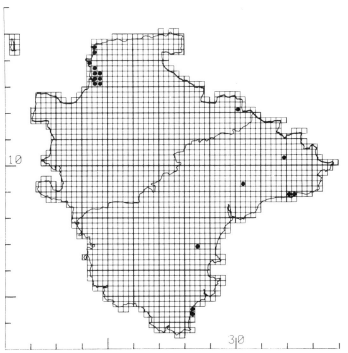

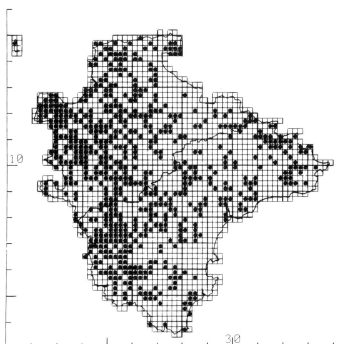

Callitriche obtusangula Le Gall   Blunt-fruited Water-starwort
In ponds and ditches. Local, but quite widely distributed and
perhaps not uncommon. (15)

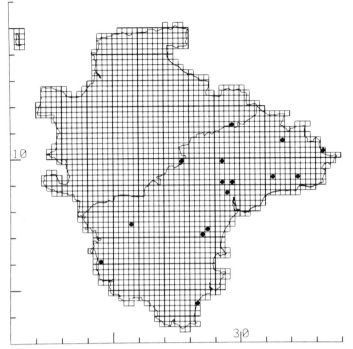

Callitriche hamulata Kütz ex Koch
Intermediate Water-starwort
(*C. intermedia* Hoffm.)
In pools, ditches and streams; thinly scattered over much of the
county and perhaps not uncommon. (98)

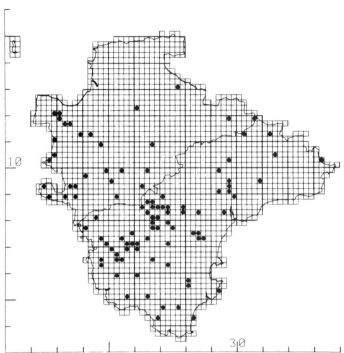

Callitriche platycarpa Koch
Various-leaved Water-starwort
(inc. *C. palustris* L.)
In ponds, ditches and streams. Widely scattered over the county
and rather rare. (13)

LABIATAE

Ajuga reptans L.   Bugle
In damp woods, pastures and damp shaded hedges. Common
and generally distributed. (1218)

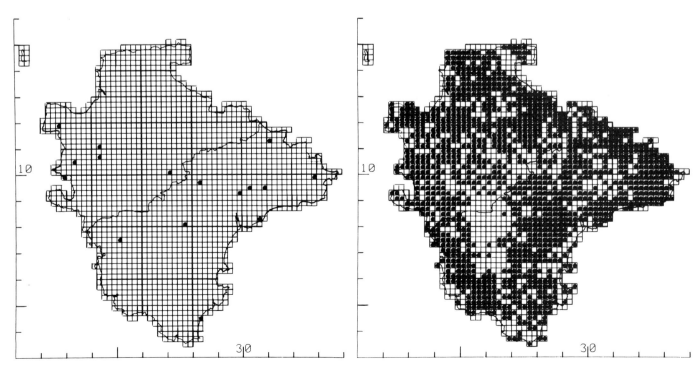

Teucrium scorodonia L.   Wood Sage
In woods, hedges, scrub, heaths and roadsides. Common and generally distributed, and sometimes very abundant on lighter or well-drained soils. (1596)

Scutellaria minor Huds.   Lesser Skull-cap
In peaty bogs and damp heathland. Not uncommon in suitable habitats, especially around Dartmoor. (256)

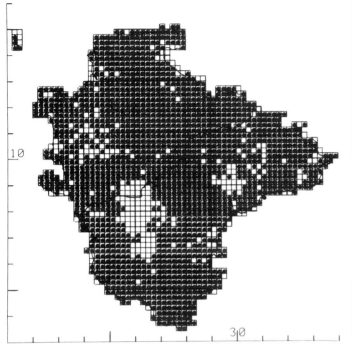

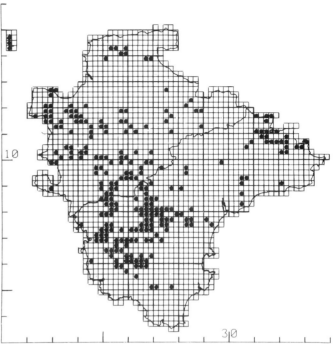

Scutellaria x hybrida Strail
(*S. galericulata* x *minor*)
This is recorded from both vice-counties (Perring in Stace, 1975), and is said to be persistent at Dartington, though has not been found there recently. There is a record for N. Devon from Ilfracombe (Perring & Sell, 1968).

Teucrium scordium L.   Water Germander
In dune-slacks; locally abundant on Braunton Burrows, and recently found on Northam Burrows, but not occurring anywhere else. (7)

Teucrium chamaedrys L. has been reported from time to time as an escape from cultivation, but there are no recent records.

Scutellaria galericulata L.   Skull-cap
Along stream-sides, by ditches and in wet meadows. Generally distributed but never common, and much less frequent than formerly. (69)

Marrubium vulgare L.   White Horehound
In waste places, roadsides and on sea cliffs. Rare, perhaps most frequent on the chalk at Beer and Branscombe, and also on Braunton Burrows. Probably not native in many of its inland sites. (16)

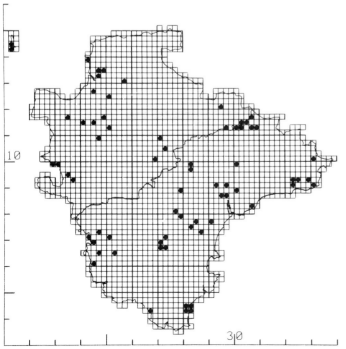

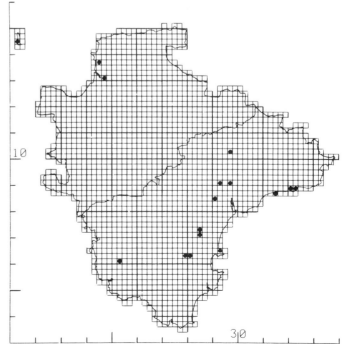

Melittis melissophyllum L.   Bastard Balm
In woods, hedges and bushy scrub. Scattered and local over much of the county, though rather frequent in the vicinity of the road between Exeter and Barnstaple and in the south-west, becoming quite common in adjacent parts of Cornwall. (79)

Galeopsis bifida Boenn., (*G. tetrahit* var. *bifida* (Boenn.) Lej. & Court.) is only distinguishable with difficulty from *G. tetrahit*; the absence of any recent records may reflect this.

Galeopsis ladanum L. has been reported from Devon but perhaps confused with *G. angustifolia*; there are no recent records. **G. segetum** Necker (*G. dubia* Leers) was reported as a casual in 1931.

Lamium maculatum L.   Spotted Dead-nettle
Introduced; a native of Europe. Cultivated in gardens and sometimes found as an escape or near rubbish tips, but not naturalised. (3)

Lamium album L.   White Dead-nettle
In hedges, waste places and along roads. Rather common and quite generally distributed. (549)

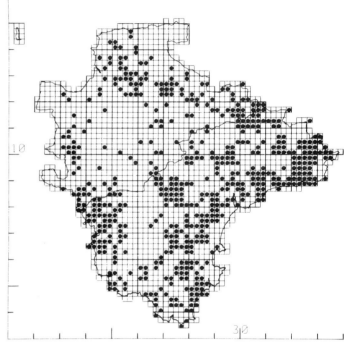

Phlomis fruticosa is a native of S. Europe which is frequently cultivated and may be found as an escape, but it not naturalised.

Galeopsis angustifolia Ehrh. ex Hoffm.
                          Narrow-leaved Hemp-nettle
In cultivated ground and waste places. Very rare, with records only from W. Devon. (2)

Galeopsis speciosa Mill.   Large-flowered Hemp-nettle
Introduced in Devon. Recorded from two localities near Tavistock and Tiverton, probably as garden escapes. (2)

Galeopsis tetrahit L.   Common Hemp-nettle
In arable land and waste places, rarely in woods or scrub. Fairly common and generally distributed. (911)

Lamium purpureum L.   Red Dead-nettle
In cultivated ground, waste places and sometimes in hedges. Very common and generally distributed. (1058)

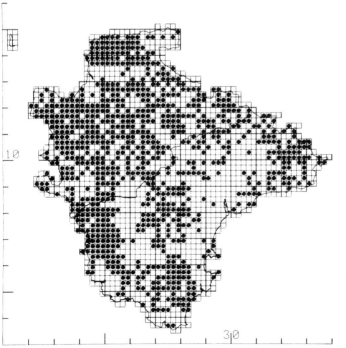

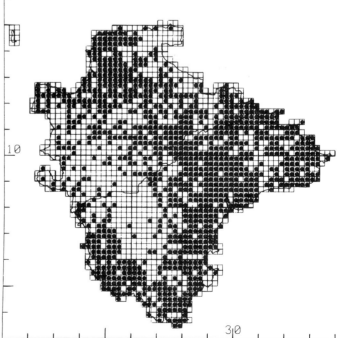

Lamium hybridum Vill. Cut-leaved Dead-nettle
In cultivated ground and waste places. Very thinly scattered over the county and becoming quite rare. (15)

Lamiastrum galeobdolon (L.) Ehrend & Polat.
Yellow Dead-nettle, Yellow Archangel
(*Lamium galeobdolon* (L.) L., *Galeobdolon luteum* Huds.)
In woods and hedges, usually on clayey or marshy soils. Generally distributed and sometimes abundant where it occurs. (515)

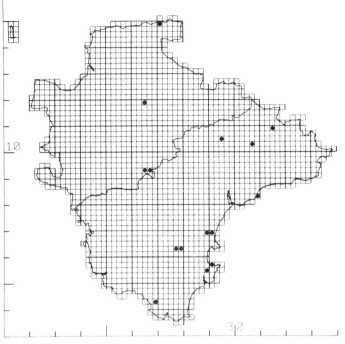

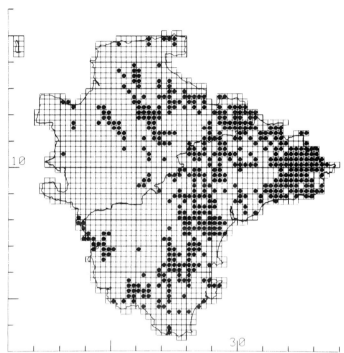

Leonurus cardiaca L. Motherwort
Introduced; a native of Europe. In hedges and waste places. Only known from the vicinity of Lustleigh, where it is probably an escape from cultivation. (1)

Ballota nigra L. Black Horehound
In hedges and along roadsides, especially at the gateways of fields. Quite common in the south and east, but apparently rare or absent from much of the west of the county. (314)
Our plant is ssp. **foetida** Hayek.

Lamium amplexicaule L. Henbit
In cultivated ground, mainly on light and often rather base-rich soils, sometimes on walls, grassy fields or in waste places. Rare, perhaps more frequent in the south and south-east. (65)

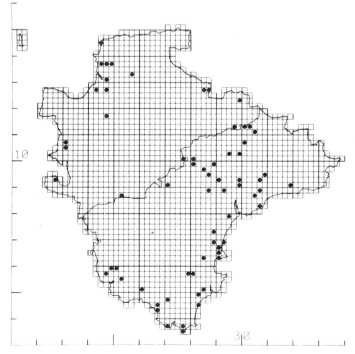

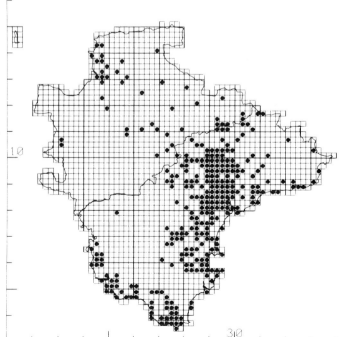

Stachys officinalis (L.) Trev.   Wood Betony, Betony
(*Betonica officinalis* L.)
In woods, scrub and hedges, along roads and on heaths.
Common and generally distributed. (999)

Stachys palustris L.   Marsh Woundwort
By rivers and streams, in damp or wet fields and in cultivated
ground. Generally distributed but only moderately common,
and probably less frequent than formerly, owing to drainage.
(549)

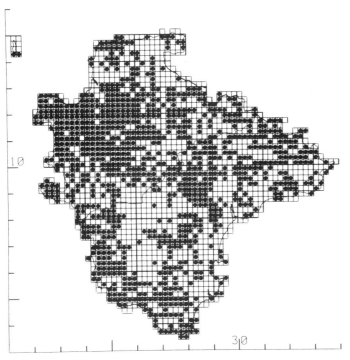

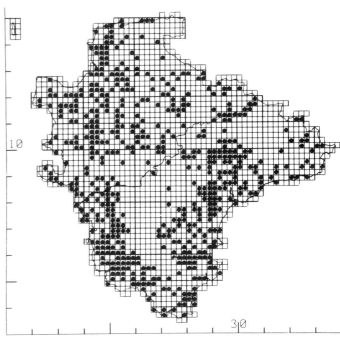

Stachys x ambigua Sm.
(*S. palustris* x *sylvatica*)
Occurs very infrequently and often in the absence of one or
other parent, but records are widely scattered and it could have
been overlooked. (4)

Stachys arvensis (L.) L.   Field Woundwort
In fields and cultivated ground; not uncommon on the Culm,
less so elsewhere, but quite generally distributed. (441)

Stachys sylvatica L.   Hedge Woundwort
In woods, hedges, shaded lanes and the edges of fields, usually
in better soils or rather damp habitats. Common and generally
distributed. (1581)

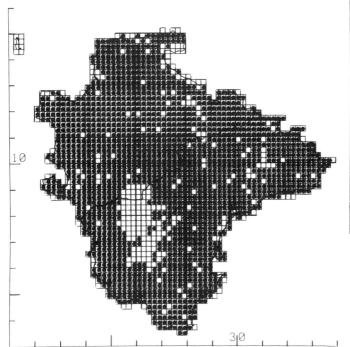

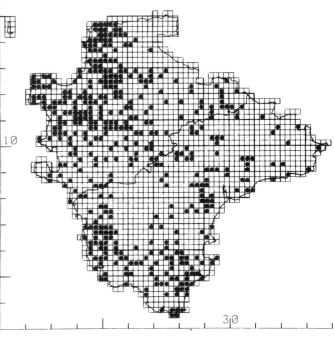

Stachys annua (L.) L. has been recorded as a casual, but there
are no recent records.

Nepeta cataria L., the Cat-mint, is a rare plant of hedgerows
which used to occur at Braunton, Croyde and Instow, but has
not been seen since 1966. Rather similar garden plants, which
may sometimes be found as escapes, are either **N. x faassenii**
Bergmans ex Stern (*N. mussinii* hort. p.p.), or **N. mussinii**
Spreng. (3)

Glechoma hederacea L.   Ground Ivy
(*Nepeta hederacea* (L.) Trev.)
In hedges, woods and waste places, often in the damper or
more clayey soils, but also in well-drained habitats. Common
and generally distributed. (1488)

Melissa officinalis L.   Balm
Introduced; a native of C. & S. Europe. Widely cultivated as a
pot-herb, and sometimes naturalised in the vicinity of habitations. (36)

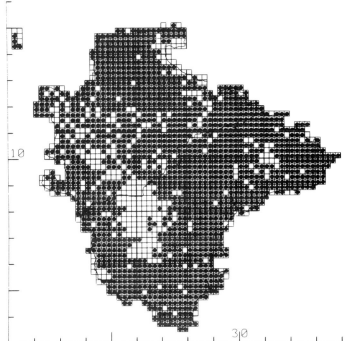

Prunella vulgaris L.   Self-heal
In grasslands, woodlands and waste places, but avoiding the
most acid soils. Very common and generally distributed. (1540)

Acinos arvensis (Lam.) Dandy   Basil-thyme
(*Calamintha acinos* Clairv.)
In open habitats in grassland or among rocks, usually in dry
calcareous soils. Scattered over the county, but most common
around Torquay and Branscombe; considerably less common
than formerly and apparently absent from N. Devon. (18)

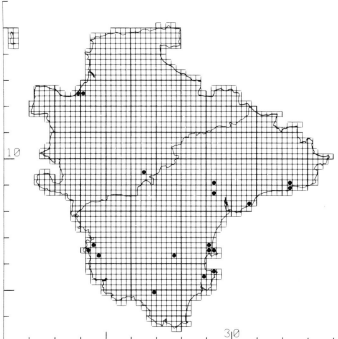

143

Calamintha sylvatica Bromf.   Calamint
(inc. *C. ascendens* Jord.)
In hedges and usually dry, sunny slopes, in calcareous or
base-rich habitats. Most frequent in the south, especially around
Torbay, but not uncommon elsewhere. (329)
Our plant is ssp. **ascendens** (Jord.) P.W.Ball.

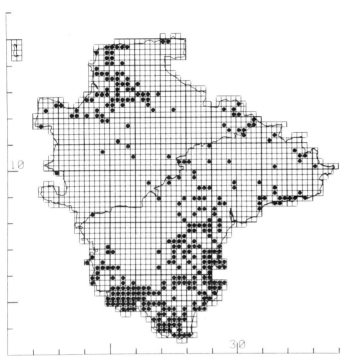

Origanum vulgare L.   Marjoram
In dry hedgebanks and scrub, usually on calcareous or base-rich
soils. Most common in the south, especially on the limestone,
but scattered elsewhere. (198)

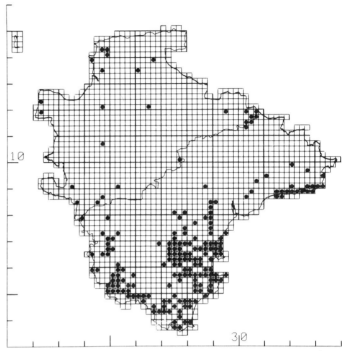

Thymus praecox Opiz   Thyme
(*T. serpyllum* auct. brit., *T. drucei* Ronn., inc. *T. pycnotrichus*
auct., *T. lanuginosus* (Mill.) Ronn., *T. neglectus* Ronn., *T.
britannicus* Ronn.)
On heaths, grasslands, fixed dunes and rocky places. Common
in coastal habitats, and around the edges of Dartmoor, rather
rare elsewhere. (207)
Our plant is ssp. **arcticus** (Dur.) Jalas.

Clinopodium vulgare L.   Wild Basil
In hedges, woods and scrub, usually in rather dry habitats. Most
frequent in the Torbay limestone region, but moderately
common elsewhere. (257)

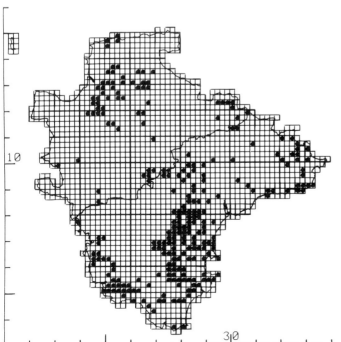

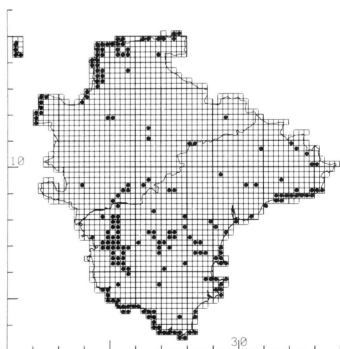

Thymus pulegioides L., the Larger Wild Thyme, has been
recorded from Braunton and Northam Burrows, and in scattered
dry habitats elsewhere, but it has not been seen recently and it is
doubtful if it still persists.

Lycopus europaeus L.   Gipsy-wort
By streams, rivers and ponds, and in marshy habitats generally.
Scattered over the county, but not very common. (188)

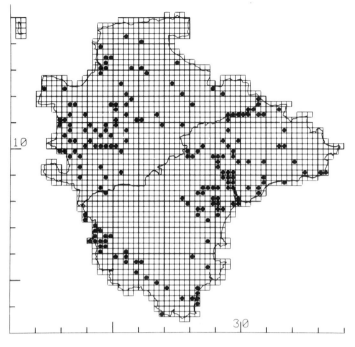

Mentha requienii Benth.
Introduced; a native of Corsica and Sardinia. Sometimes grown
in gardens and escaping, but usually found in the immediate
vicinity of habitations and scarcely naturalised. (2)

Mentha pulegium L.   Penny-royal
In wet places in heaths or on sandy soil, often near the sea, or on
sea cliffs. Very local around the south coast, and also occurring
at Braunton, but often threatened by intensive agriculture near
to cliff edges. (5)

Mentha arvensis L.   Corn Mint
In fields and damp scrubby grassland. Fairly common and
generally distributed. (460)

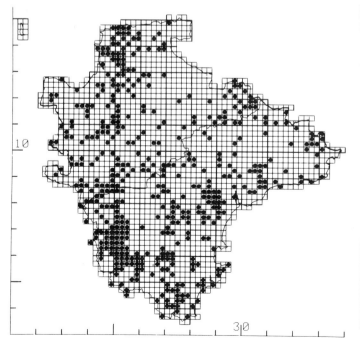

Mentha x muellerana F.W.Schultz, (*M. arvensis* x *suaveolens*),
was planted in the Scabbacombe valley, Brixham, in 1936,
following the destruction of its habitat at Salcombe (Fl. Dev.).
There are no records of its continuing survival.

Mentha x verticillata L.   Whorled Mint
(*M. arvensis* x *aquatica*)
By rivers, ponds and ditches, and in damp grassland; frequently
found growing with *M. aquatica* and not always easy to separate
from this. Generally distributed and probably more frequent
than the records suggest. (42)

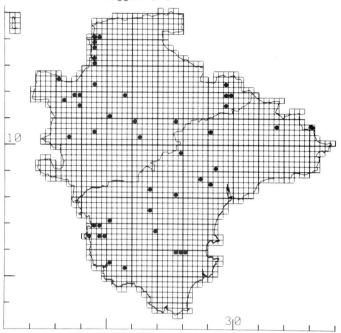

Mentha x gentilis L.   Bushy Mint
(*M. arvensis* x *spicata*)
In damp and marshy grassland. An apparently rare hybrid which
may well occur more frequently than records suggest. (3)

Mentha x smithiana R.A.Graham   Tall Mint
(*M. x rubra* Sm., *M. aquatica* x *arvensis* x *spicata*)
In damp grassland and waste ground. Rare, with only scattered
records, mostly in E. Devon. (5)

Mentha aquatica L.   Water Mint
In marshes, wet woods and grassland, and beside rivers and
streams. Common and generally distributed, and often abundant where it occurs. (1069)

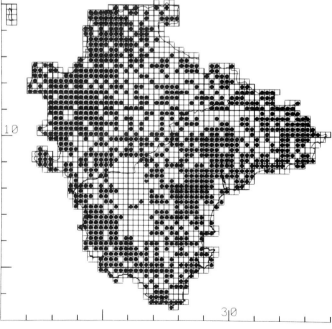

Mentha x piperita L.   Peppermint
(*M. aquatica* x *spicata*)
By ditches and streams, and along roadsides. It has been
extensively cultivated and many records are probably escapes
from cultivation. Not very common, but widely distributed. (20)

Mentha x piperita L.   Peppermint

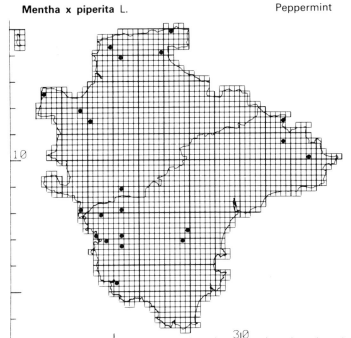

Mentha x maximilianea F.W.Schultz (*M. aquatica x suaveolens*) was recorded from Man Sands, Brixham in 1955 (Graham, 1958), but it is not known if it persists. **M. x dumetorum** Schultes (*M. x palustris* Sole, *M. aquatica x longifolia*), is reported from Otterton (Herb. Kew, 1936), and also from Plymouth, but there are no recent records.

Mentha suaveolens Ehrh.   Apple-mint
(*M. rotundifolia* auct., non (L.) Huds.)
In grassy waste places, roadsides and ditches; perhaps most frequent near the sea. Not uncommon in S. Devon, scattered elsewhere. Sometimes cultivated and some records are probably escapes from cultivation. (62)

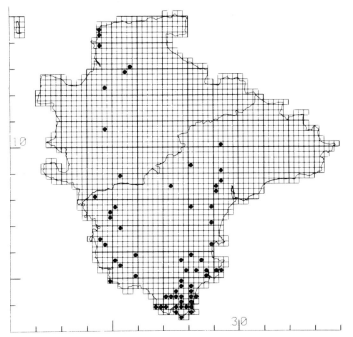

Mentha x villosa Huds.   Large Apple-mint
(*M. niliaca* auct., *M. cordifolia* auct., *M. alopecuroides* Hull, *M. spicata x suaveolens*)
In damp grassland, roadsides and waste places. Has been recorded on very few occasions, and is possibly more common than this. (6)
All records for **M. x rotundifolia** (L.) Huds., (*M. x niliaca* Juss. ex Jacq., *M. longifolia x suaveolens*), should be referred here.

Mentha spicata L.   Spear-mint, Garden Mint
(*M. viridis* auct.)
Introduced; a native of Europe. Widely cultivated in gardens and frequently escaping; often naturalised in damp waste ground and along roads. (75)

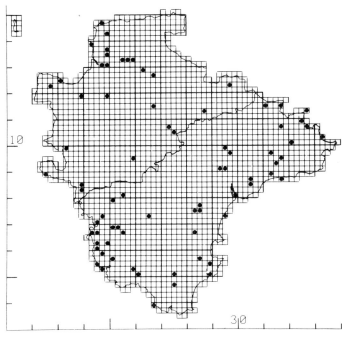

All records of **M. longifolia** (L.) Huds. (which does not occur in Britain) should be referred to this species.

Salvia verbenaca L.   Clary
(*S. horminoides* Pourr.)
In dry sandy or calcareous soil, mostly near the sea. Rather rare; scattered around the south coast and also at Saunton and Westleigh. (10)

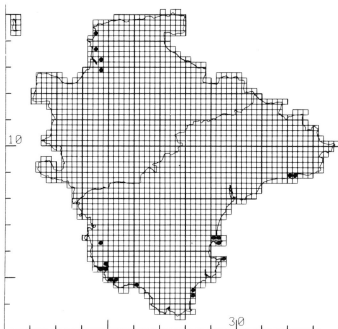

Other species of **Salvia** (**S. verticillata** L., **S. sclarea** L. and **S. virgata** Jacq.) have been recorded from time to time, but all are probably garden escapes.

SOLANACEAE

Nicandra physalodes (L.) Gaertn.
Shoo-fly Plant, Apple of Peru
Introduced; a native of Peru. Quite frequently cultivated in gardens and a rare weed of arable fields and waste places, but not naturalised. (1)

Lycium chinense Mill.
Tea-plant
Introduced; a native of E. Asia. Widely cultivated as a hedge and sometimes naturalised, especially near the sea. (26)

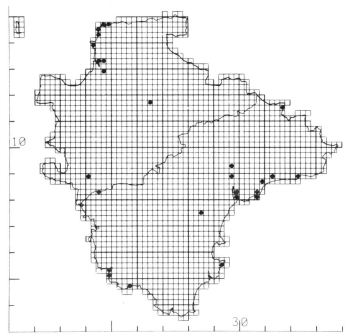

L. barbarum L. is also sometimes cultivated, but it is not clear that it is naturalised.

Atropa belladonna L.
Deadly Nightshade
Introduced in Devon. Confined to base-rich soils, but with only a single record from Sidmouth which is probably a garden escape. (1)

Hyoscyamus niger L.
Henbane
On sandy or rocky ground on or near the shore, very rarely inland, as a weed of arable ground. Rare, with scattered records around both coasts. (14)

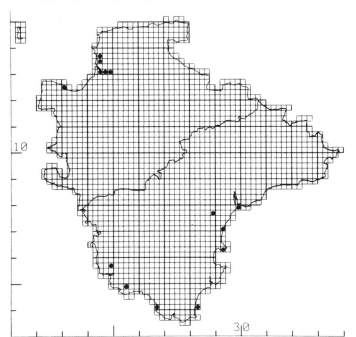

Solanum nigrum L.
Black Nightshade
In waste places and as a weed in cultivated fields and gardens. Not very common, perhaps more frequent near the coast, but quite generally distributed. (187)

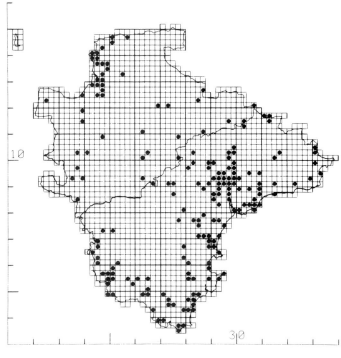

Solanum dulcamara L.
Woody Nightshade
In hedges, scrub and waste places, especially if rather damp, and on or near the coast. Common and fairly generally distributed. (1138)

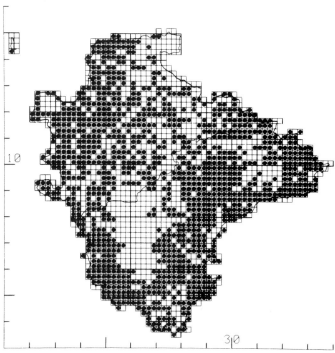

Solanum tuberosum L., the Potato, is very widely cultivated, and is sometimes found in the vicinity of rubbish tips, and as a residue from field crops, but is not naturalised.

147

Lycopersicon esculentum Mill. Tomato

Introduced; a native of S. America. Occasionally found in the vicinity of rubbish tips, as a relic of cultivation, and seedlings may appear in river gravel, but they do not persist. It is not naturalised. (3)

Datura stramonium L. Thorn-apple

Introduced; a native of north temperate regions; it occurs in waste places and as a weed of cultivated ground. Rare, perhaps sometimes introduced with crops, but not naturalised. (13)

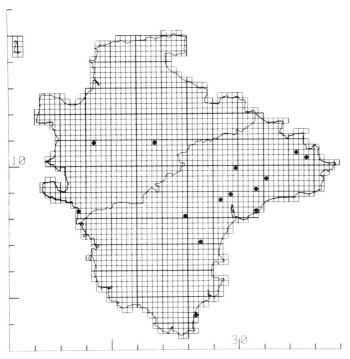

SCROPHULARIACEAE

Mimulus guttatus DC. Monkey-flower

Introduced; a native of N. America, and now found in many streams and rivers, and in boggy places along roads. Quite generally distributed, but not very common. (112)

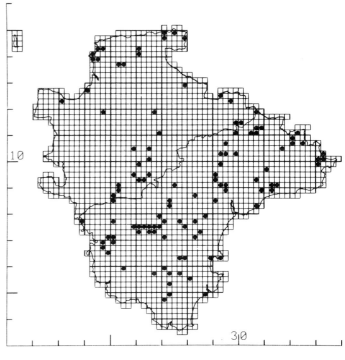

BUDDLEJACEAE

Buddleja davidii Frauchet Buddleia

Introduced; a native of China. Commonly grown in gardens and now widely naturalised in waste places, on dry heaths and coastal cliffs, and at the margins of woods and scrub, especially in the southern half of the county. (321)

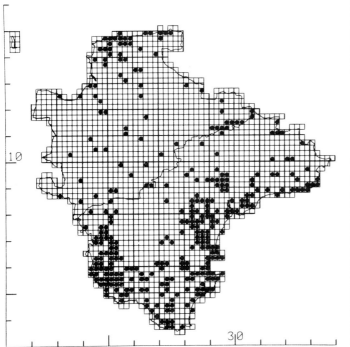

Mimulus luteus L. Blood-drop Emlets

Introduced; a native of Chile. In streams and marshy places often along roads. Rare, but thinly scattered over the county. (20)

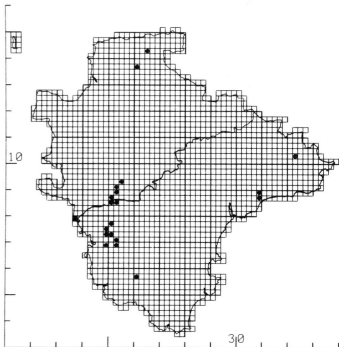

Mimulus moschatus Dougl. ex Lindl.   Musk
Introduced; a native of the United States. Sometimes cultivated and locally naturalised in damp or shaded habitats. (15)

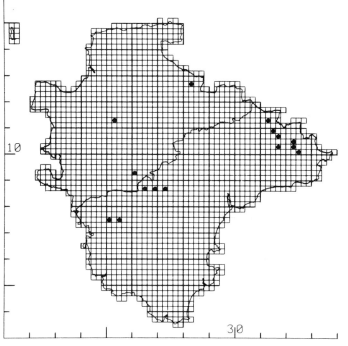

Verbascum thapsus L.   Aaron's Rod, Mullein
In dry waste places, by roadsides and on cliffs. Most common in the south of the county, rather rare elsewhere. Sometimes occurs as an escape from cultivation. (466)

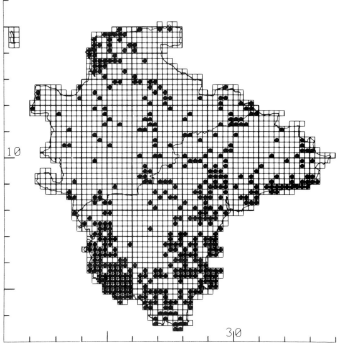

Verbascum lychnitis L.   White Mullein
In waste places and on grassy banks, usually on calcareous soil. Very rare, only recorded from the Landscove slate quarries. (2)

Verbascum nigrum L.   Dark Mullein
In open grassy places on roadsides and banks, usually on base-rich soils. Scattered over S. Devon, but quite rare and probably less common than formerly. (13)

Verbascum blattaria L.   Moth Mullein
Introduced; a native of Europe. In fields and waste places. Rare, and perhaps sometimes confused with *V. virgatum,* when not in flower. (2)

Verbascum virgatum Stokes in With.   Twiggy Mullein
In fields, waste places and dry banks. Not uncommon around Plymouth and in a few other localities in S. Devon, but rare elsewhere and perhaps always introduced. (42)

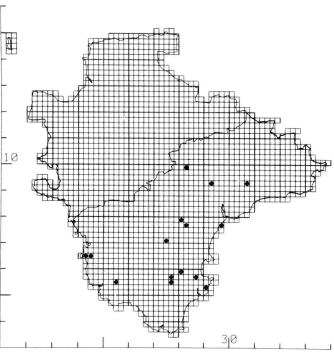

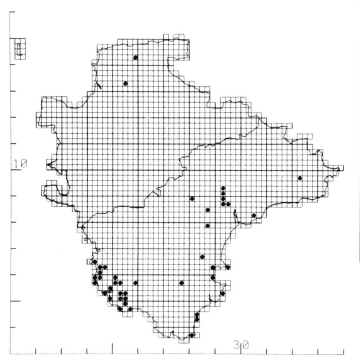

Verbascum phlomoides L., **V. phoenicium** L. and **V. pulverulentum** L. have all been recorded in the past, probably as escapes from cultivation. Only the first can still be found in a few localities. **Verbascum x lemaitrei** Bor., (*V. thapsus* x *virgatum*), was reported from Trusham in 1929; **V. x regelianum** Wirtg., (*V. lychnitis* x *pulverulentum*), has been recorded from both vice-counties without locality (Ferguson in Stace, 1975).

149

Scrophularia vernalis L.   Yellow Figwort
Introduced; a native of C. & S. Europe. In plantations, hedges and waste places; it was still present at an old site at Estover, Plymouth, in 1980. (1)

Scrophularia scorodonia L.   Balm-leaved Figwort
In hedges and along roadsides. Locally frequent around Kingsbridge and also occurring on Lundy, but elsewhere, records are very scattered and it is rare. (31)

Scrophularia auriculata L.   Water Figwort, Water Betony
(*S. aquatica* auct. non L.)
At the edges of streams, ditches and ponds, and in wetter parts of woods and in marshes, though also occurring in relatively dry habitats. Common and generally distributed, but particularly frequent in the south and east. (676)

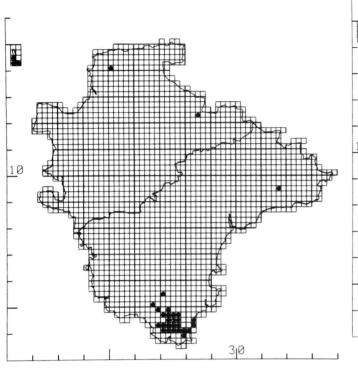

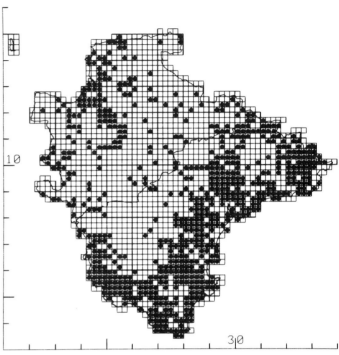

Scrophularia nodosa L.   Knotted Figwort
In damp hedges, scrub and woodland. Common and generally distributed. (1108)

Antirrhinum majus L.   Snapdragon
Introduced; a native of the Mediterranean region. Widely grown in gardens and naturalised on walls and quarries and also found around rubbish tips. (40)

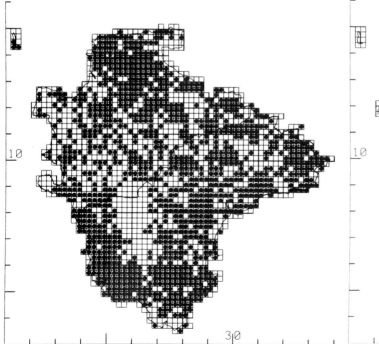

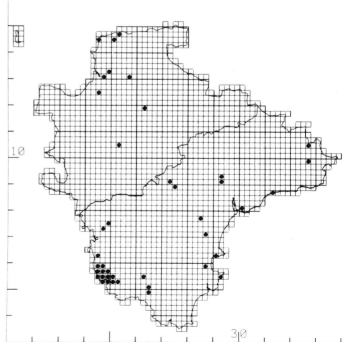

150

Misopates orontium (L.) Rafin.

Corn Snapdragon, Weasel's Snout

(*Antirrhinum orontium* L.)

In cultivated and waste ground. Local, but fairly generally distributed. (72)

Linaria purpurea (L.) Mill.   Purple Toadflax

Introduced; a native of Italy. Often grown in gardens and naturalised on walls and in waste places, usually near habitations. (156)

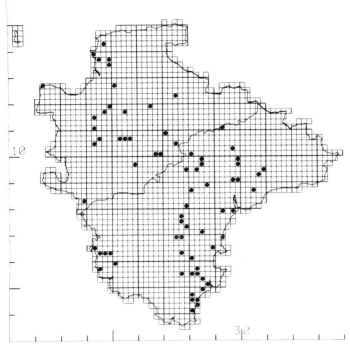

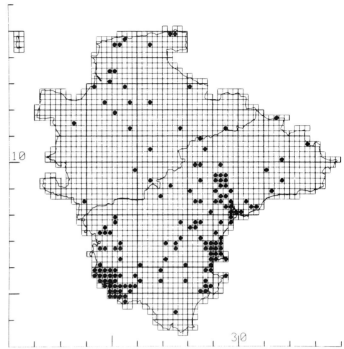

Linaria repens (L.) Mill.   Pale Toadflax

In dry stony or waste places, usually on calcareous or base-rich soils. Scattered over the county, sometimes as an escape, but rare. (28)

Chaenorrhinum minus (L.) Lange   Small Toadflax

(*Linaria minor* (L.) Desf.)

In cultivated ground, on railway banks and in waste places. Scattered over the southern half of the county, rare in the north, and nowhere common. (68)

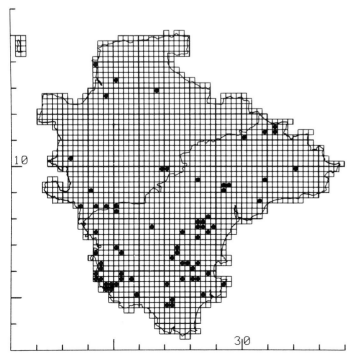

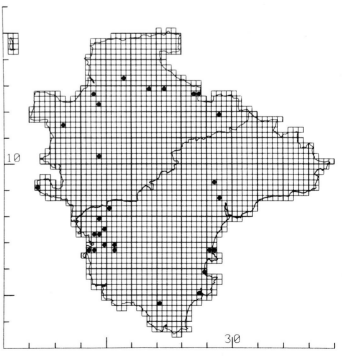

Linaria x sepium Allman

(*L. repens* x *vulgaris*)

Occurs occasionally with its parents, and is perhaps more common than the number of records suggests. (3)

151

Linaria vulgaris Mill.   Yellow Toadflax
In hedges, on railway banks and at the edges of fields. Common and generally distributed. (1027)

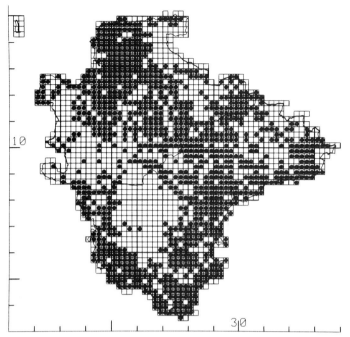

Kickxia elatine (L.) Dum.   Sharp-leaved Fluellen
(*Linaria elatine* (L.) Mill.)
In arable fields, usually on light or sandy soils. Fairly generally distributed, but not very common and quite rare in some localities. (125)

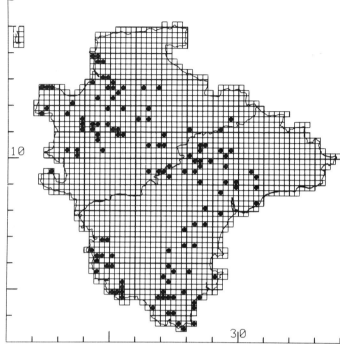

Linaria supina (L.) Chaz.   Decumbent Toadflax
Introduced; a native of S.W. Europe. In waste places and rubble around Plymouth and perhaps extending a little way to the east, with a record from near South Brent, and it appears to spread in railway ballast. (8)

Linaria arenaria DC.   Sand Toadflax
Introduced; a native of France. Quite widespread on semi-fixed dunes on Braunton Burrows, but found nowhere else. (4)

Linaria genistifolia (L.) Mill. ssp. **dalmatica** (L.) Maire & Petitm. (*L. dalmatica* (L.) Mill., inc. *L. macedonica* Griseb.), has been reported as a casual, probably a garden escape, but there are no recent records.

Cymbalaria muralis Gaertn., Mey. & Scherb.
                       Ivy-leaved Toadflax
(*Linaria cymbalaria* (L.) Mill.)
Introduced; a native of S. Europe. Widely naturalised on walls, banks and in stony hedges; generally distributed, and very common and abundant in some habitats. (868)

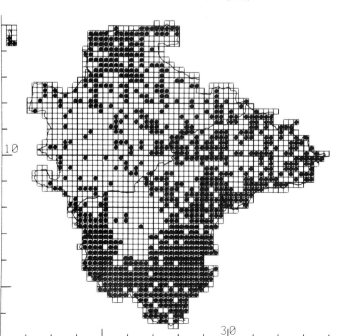

Kickxia spuria (L.) Dum.   Broad-leaved Fluellen
(*Linaria spuria* (L.) Mill.)
In light arable land and by roadsides. Rare, in very scattered localities and mostly around the coast. (11)

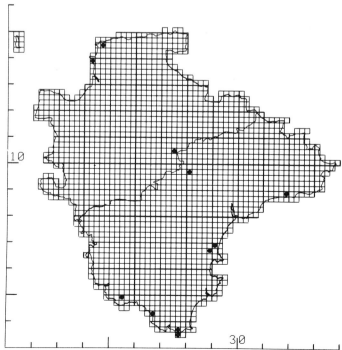

Digitalis purpurea L.   Foxglove
In hedges, woods, scrub, waste ground and also on sea cliffs;
very common and often abundant except on calcareous soils,
penetrating the moors along stream-banks and occurring in the
shade on some tors. (1707)

Veronica officinalis L.   Common Speedwell
In grassland, heaths and in open woodland, usually on acid
soils. Common and generally distributed. (550)

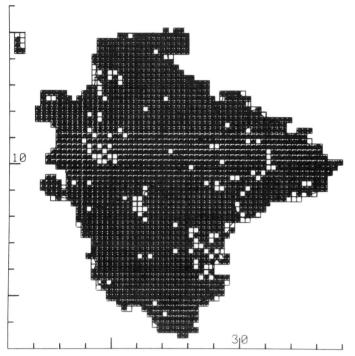

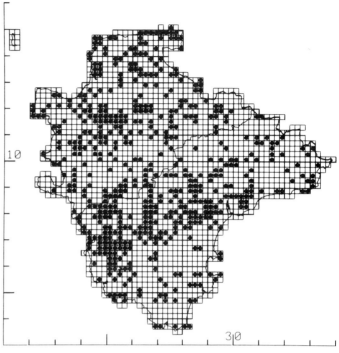

Erinus alpinus L.
Introduced; a native of Europe. Frequently grown in gardens
and naturalised on or at the base of walls in a few localities, and
rather common in Tavistock. (6)

Veronica serpyllifolia L.   Thyme-leaved Speedwell
In damp grassland, on heaths and in waste places. Very
common and generally distributed. (1041)

Veronica chamaedrys L.   Germander Speedwell
In grassland, woods and hedges. Very common and generally
distributed. (1672)

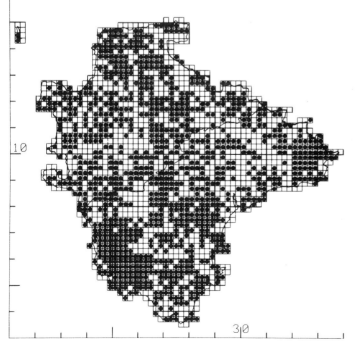

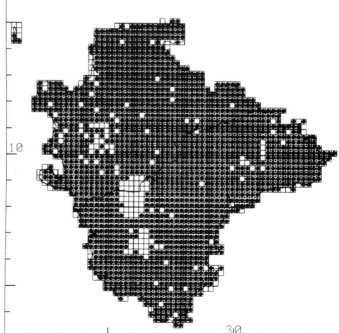

Veronica montana L.   Wood Speedwell
In damp woodland and shaded hedges, especially in clayey soils. Fairly common and generally distributed in suitable habitats. (858)

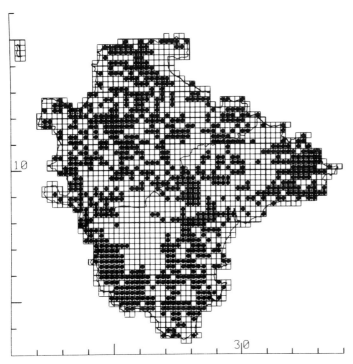

Veronica beccabunga L.   Brooklime Speedwell
Beside ponds, streams and rivers, and in marshes and ditches. Common and generally distributed. (989)

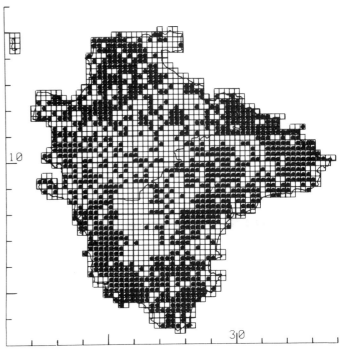

Veronica scutellata L.   Marsh Speedwell
Beside ponds and streams and in wet alluvial meadows, usually on acid soils, and ascending to 330 m (1100 ft.) on Dartmoor. Not very common, most frequent in the wet heaths in the north-west. (125)

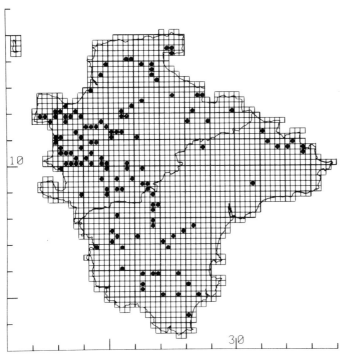

Veronica anagallis-aquatica L.   Water Speedwell
In ponds, streams and wet meadows. Quite rare, most frequent in the meadows behind Braunton Burrows, and in river valleys in the east of the county. (26)

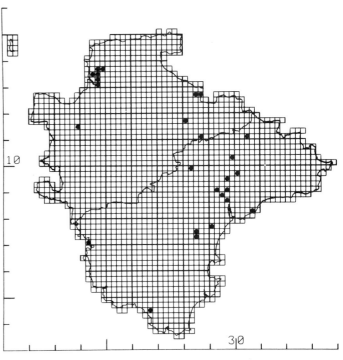

Veronica catenata Pennell
(*V. aquatica* Bernh.)
In streams and ponds, and on wet mud; in similar localities to the previous species, but often rather more abundant. (8)

154

Veronica arvensis L.   Wall Speedwell
On banks, paths and walls, and in cultivated ground. Common
and generally distributed. (828)

Veronica polita Fries   Grey Speedwell
In cultivated ground, on roadsides and in dry banks. Uncommon, but widely distributed. (60)

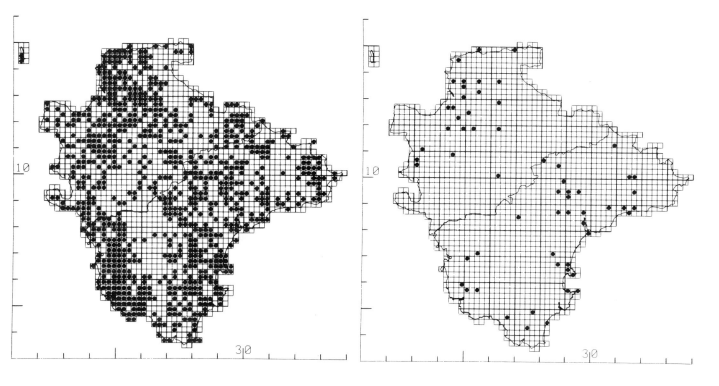

Veronica agrestis L.   Field Speedwell
In fields and cultivated ground, generally preferring more acid
soils. Rare, but widely distributed. (92)
Some records could be small forms of *V. persica*.

Veronica persica Poir.   Buxbaum's Speedwell
Introduced; a native of W. Asia. A common weed of cultivated
ground, gardens and also on dry banks. Generally distributed.
(1181)

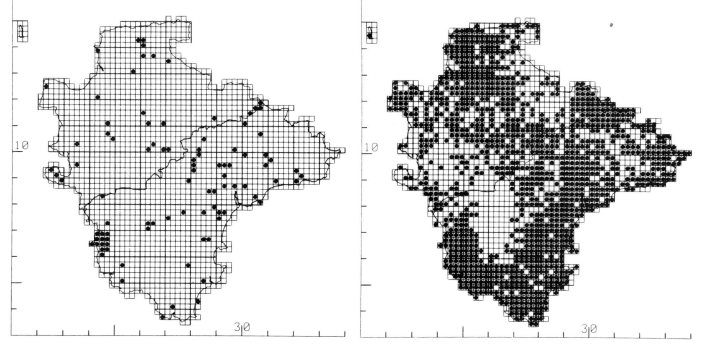

155

Veronica filiformis Sm.   Slender Speedwell
Introduced; a native of Asia Minor and the Caucasus. Once
grown in gardens as a decorative plant, now extensively
naturalised in lawns, damp grassland and waste places, and
spreading quite rapidly. (460)

Sibthorpia europaea L.   Cornish Moneywort
On moist shaded banks by rivers and streams. Almost entirely
confined to the southern and south-western edges of Dartmoor,
where small patches occur locally. (66)

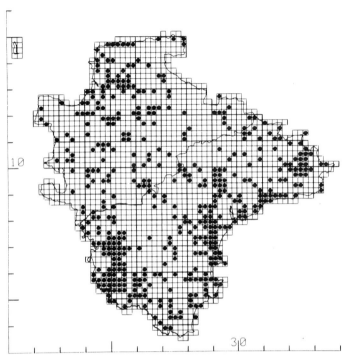

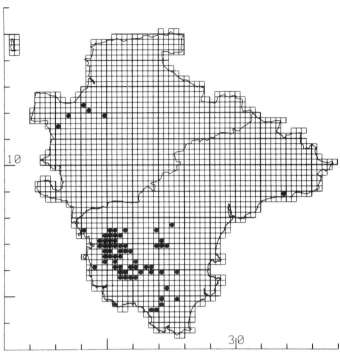

Veronica hederifolia L.   Ivy-leaved Speedwell
In arable land, gardens, hedges and on roadsides. Common and
generally distributed. (856)

Melampyrum pratense L.   Common Cow-wheat
In woods and scrub, and nearby hedges and banks, always on
acid soils. Fairly common, though local, and quite generally
distributed. (465)

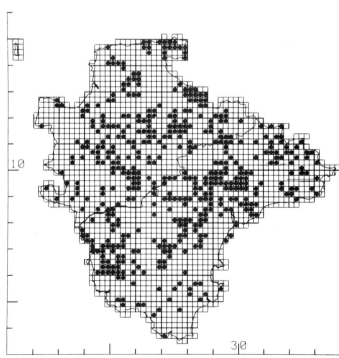

Veronica longifolia L.
Introduced; a native of Europe. Occurs rarely as a garden
escape, and is scarcely naturalised. (1)

Euphrasia officinalis L. s.l.   Eyebright
In grassland, heaths and waste places. Fairly common in dry,
base-rich habitats, rather rare elsewhere. (298)

Euphrasia tetraquetra (Bréb.) Arrond.
(inc. *E. occidentalis* Wettst.)
In dry grassland, especially on sea cliffs, but also found inland to
some extent. (15)

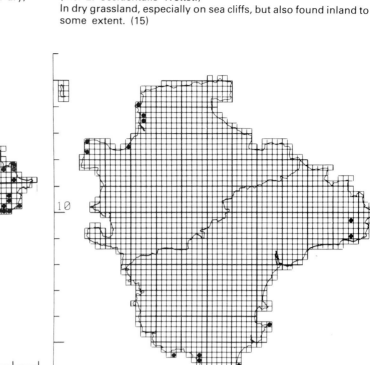

This aggregate is usually considered to include a number of
microspecies which are difficult to distinguish. Several of these
occur in Devon, but it is unlikely that the maps reflect their true
distribution patterns.

Euphrasia anglica Pugsl.
In pastures on clayey soils, and also on heaths. Fairly common
and reasonably generally distributed. (118)

Euphrasia nemorosa (Pers.) Wallr.
(inc. *E. curta* (Fries) Wettst.)
In grassy places, on heaths and dunes. Probably the commonest
of the species in the county, and very variable. (180)

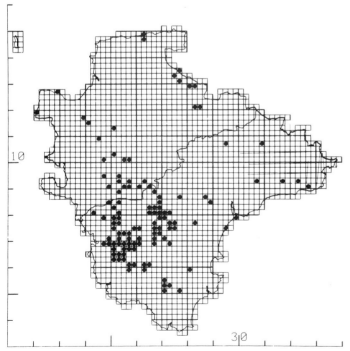

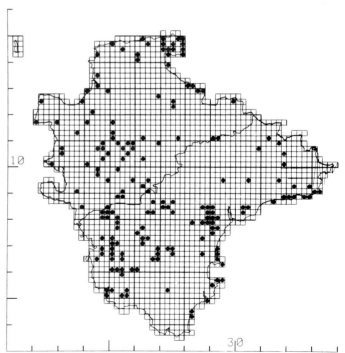

Euphrasia vigursii Davey
Usually confined to dry heathland; probably considerably
under-recorded. (8)
It has been suggested that this is the hybrid *E. anglica* x
micrantha.

Euphrasia pseudokerneri Pugsl.
In calcareous grassland. Very rare, with only a single record
from Salcombe Regis, in E. Devon. (1)

Euphrasia confusa Pugsl.
In grassland and on heaths, usually in acid soils. Quite common around Dartmoor and also on the heaths east of Exeter, but not seen recently on Exmoor. (35)

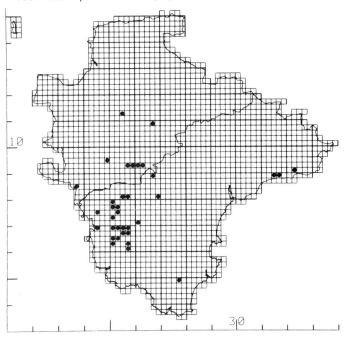

Euphrasia stricta D.Wolff & J.F.Lehm.
(*E. brevipila* Burn. & Gremli)
In meadows and pastures. Only known from the vicinity of Tavistock. (7)

Euphrasia micrantha Reichb.
On heaths and moors, on light and usually dry soils. Almost confined to the periphery of Dartmoor, and some heathy areas in S. Devon. (23)

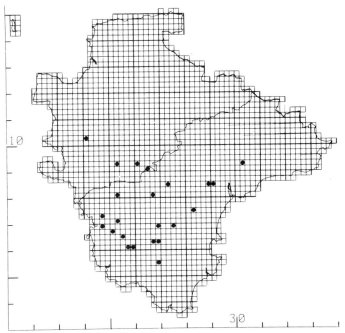

Euphrasia *Hybrids.*
A number of hybrids were reported in Fl. Dev., but in view of the difficulty in determining them, and the work which has been done on the genus since that account was prepared, it seems best to disregard them. The following hybrids are accepted for Devon by Stace (1975):
E. anglica x *vigursii* in S. Devon;
E. confusa x *tetraquetra* without locality;
E. confusa x *nemorosa*;
E. anglica x *micrantha* (?=*E. vigursii*);
E. anglica x *nemorosa* (*E. x glanduligera* Wettst.) in N. Devon.

Odontites verna (Bell.) Dum.   Red Bartsia
(*Bartsia odontites* Huds. agg.)
In grassland, on roadsides, in fields and waste places. Quite common and generally distributed, more especially in western parts of the county. (412)

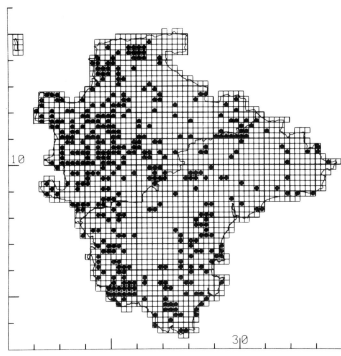

The most common form is probably ssp. **serotina** (Dum.) Corb., but ssp. **verna** has been recorded from the vicinity of Plymouth (Perring & Sell, 1968).

Parentucellia viscosa (L.) Caruel   Yellow Bartsia
(*Bartsia viscosa* L.)
In damp grassland, usually near the sea, and in grey dunes. Not uncommon around the coast, and occasionally some distance inland; locally abundant on Braunton Burrows. (43)

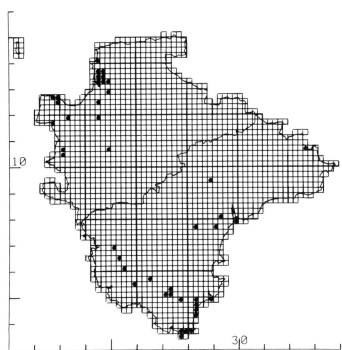

Pedicularis palustris L.　　　Red Rattle, Marsh Lousewort
In wet heaths and bogs. Scattered over the county, most frequent on parts of Dartmoor and in the north-west. (111)

Rhinanthus minor L.　　　Yellow Rattle
In grassland, on banks and in waste places. Common and generally distributed, and locally abundant in the dune slacks on Braunton Burrows. (468)

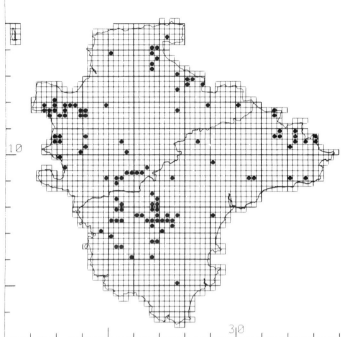

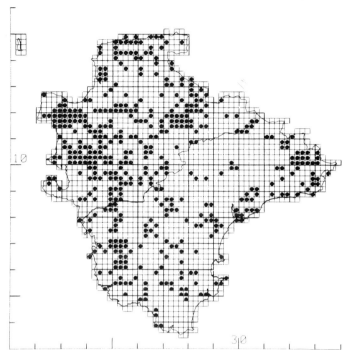

This species shows the ecotypic variation characteristic of the genus; the autumnal variant has been separated as var. *stenophyllus* Schur.

Lathraea squamaria L.　　　Toothwort
Parasitic on the roots of woody plants, especially elm and hazel, and can be found in woods and moist hedgerows. Very rare, and apparently appreciably less common than formerly. (5)

Lathraea clandestina L.
This was recorded in the grounds of Sydenham House in 1938, and has been confirmed there recently. It occurs on the banks of the Tamar at Horsebridge and in some quantity above Morwellham; it also occurs on the Cornish side of the river. (3)

Pedicularis sylvatica L.　　　Lousewort
In damp heaths, moorland and upland acid pastures. Quite common on Dartmoor and Exmoor, and in some lowland heaths, preferring drier habitats than *P. palustris*. (429)

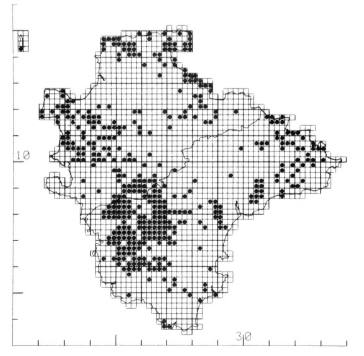

ACANTHACEAE

Acanthus mollis L.　　　Bear's Breech
Introduced; a native of S. Europe. Sometimes cultivated in gardens and naturalised in a few places; it can be a very persistent weed. (7)

OROBANCHACEAE

Orobanche minor Sm.   Lesser Broomrape
Parasitic, most frequently on *Trifolium* species and other legumes. Locally common but less frequent than formerly. (45)

Orobanche hederae Duby   Ivy Broomrape
Parasitic on *Hedera helix*. The commonest species around the coast, especially in the south, and may occasionally be found inland. (50)

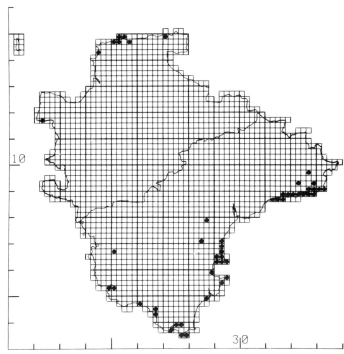

Orobanche maritima Pugsl.   Carrot Broomrape
(*O. amethystea* auct. non Thuill.)
Parasitic on *Daucus carota*. Confined to the south coast, where it may be locally plentiful in some years. There are no recent records from Braunton Burrows. (10)

Orobanche rapum-genistae Thuill.   Greater Broomrape
Parasitic on shrubby legumes, especially *Ulex* and *Cytisus*. Rare, but records are widely scattered and it could be rather under-recorded, though is undoubtedly less frequent than formerly. (11)

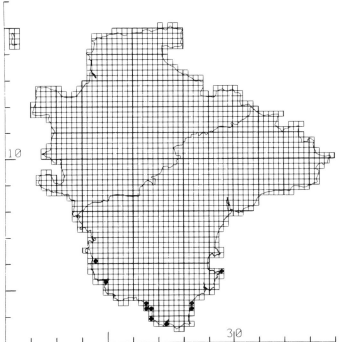

It has been suggested that this is only a variety of *O. minor*.

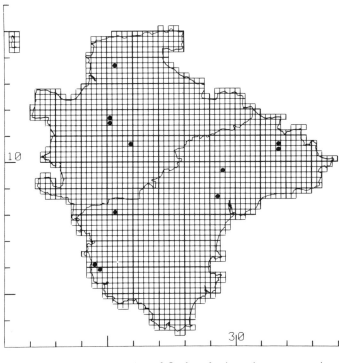

A number of other species of **Orobanche** have been reported from time to time, including **O. purpurea** Jacq., **O. loricata** Reichenb. (inc. *O. picridis* F.W.Schultz ex Koch) and **O. ramosa** L. It seems unlikely that any of them were correctly identified, and there are no recent records or specimens.

LENTIBULARIACEAE

Pinguicula lusitanica L.   Pale Butterwort
In *Sphagnum* bogs and wet heaths. Not difficult to find on
Dartmoor and in several wet heaths in the lowlands, but local. It
frequently grows on peat at the sides of *Sphagnum* clumps, but
may prefer rather base-rich conditions. (88)

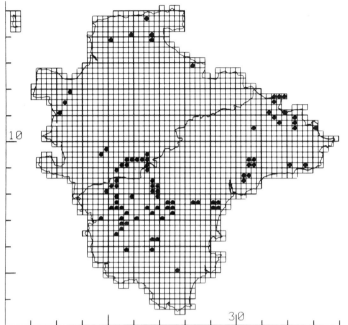

Pinguicula vulgaris L., the Common Butterwort, was recorded at
Clawton in 1940, but is probably extinct in Devon. **P. grandiflora**
Lam. has been introduced on two or three occasions and still
remains in very small quantities on one or two of the Pebble-bed
Commons. (2)

Utricularia australis R.Br.   Greater Bladderwort
(*U. neglecta* Lehm., *U. major* auct.)
In ditches and pools around clay workings, in base-poor or acid
water. There is a single record from a clay pool near Kingsteign-
ton, and it also occurs in the lake in Stover Park. (2)

RUBIACEAE

Sherardia arvensis L.   Field Madder
In cultivated ground and dry grassland, on light soils. Widely
distributed, but not very common. (270)

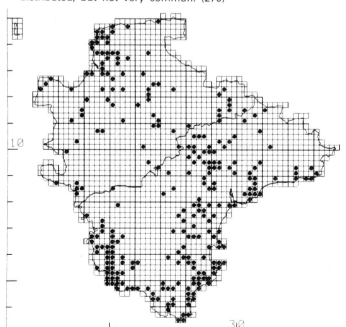

Asperula cynanchica L.   Squinancy-wort
In dry grassland, strictly confined to calcareous soils, and only
found in the south of the county. (8)

Asperula arvensis L. has been reported as a casual around
Plymouth and Salcombe, but has not been seen for many years
and is undoubtedly extinct.

Galium odoratum (L.) Scop.   Sweet Woodruff
(*Asperula odorata* L.)
In woods and on banks, usually on base-rich soils. Generally
distributed throughout the county but local, though often quite
abundant where it occurs. (277)

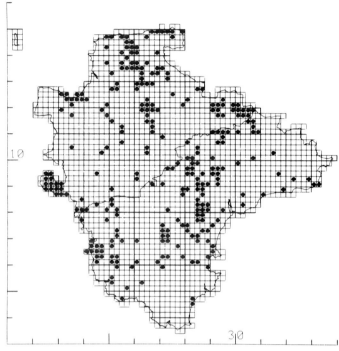

Galium uliginosum L.   Fen Bedstraw
In wet bogs and marshes, usually on base-rich soils and rather
frequent on the Culm; largely absent from the South Hams.
(109)

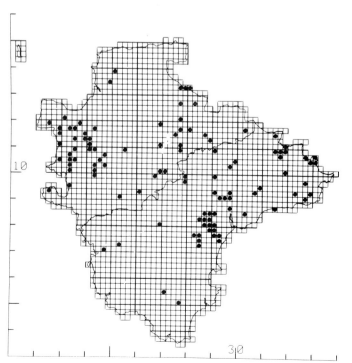

161

Galium palustre L.   Marsh Bedstraw
In damp grassland beside pools, streams and ditches. Common
and generally distributed. (888)

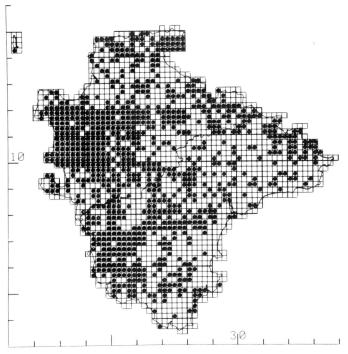

There are no records for the related **G. elongatum** C.Presl, (*G. palustre* ssp. *elongatum* (C.Presl) Lange), though it is likely to occur in the county. **G. palustre** ssp. **tetraploideum** Clapham has been reported from 'a pond in Devon' (Clapham, Tutin & Warburg, 1962).

Galium verum L.   Lady's Bedstraw, Yellow Bedstraw
In pastures, on banks and in fixed dune grassland. Most
common around the coast, but local in scattered habitats inland.
(164)

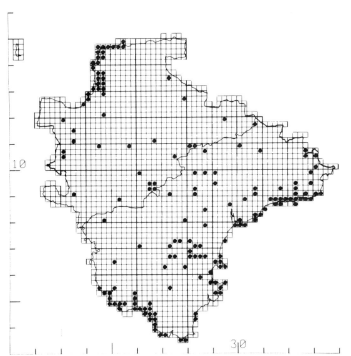

Galium mollugo L.   Hedge Bedstraw
In hedges, scrub and on banks, usually in base-rich soils. Very
common in the southern half of the county, but quite rare in the
north. (977)

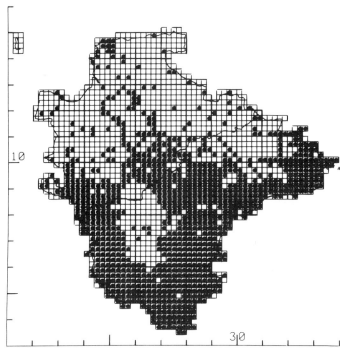

Galium album Mill., (*G. erectum* Huds., *G. mollugo* ssp. *erectum* Syme), the Upright Hedge Bedstraw, is now generally considered to be a distinct species. It has been recorded on several occasions, but often not distinguished from *G. mollugo.*

Galium x pomeranicum Retz   Hybrid Yellow Bedstraw
(*G. verum* x *mollugo*)
This hybrid occurs with its parents, and has been recorded on two occasions on the coast near Thurlestone. It also occurs in the Axmouth-Lyme Regis Undercliffs NNR. Perring & Sell (1968) give several localities along the south coast. (2)

Galium saxatile L.   Heath Bedstraw
On heaths, moors and in acid grassland. Very common on
Dartmoor and Exmoor, and locally frequent elsewhere in
suitable habitats. (683)

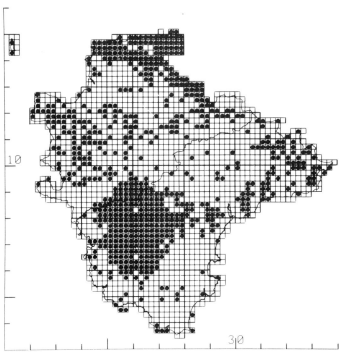

Galium aparine L.   Cleavers, Goose-grass
In hedges, scrub and waste places. Common everywhere,
except on the higher moors, and sometimes a vexatious garden
weed. (1674)

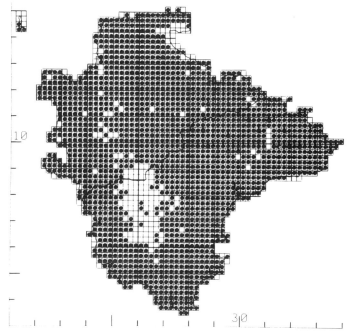

Galium parisiense L.   Wall Bedstraw
In dry sandy places. Very rare; a species of S.E. England which
has a single station in a field on Saunton Cliffs, but has not been
seen since 1966. (1)

Galium cruciata (L.) Scop.   Cross-wort
(*Cruciata chersonensis* auct.)
In scrub, hedges and on roadsides, especially on calcareous or
base-rich soils. Almost totally confined to southern and eastern
parts of the county, where it is locally frequent. (297)

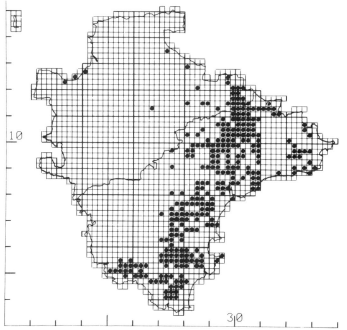

Galium debile Desv., the Slender Marsh Bedstraw, used to occur
in pools around clay workings at Chudleigh Knighton, but the
habitat has been destroyed and the species is believed extinct.
Galium tricornutum Dandy, (*G. tricorne* Stokes), the Rough Corn
Bedstraw or Three-horned Goose-grass, has been reported from
cultivated fields in S. Devon, but there are no recent records and
it is believed extinct.

Rubia peregrina L.   Wild Madder
In hedges and scrub. Most common around the coast, and
especially in the base-rich soils around Torbay, where it can be
found some distance inland. (259)

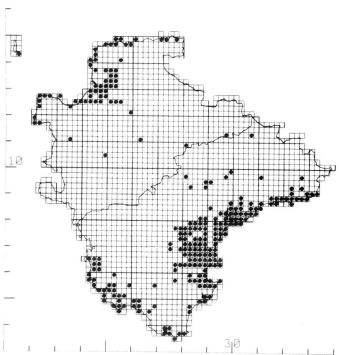

PLANTAGINACEAE

Plantago major L.   Rat-tail Plantain, Great Plantain
In grassland, along roads and in waste places. Very common
and generally distributed. (1732)

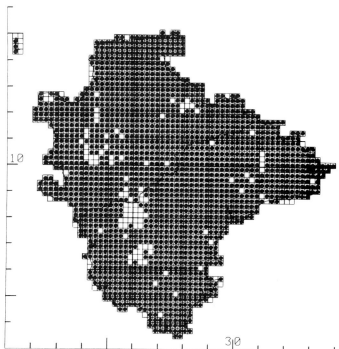

Plantago coronopus L.   Buck's-horn Plantain
In dry sandy soils near the sea, also occurring in open habitats
and dry grassland elsewhere. Most common around the coast,
where it may be locally abundant; less frequent inland. (214)

Plantago media L.   Hoary Plantain, Lamb's-tongue
In grassland on base-rich or calcareous soils. Quite common on
the chalk in E. Devon, local on the Torbay limestone, rare and
scattered in the rest of the county. (44)

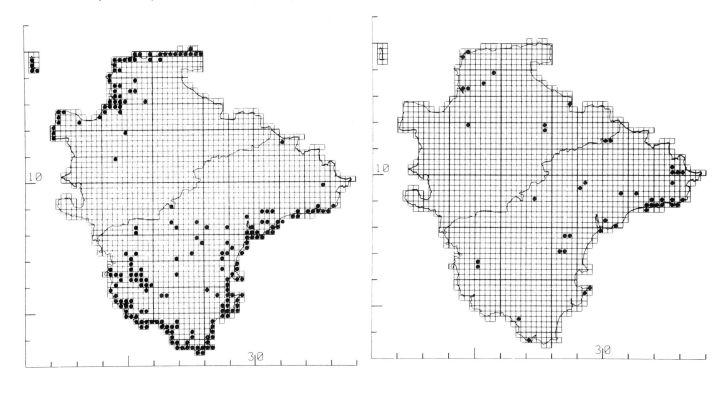

Plantago maritima L.   Sea Plantain
In salt-marshes, around the shores of estuaries and in coastal
rock crevices, occasional inland. Quite common and often
abundant in maritime habitats. (138)

Plantago lanceolata L.   Ribwort Plantain
In pastures, on roadsides and in cultivated and waste ground.
Very common and generally distributed. (1739)

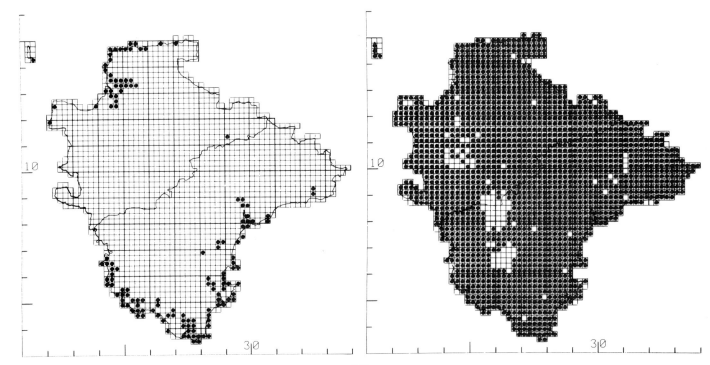

Plantago indica L. has been reported as a casual in the past, but there are no recent records.

Littorella uniflora (L.) Aschers.   Shore-weed
On the sandy and gravelly edges of non-calcareous ponds and reservoirs, both above and below water level. Locally abundant on Dartmoor, and sometimes forming a sward in suitable habitats, rare elsewhere. (24)

Viburnum opulus L.   Guelder Rose, Water Elder
In scrub and hedges, especially on damper soils. Common in the north and west of the county, especially on the Culm, less frequent elsewhere. (713)

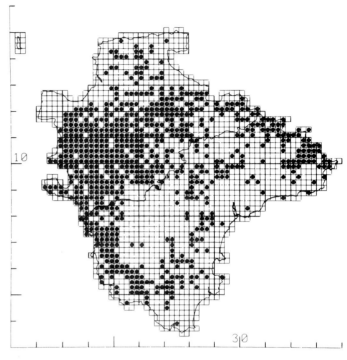

CAPRIFOLIACEAE

Sambucus ebulus L.   Danewort, Dwarf Elder
Introduced; a native of Europe. In waste places in villages and by farms. Only known from two localities near Thurlestone and Plymouth, and now a very rare plant. (3)

Sambucus nigra L.   Elder
In disturbed and enriched sites in woods, scrub and hedges. Very common and generally distributed. (1639)

Viburnum lantana L.   Wayfaring Tree
In scrub and hedges, especially common on the chalk in E. Devon and around Torbay, but very scattered elsewhere and always in base-rich habitats. (139)

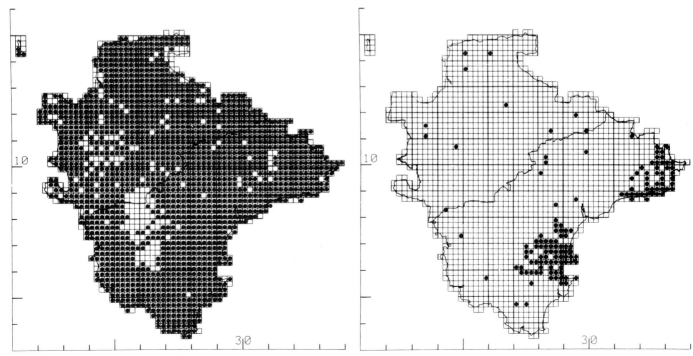

Symphoricarpos rivularis Suksdorf Snowberry
(*S. racemosus* Michx)
Introduced; a native of N. America and sometimes planted as a hedge. Naturalised in many places and quite widely distributed. (383)

Lonicera periclymenum L. Honeysuckle
In woods, scrub and hedges. Common and generally distributed, especially in the lowlands. (1650)

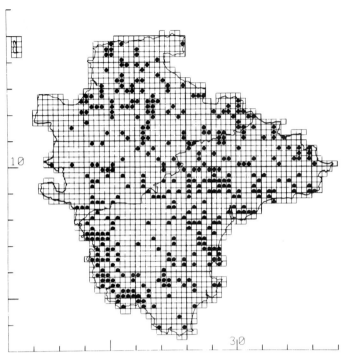
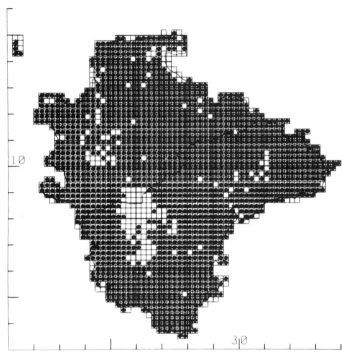

Leycesteria formosa Wall.
Introduced; a native of China and quite frequently planted in gardens. It is established in hedges in several localities, probably from bird-sown seed. (30)

Lonicera japonica Thunb.
Introduced; a native of E. Asia, sometimes cultivated and occasionally escaping, but scarcely naturalised. (4)

Lonicera nitida Wils.
Introduced; a native of China. Quite frequently grown in gardens as a hedge, and naturalised in many places on banks and in hedges near habitations. (54)

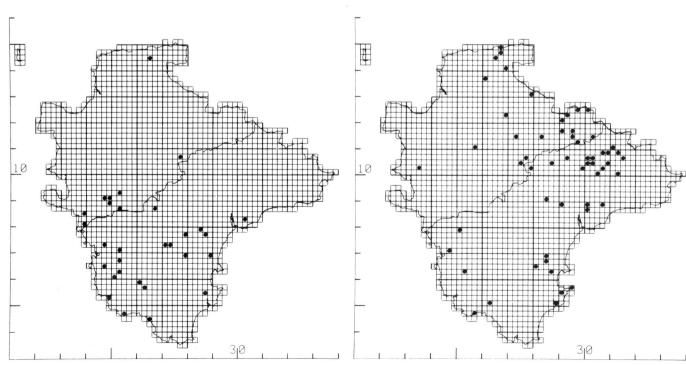

ADOXACEAE

Adoxa moschatellina L.   Moschatel

In shaded woods and damp hedges. Local, but scattered over the county, avoiding acid habitats and the immediate vicinity of the south coast. (374)

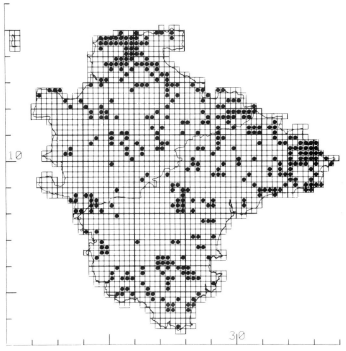

VALERIANACEAE

Valerianella locusta (L.) Betcke

                               Lamb's Lettuce, Corn Salad

(*V. olitoria* (L.) Poll.)

In arable fields, gardens and by roadsides; quite frequent in the south of the county, much rarer in the north, except on sand-dunes. (349)

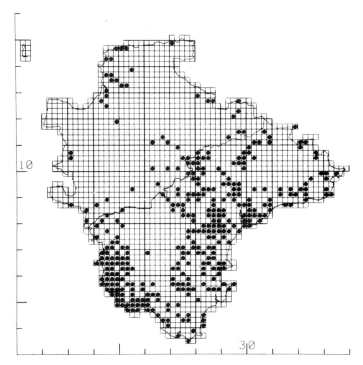

Valerianella carinata Loisel.

In hedges and gardens and especially on walls. Rare in the north, though fairly frequent on Braunton Burrows, rather more common in the south, especially around the major towns. (117)

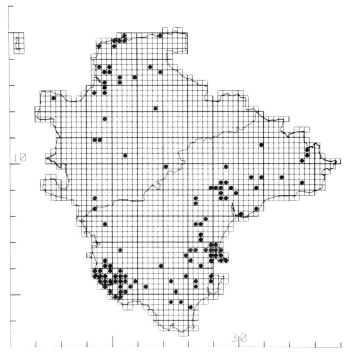

Valerianella dentata (L.) Poll.

In arable fields. Apparently rare, formerly found on the Braunton bulb-farm and also known from around Plymouth. (13)

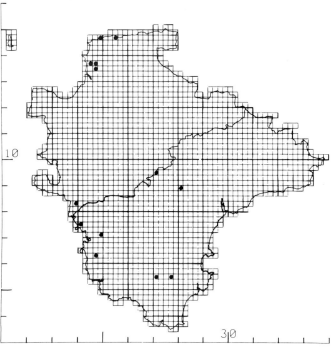

Valerianella rimosa Bast.

In cornfields and cultivated ground. Apparently very rare, with records only from near Crediton and Chudleigh. (3)

Valerianella eriocarpa Desv.

Introduced; a native of Europe. It has been reported from various localities, but only found recently in an arable field at Exeter, and near Saunton Sands car park in 1979. (2)

Valeriana officinalis L. Valerian
(inc. *V. sambucifolia* Mikan f.)
Along wet roadsides, in hedges and scrub and by streams, rarely on drier soils. Common in the west, where it is locally abundant, rather less frequent in the south and east. (932)

Centranthus ruber (L.) DC. Red Valerian, Wall Valerian
Introduced; a native of Europe. Widely naturalised on walls, buildings and in rocky places, most common around the coast, but frequent inland and a persistent weed in some places. (531)

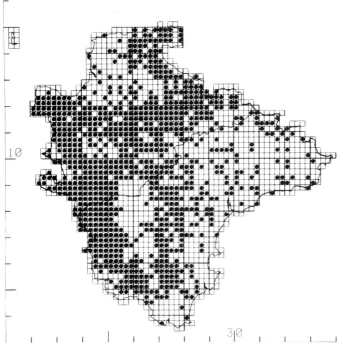

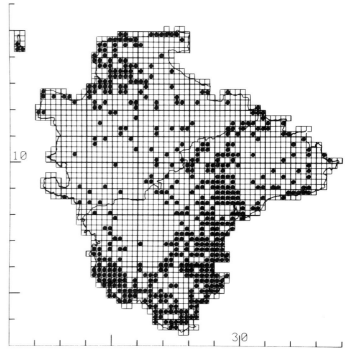

Most records seem to fall within ssp. **sambucifolia** (Mikan f.) Čelak., which is the common form in damp and usually non-calcareous soils.
Ssp. **collina** (Wallr.) Nym. is found in drier and more calcareous habitats, but this taxon has not been found in the county.

Valeriana pyrenaica L. Pyrenean Valerian
Introduced; a native of S. Europe. Recorded from the vicinity of Bampton and at Widecombe, probably as an escape, and long naturalised at the latter locality. (2)

Valeriana dioica L. Marsh Valerian
In wet meadows, marshes and bogs in the lowlands. Rare, scattered over the county, but mostly in the south, usually in moderately base-rich soils. (64)

DIPSACACEAE

Dipsacus fullonum L. Teasel
(*D. sylvestris* Huds.)
In hedges, scrub, along roadsides and in rough pasture; rather uncommon, most frequent in the south-east. Mostly on clayey or marly soils, and absent from the moors. (277)

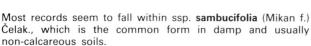

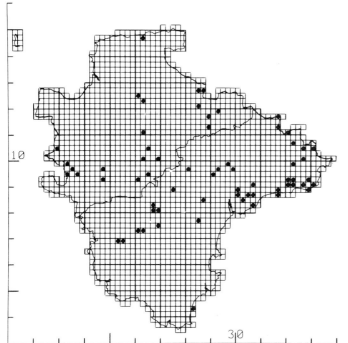

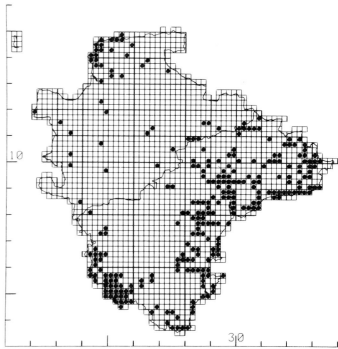

Dipsacus pilosus L. Small Teasel
In damp shaded places, usually by streams, in calcicole habitats. Very rare, but capricious and erratic in its appearances, with one record from Torbay and also occurring at Membury and Dalwood, near Axminster. (3)

Succisa pratensis Moench   Devil's-bit Scabious
In damp fields and meadows, and on wet and often somewhat
calcareous heaths. Quite common and generally distributed.
(730)

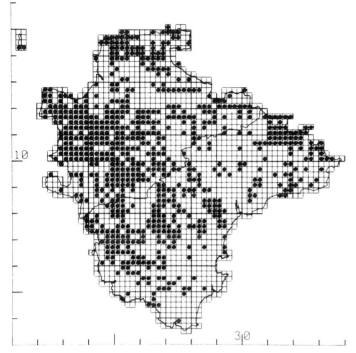

Knautia arvensis (L.) Coult.   Field Scabious
In dry fields, pastures and hedgebanks. Fairly common in the
south and especially in base-rich habitats, rare elsewhere. (397)

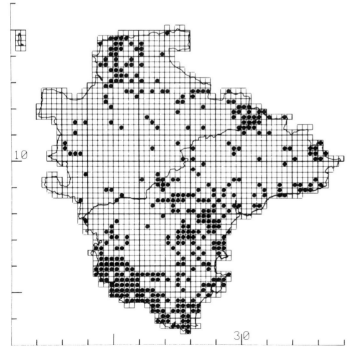

Scabiosa columbaria L.   Small Scabious
In dry pastures and hedges, usually on calcareous soils, where it
is quite frequent; rare elsewhere, but quite widely scattered
over the county, mostly in the south. (57)

Scabiosa columbaria L.   Small Scabious

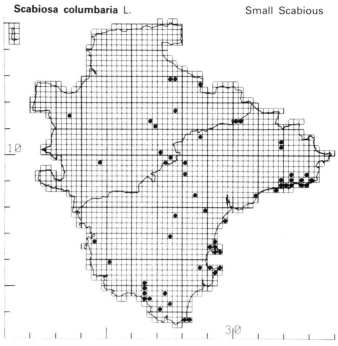

CAMPANULACEAE

Campanula medium L.   Canterbury Bell
Introduced; a native of Europe. Quite commonly grown in
gardens, and sometimes found as an escape or near rubbish,
but not naturalised. (2)

Campanula trachelium L.
                Nettle-leaved Bell-flower, Bats-in-the-Belfry
In woods and hedges, usually on fairly dry soils. Perhaps native
near Lynton, doubtfully so elsewhere. (3)

Campanula rapunculoides L.   Creeping Campanula
Introduced; a native of Europe. A very rare plant, only known
from near Sidmouth, and doubtfully naturalised. (2)

Campanula rotundifolia L.   Hare-bell
In grassland and dry heathland. Rare, with few and rather
scattered records. (10)

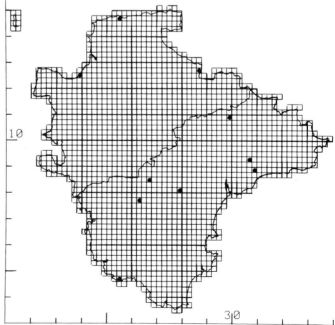

Campanula persicifolia L. has been recorded as naturalised at
Budleigh Salterton and Gidleigh, but has not been seen recently.

Legousia hybrida (L.) Del., the Venus' Looking-glass, is a
cornfield weed which has not been found for many years and is
probably extinct.

Wahlenbergia hederacea (L.) Reichb.   Ivy-leaved Bell-flower
In damp peaty grassland, often by streams. Quite common around the periphery of Dartmoor, rather scattered over Exmoor and on the heaths on the Somerset border. (168)

Eupatorium cannabinum L.   Hemp Agrimony
In moist shaded places, ditches and river banks, and in scrubby moorland. Generally distributed and absent only from the higher moors. (1241)

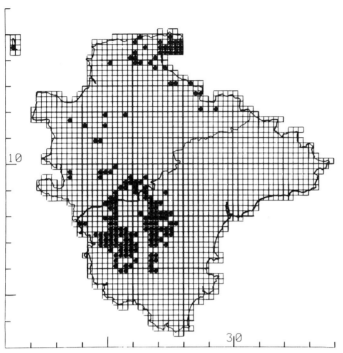

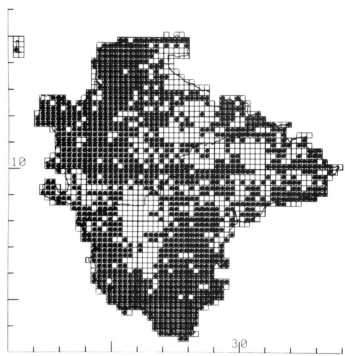

Solidago virgaurea L.   Goldenrod
On dry heathy ground, banks and in woodland, usually on acid soils. Quite common in lowland habitats, and reaching a considerable altitude on Dartmoor, where it can be found on several tors, and some plants seems to be var. *cambrica* L. (541)

Jasione montana L.   Sheep's-bit Scabious
On heaths, in hedgebanks and on walls, and in rocky habitats around the coast; always on acid soils. Common and locally abundant. (588)

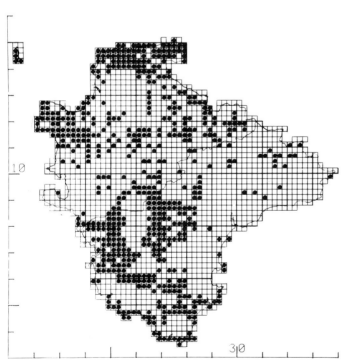

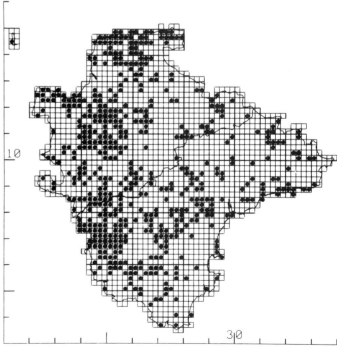

Solidago canadensis L.   Canadian Goldenrod
Introduced; a native of N. America. Widely cultivated in gardens and sometimes escaping, but scarcely naturalised. (2)

Solidago graminifolia L.
Introduced; a native of N. America. Grown in gardens to some extent and occasionally escaping, but probably only naturalised in a wood near Barnstaple. (4)

Lobelia urens L.   Heath Lobelia
In damp meadows and scrub. Very rare, and only known from E. Devon and in the Devon Trust Nature Reserve near Loddiswell, in the South Hams. (5)

Bellis perennis L.   Daisy
Abundant in grassland, short turf and roadsides everywhere except in very peaty habitats. Occurs in turf at over 610m (2000 ft.) on High Willhay. (1714)

Aster tripolium L.   Sea Aster
In the upper reaches of salt-marshes, more rarely on maritime cliffs, rocks and walls. Quite common around the coast, and sometimes a little way inland along estuaries. (70)

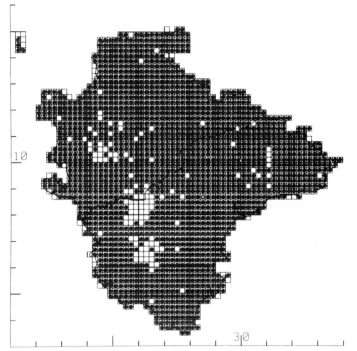

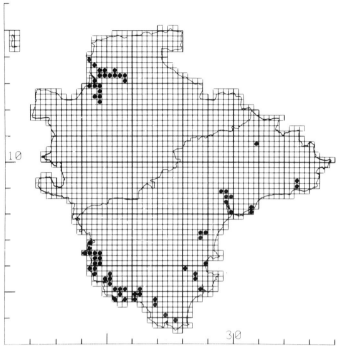

Aster linosyris (L.) Bernh.   Goldilocks
Confined to limestone sea cliffs at Berry Head and near Shaldon, where it is very rare, with only rather few plants. (3)

Aster x salignus Willd. has been reported as an escape from cultivation, but there are no recent records. It was probably a form of *A. novi-belgii*.

Aster novi-belgii L.   Michaelmas Daisy
Introduced; a native of N. America. Commonly cultivated and frequently found as an escape near rubbish tips and sometimes naturalised in damp or waste ground and hedges. (37)

Erigeron mucronatus DC.   Mexican Fleabane
Introduced; a native of Mexico. Now well established on walls in many parts of S. Devon, and also around Barnstaple and Ilfracombe. Often abundant where it occurs. (70)

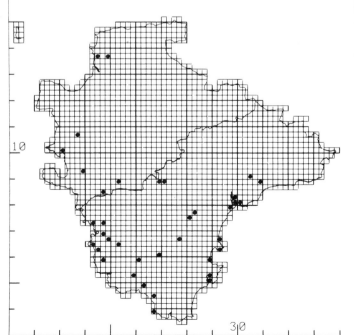

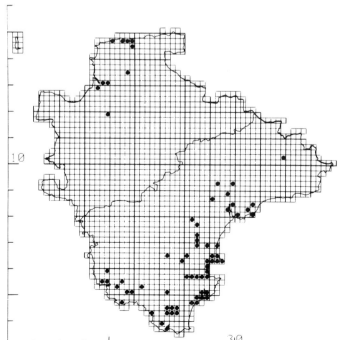

Erigeron acer L.   Blue Fleabane
On dry banks and walls, and also on sand-dunes. Rare, and usually near the sea. Quite frequent on Braunton Burrows, and also on the Axmouth-Lyme Regis Undercliff. (28)

Filago vulgaris Lam.   Cudweed
(*F. germanica* L. non Huds.)
In dry heaths and pastures and on banks. Rather rare, but scattered over the county, usually in acid soils. (62)

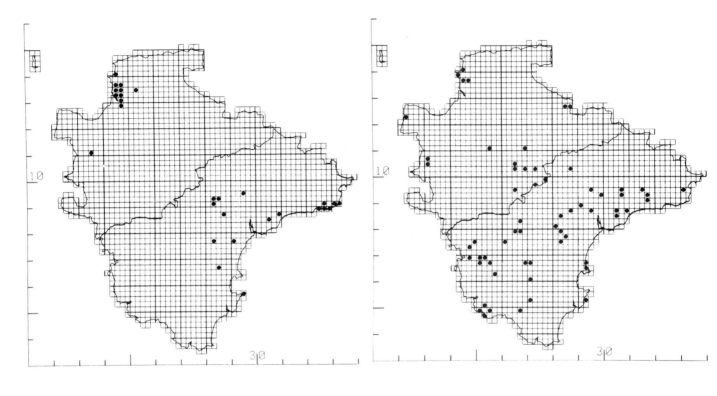

Erigeron canadensis L.   Canadian Fleabane
(*Conyza canadensis* (L.) Cronq.)
Introduced; a native of N. America. On waste ground, roadsides and in cultivated land, usually on sandy soils. Rather rare, most frequent on Braunton Burrows and around Plymouth and Exeter. (37)

Filago minima (Sm.) Pers.   Small Cudweed
(*Logfia minima* (L.) Dum.)
On dry heaths and walls and in waste places. Very scattered and quite rare, though rather easily overlooked. (13)

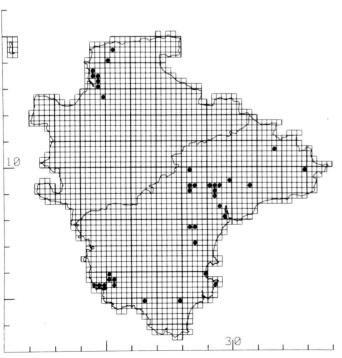

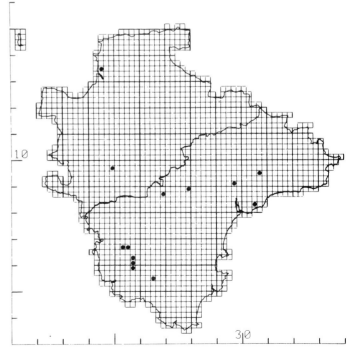

Erigeron x huelsenii Vatke, (*E. acer* x *canadensis*), has been recorded from Braunton Burrows, but has not been seen there recently.

Filago pyramidata L., (*F. spathulata* C.Presl), has been reported from sandy fields in various parts of the county, but has not been seen for many years and is probably extinct.

Gnaphalium sylvaticum L.   Wood Cudweed, Heath Cudweed
(*Omalotheca sylvatica* (L.) Schultz & F.W. Schultz)
In dry heaths and open woodland on acid soils. Rare, with few and scattered records, and usually only found in small quantities. (19)

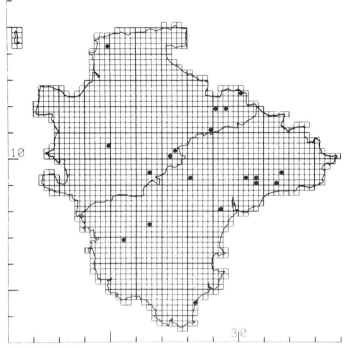

Inula conyza DC.   Ploughman's Spikenard
Along roadsides, in banks and dry waste places. Quite common in dry calcareous grassland and open scrub around Torbay and in E. Devon, frequent along the south coast and on Braunton Burrows. (154)

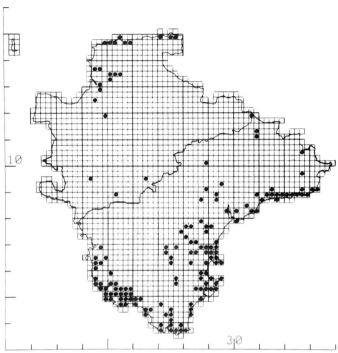

Gnaphalium uliginosum L.   Marsh Cudweed
(*Filaginella uliginosa* (L.) Opiz)
In damp fields and waste places, particularly in the wet edges of roads and in muddy gateways. Common over much of the county, in acid soils. (871)

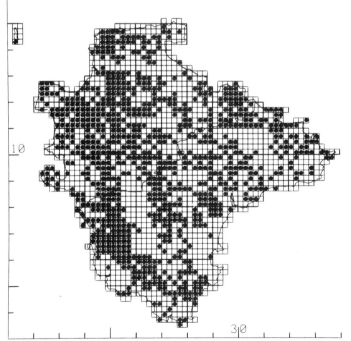

Inula crithmoides L.   Golden Samphire
On maritime cliffs and rocks. Rare, but can be found in several localities along the south coast between Torbay and Plymouth. (7)

Pulicaria dysenterica (L.) Bernh.   Fleabane
In damp grassland, meadows and roadsides, often by ditches or streams. Quite common and fairly generally distributed. (1063)

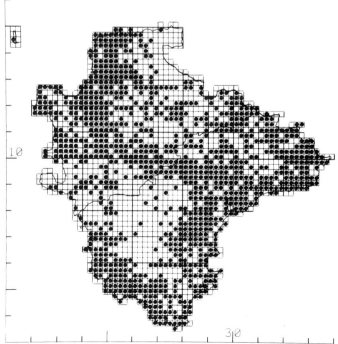

Anaphalis margaritacea (L.) Benth.   Pearly Everlasting
Introduced; a native of Europe. In waste ground near Chudleigh, Cullompton and Plymouth, probably always as escapes from cultivation. (3)

Inula helenium L.   Elecampane
Introduced; a native of Europe. In fields and hedges, probably a relic of cultivation. Well established in a hedge near Exeter, and also recorded from near Lyme Regis. (3)

Bidens tripartita L.   Trifid Bur-marigold
In wet meadows and on river banks. Rare, though rather less so
than *B. cernua,* and mostly along rivers in E. Devon. (39)

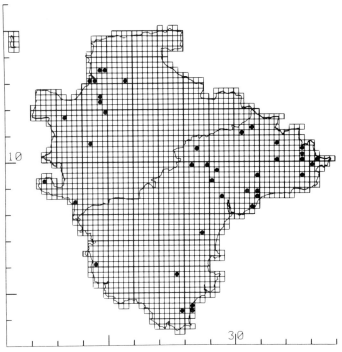

Bidens cernua L.   Nodding Bur-marigold
Around the edges of pools and streams and in wet meadows.
Rare, with very scattered records. (20)

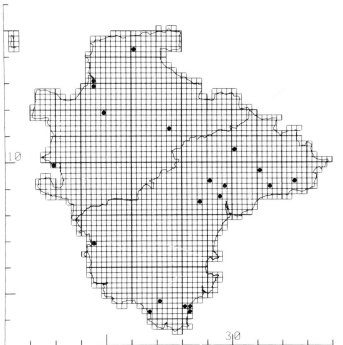

Ambrosia artemisiifolia L. was once reported from Torquay, but
has not been seen since.

Xanthium spinosum L.   Spiny Cocklebur
Introduced; a native of America. Occurs as a wool alien at
Bradley Mill, Newton Abbot. (1)

Galinsoga parviflora Cav.   Gallant Soldier
Introduced; a native of S. America. A single record from the
banks of the R. Taw at Appledore, near Barnstaple, but it also
has been found previously elsewhere in the vicinity. (1)

Galinsoga ciliata (Rafin.) S.F.Blake   Hairy Gallant Soldier
Introduced; a native of America. In cultivated land and waste
places; only known from Plymouth, Exeter and Exmouth. (4)

Anthemis arvensis L.   Corn Chamomile
In arable land and waste places, usually on base-rich soils.
Rather rare and local, with a very scattered distribution. (64)

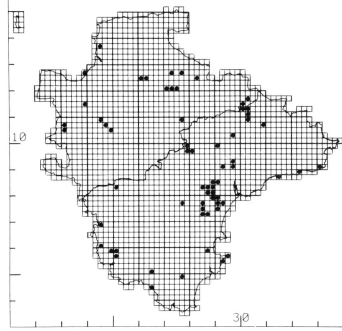

Anthemis cotula L.   Stinking Mayweed
A weed of arable land and gardens. Quite rare, most frequent on
rather clayey soils. (51)

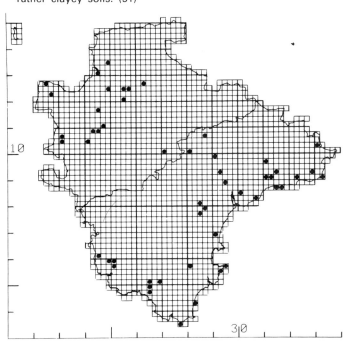

Anthemis tinctoria L.   Yellow Chamomile
Introduced; a native of Europe. In waste places and on dry
banks. Very rare, known only from Lapford and Tiverton. (2)

174

Achillea millefolium L.   Yarrow Milfoil

In grassland, lawns, hedges and by roadsides. Abundant, and
generally distributed except on the higher moors. (1723)

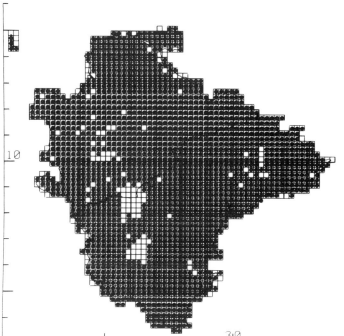

Chamaemelum nobile (L.) All.   Chamomile
(*Anthemis nobilis* L.)

On heaths, moors and commons, usually in short turf along
roads and at the margins of heaths. Locally common around
Dartmoor, elsewhere scattered and rather rare. (68)

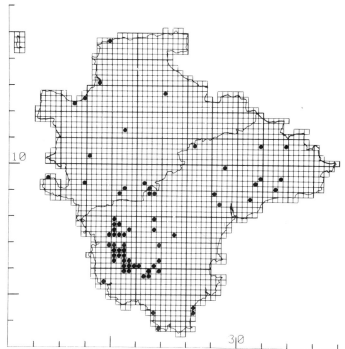

Achillea ptarmica L.   Sneezewort

In marshes, wet meadows and roadside ditches; particularly
characteristic of meadows on the Culm in central and N.W.
Devon, and rather scattered elsewhere. (464)

Tripleurospermum inodorum Schultz   Scentless Mayweed
(*Matricaria perforata* Mérat, *M. inodora* L. nom. illeg.)

In cultivated and waste ground, particularly in gateways.
Abundant around the coast and quite common on the Culm and
other clayey soils; much less frequent in heathy areas. (797)

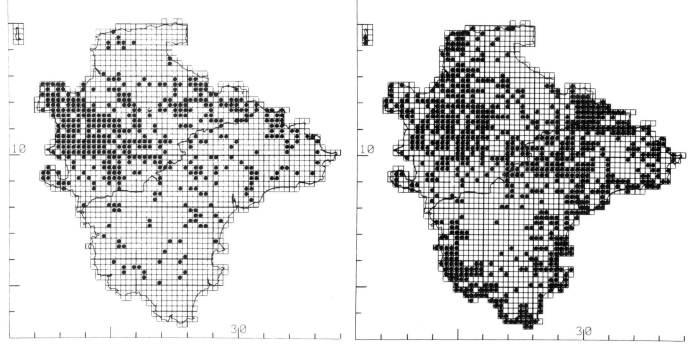

Matricaria recutita L.   Wild Chamomile
(*Chamomilla recutita* (L.) Rauschert., *M. chamomilla* L. p.p.)
A weed of cultivated ground and waste places. Local in lowland
areas, and mostly in clayey habitats on the Culm. (186)

Chrysanthemum segetum L.   Corn Marigold
Introduced; a native of Europe. A weed of arable soils and waste
places, usually on fairly light or sandy soils. Local, but scattered
over the county and sometimes abundant where it occurs. (86)

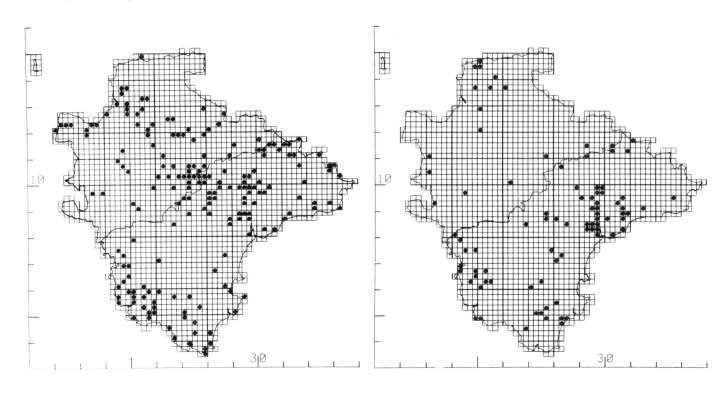

Chrysanthemum coronarium L. has been reported from S.
Molton as an alien, but has not been seen recently.

Matricaria matricarioides (Less.) Porter
                    Pineapple-weed, Rayless Mayweed
(*Chamomilla suaveolens* (Pursh) Rydb.)
Introduced; a native of N.E. Asia. On paths, waysides and in
waste places, especially where these are trampled. Very common, often abundant, and generally distributed. (1585)

Leucanthemum vulgare Lam.   Moon Daisy, Ox-eye Daisy
(*Chrysanthemum leucanthemum* L.
In meadows, grassland and on grassy banks. Common and
generally distributed except on the moors. (947)

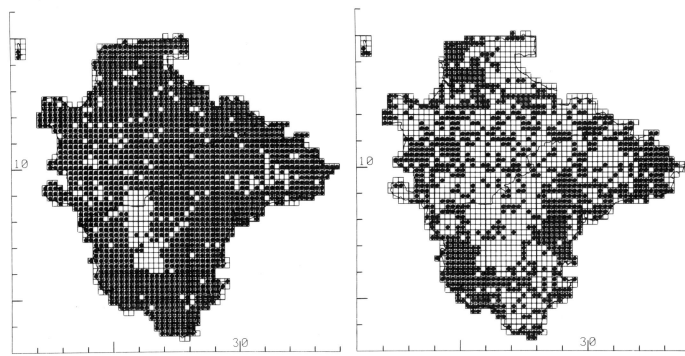

Leucanthemum maximum (Ramond) DC.   Shasta Daisy
(*Chrysanthemum maximum* Ramond)
Introduced; a native of the Pyrenees. Widely cultivated in gardens and often escaping, and becoming naturalised in hedges and banks, usually fairly near habitations. (15)

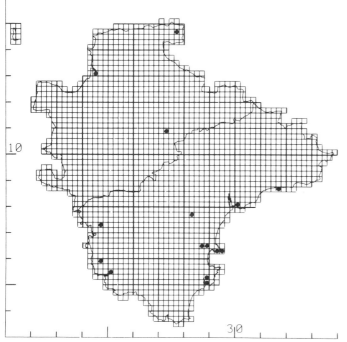

Tanacetum vulgare L.   Tansy
(*Chrysanthemum vulgare* (L.) Bernh.)
In rough pastures, hedgebanks and on roadsides, often in rather damp and sandy soils. Common around Exeter, more local elsewhere, and often rather frequent where it occurs. (421)

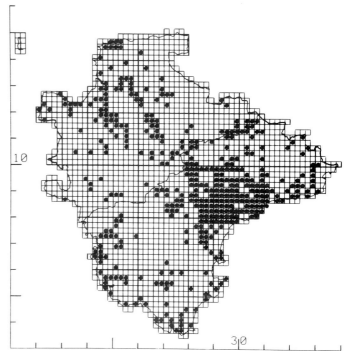

Tanacetum parthenium (L.) Schultz   Feverfew
(*Chrysanthemum parthenium* (L.) Bernh.)
On walls and by roadsides, often in the vicinity of habitations. Fairly common and generally distributed in the lowlands. (338)

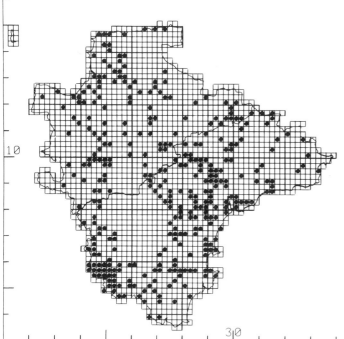

Artemisia vulgaris L.   Mugwort
In waste places, hedges and on roadsides. Common in the south and east, very much less so in the north and west, except around the coast from Barnstaple to Ilfracombe. (692)

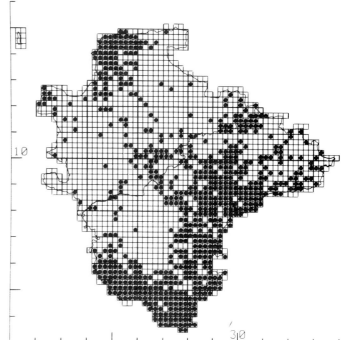

Artemisia absinthium L.   Wormwood
In waste places and on roadsides, usually rather near the sea,
where it is local; very rare inland. (30)

Tussilago farfara L.   Coltsfoot
In fields, on banks and in waste ground, usually where this is
damp and clayey. Common over much of the county, particularly in coastal districts; less frequent in the agricultural regions
in the centre. (714)

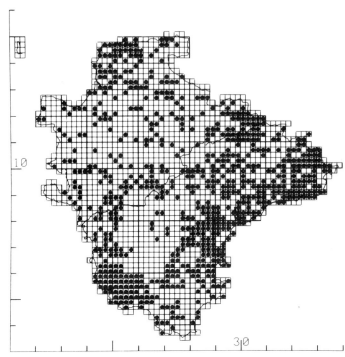

Artemisia maritima L.   Sea Wormwood, Sea Mugwort
In the drier parts of salt-marshes and estuaries, and in waste
ground near the sea. Rare, most frequent around Barnstaple,
very occasional elsewhere. (14)

Petasites hybridus (L.) P.Gaertn., B.Mey. & Scherb.
                                                    Butterbur
In wet meadows and on banks, by streams and rivers, often on
alluvial or clay soils. Locally abundant, but most frequent along
the rivers in the east of the county. (186)

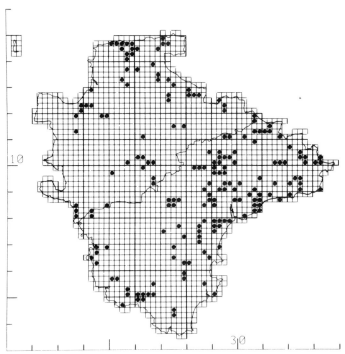

Artemisia stellerana Besser has been reported from Ilfracombe
and Branscombe, but has not been seen recently.

Petasites fragrans (Vill.) C.Presl   Winter Heliotrope
Introduced; a native of S. Europe. Extensively naturalised in
damp hedges, along roadsides and in waste places. Most
frequent in southern and eastern parts of the county, scattered
elsewhere, but often locally abundant. (467)

Senecio cineraria DC.   Cineraria
Introduced; a native of S. Europe. Naturalised in a number of
places around both N. and S. coasts, where it is often quite
abundant. (27)

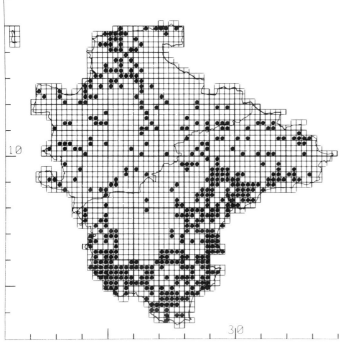

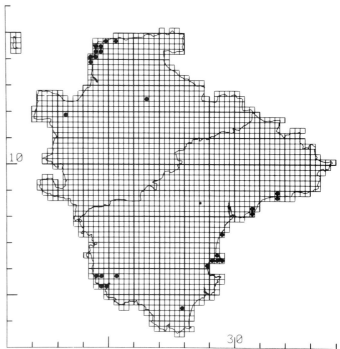

Petasites albus (L.) Gaertn. has been reported from Torquay, but
has not been seen recently.

Doronicum pardalianches L.   Leopard's Bane
Introduced; a native of W. Europe. In woods and plantations,
where it is naturalised in a few scattered localities. (13)

Senecio jacobaea L.   Ragwort
In waste places, neglected pastures and on sand-dunes. Common and generally distributed except on the moors. (1435)

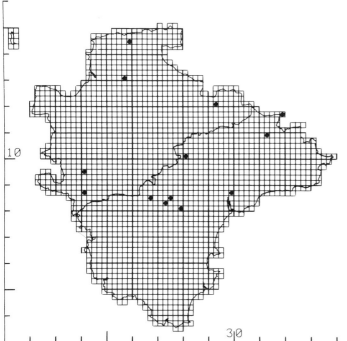

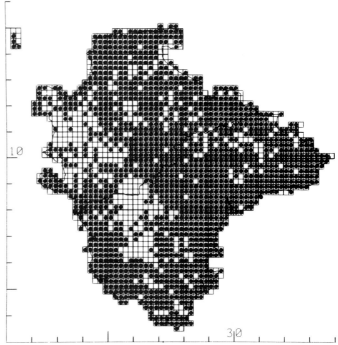

Doronicum plantagineum L. is frequently grown in gardens
and may escape into hedges and waste places, but is not
naturalised.

Senecio x albescens Burbidge & Colgan, (*S. cineraria* x *jacobaea*), has been recorded from Budleigh Salterton and Saunton
(Benoit, Crisp & Jones in Stace, 1975).

179

Senecio aquaticus Hill   Marsh Ragwort
In marshes, wet meadows and ditches. Abundant in the
north-west of the county, especially on clayey soils, local and
scattered elsewhere. (710)

Senecio squalidus L.   Oxford Ragwort
Introduced; a native of S. Europe. On walls, railway banks and in
waste ground, usually in or near towns. Not uncommon around
Plymouth and Exeter, scattered elsewhere. (89)

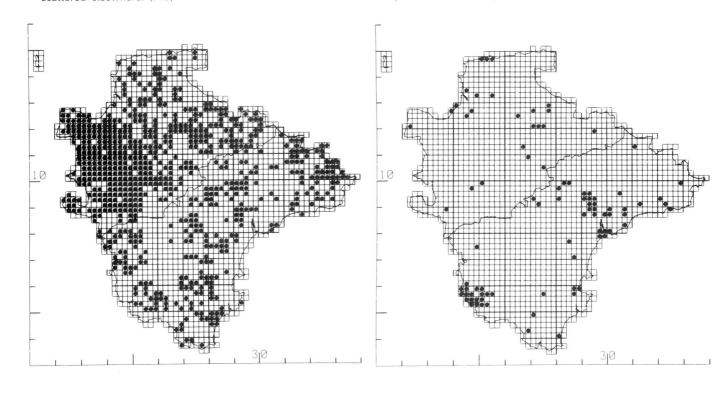

Senecio erucifolius L.   Hoary Ragwort
On dry banks, in fields and waste places, often in lowland
base-rich or calcareous soils. Frequent around Plymouth and
Barnstaple, local elsewhere but widely scattered. (186)

Senecio sylvaticus L.   Wood Groundsel, Mountain Groundsel
On dry banks, heaths and tracks on sandy acid soils. Fairly
common and generally distributed. (362)

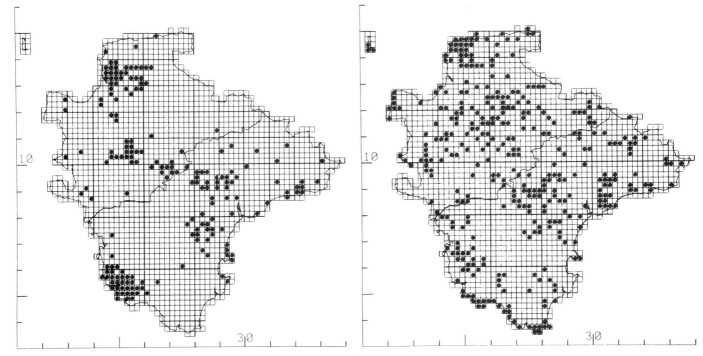

Senecio viscosus L.   Stinking Groundsel
In waste ground, on railway tracks and paths, on sandy soils.
Very local but scattered throughout the county. Some records
could be of viscid forms of *S. sylvaticus.* (64)

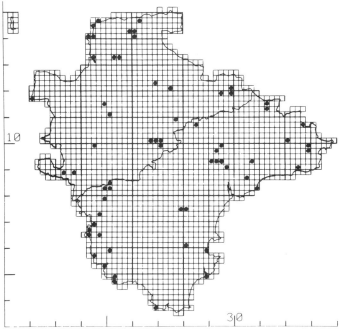

Senecio vulgaris L.   Groundsel
In cultivated ground, sand-dunes and waste places. Very
common and generally distributed, though absent from much of
Dartmoor. (1444)

Carlina vulgaris L.   Carline Thistle
In dry grassland on calcareous substrata, where it is often
common, but also in dry and not always obviously base-rich
habitats on heaths. Local, and very unevenly distributed; most
frequent near the coast. (81)

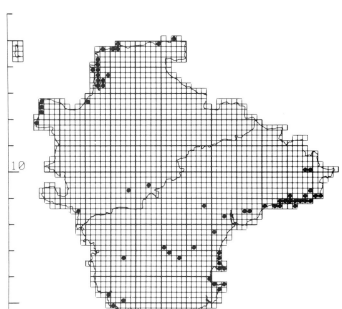

Arctium lappa L.   Great Burdock
In grassland and waste places. Scattered over the county, but
not very common. (159)

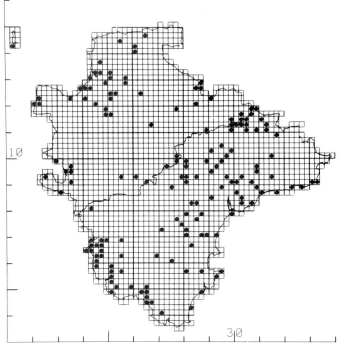

Forms with well-marked ray florets are sometimes separated as
ssp. **denticulatus** (O.F.Mueller) P.D.Sell (var. *radiatus* Koch).
These tend to be mainly coastal in distribution and it has been
suggested some of them could be hybrids with *S. squalidus.*

Neither **Senecio mikanioides** Otto ex Walp., the German Ivy,
which has been reported as established at Torquay, nor **Senecio
tanguticus** Maxim., which has been reported from Buckland
Monachorum, have been seen recently.

Calendula officinalis L. and **C. arvensis** L. are both grown in
gardens and sometimes found in the vicinity of rubbish heaps,
but are not naturalised.

Arctium minus Bernh.   Lesser Burdock
In waste places, on roadsides and in scrub and open woodland.
Common and generally distributed in lowland areas. (1228)

Carduus nutans L.   Musk Thistle
In dry fields, on roadsides and in waste places, usually on
calcareous or base-rich soils. Local in suitable habitats. (198)

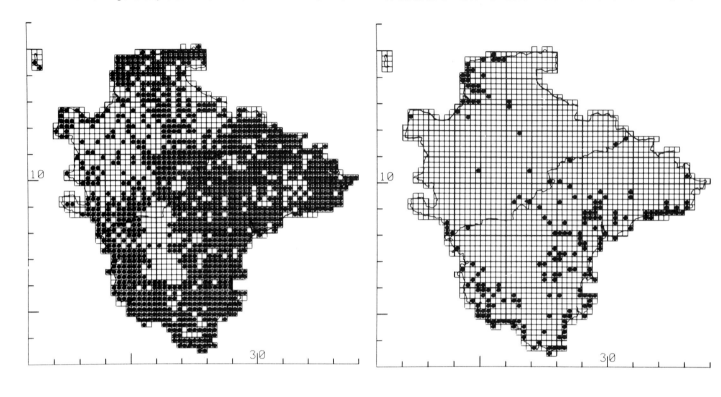

Most records fall within the range of ssp. **minus**.
Ssp. **pubens** (Bab.) J. Arènes (*A. vulgare* Hill, *A. pubens* Bab.)
has been recorded on a number of occasions, mostly from more
shaded areas. It is locally frequent in parts of W. Devon and on
the Pebble Bed heaths in the east, but rare elsewhere. It is
thought that it may have originated as the hybrid *A. lappa* x
minus. (46)

Carduus acanthoides L.   Welted Thistle
(*C. crispus* auct. non L.)
In hedges, streamsides and waste places; scattered over the
county, and generally not at all common. (84)

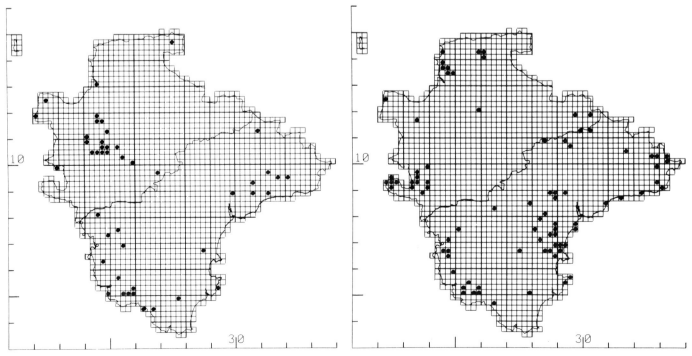

Carduus tenuiflorus Curt.   Slender Thistle
In dry pastures and waste ground near the sea. Quite common on chalk and limestone cliffs, and fairly frequent elsewhere around the coast, especially in the south. (72)

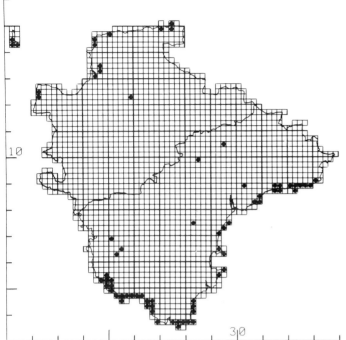

Cirsium dissectum (L.) Hill   Marsh Plume Thistle
(*C. anglicum* (Lam.) DC.)
In marshes, wet meadows and on heaths where there is an inflow of base-rich water. Local, but often abundant where it occurs. (238)

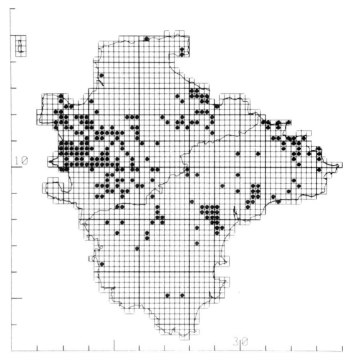

Carduus pycnocephalus   Plymouth Thistle
Introduced; a native of S. Europe. Well known from two localities on Plymouth Hoe, though now reduced to very few plants. It can also be found on sand-dunes at Instow. (3)

Cirsium eriophorum (L.) Scop.   Woolly-headed Thistle
Recorded from grassland on the chalk at Branscombe and also from the vicinity of Honiton, but now very rare in Devon. (2)

Cirsium vulgare (Savi) Ten.   Spear Thistle
(*C. lanceolatum* (L.) Scop.)
In fields, hedges, cultivated ground and waste places. Very common and generally distributed. (1672)

Cirsium acaule Scop.   Stemless Thistle
In short grassy turf, usually on chalk or limestone, and also on Northam Burrows. Very local, but common in suitable habitats. It has been recorded from scattered localities elsewhere in the county, but often in error for prostrate or small forms of *C. arvense*. (36)

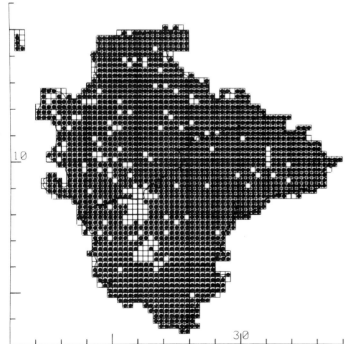
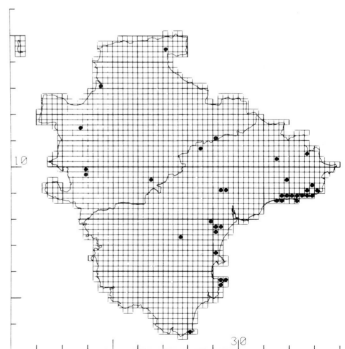

Cirsium palustre (L.) Scop.　　　　　Marsh Thistle
In moist grassland, hedges and waste places. Common and
generally distributed. (1587)

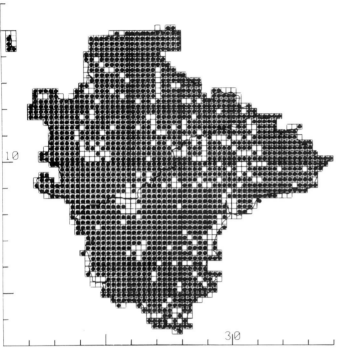

Cirsium x forsteri Loud., (*C. palustre* x *dissectum*), was reported
from Clawton, King's Nympton and Aylesbeare Common (Fl.
Dev.), but has not been seen recently.

Cirsium arvense (L.) Scop.　　Field Thistle, Creeping Thistle
In cultivated ground, pastures, scrub and waste places. Very
common everywhere except on the highest moors. (1683)

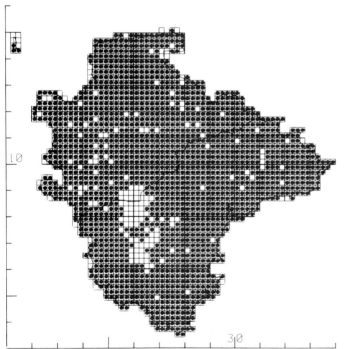

Cirsium x celakovskianum Knaf, (*C. arvense* x *palustre*), has
been reported from Great Torrington (Sledge in Stace, 1975).

Onopordum acanthium L.　　Cotton Thistle, Scottish Thistle
Perhaps native. In dry places on roadsides and sea cliffs. Very
rare, and in very scattered localities, and it does not seem to
persist for any length of time. (5)

Silybum marianum (L.) Gaertn.　　　　　Milk Thistle
Introduced; a native of S. Europe. In grassland and waste
places; local in calcareous habitats around the coast, very rare
elsewhere. (13)

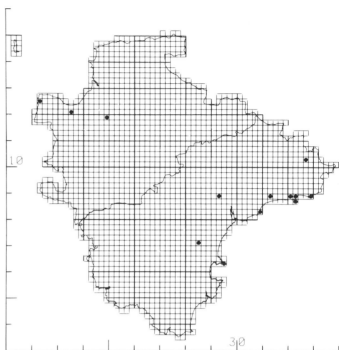

Cynara cardunculus L., the Cardoon, has been reported from the
vicinity of Braunton but there are no recent records.

Serratula tinctoria L.　　　　　　　　　Saw-wort
In scrub and damp grassland, often on calcareous soils; also in
marshes and wet heaths where there is an inflow of calcareous
water. Local, though often abundant where it occurs. (235)

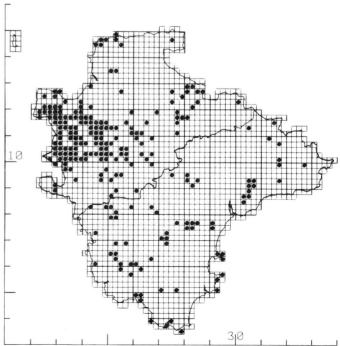

184

Centaurea scabiosa L.   Greater Knapweed
In pastures and on banks and roadsides, usually on calcareous or base-rich soils. Not uncommon on the chalk and limestone, rather rare elsewhere. (308)

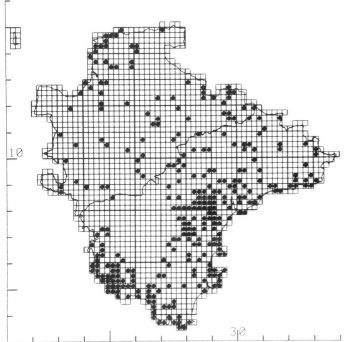

Centaurea cyanus L.   Cornflower
Introduced; a native of Europe. A weed of cultivated land, though probably not now found as such, all records being escapes from cultivation. (14)

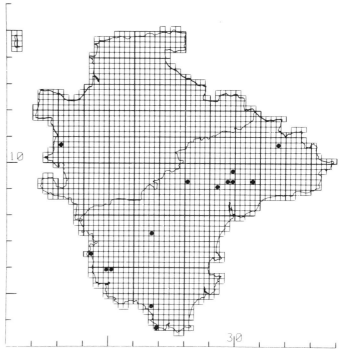

Centaurea montana L. is frequently grown in gardens and can escape; it is semi-naturalised in hedges in some districts. **C. solstitialis** L., St. Barnaby's Thistle, has been reported as a casual from several localities, but only seen recently at South Brent. **C. jacea** L. has been reported from Lundy and Exmouth, but not recently in either locality, and there have been no recent reports of **C. calcitrapa** L., the Star Thistle.

Centaurea nigra L.   Lesser Knapweed, Hard-heads
(inc. *C. nemoralis* Jord., *C. obscura* Jord.)
In fields, hedgerows and on sea cliffs. Common and generally distributed, except on the moors. *C. nemoralis* Jord. (*C. nigra* ssp. *nemoralis* (Jord.) Dorstál) and *C. obscura* Jord. (*C. nigra* ssp. *nigra*) cannot be clearly separated, as the distinguishing characters appear to vary independently, though the former appears to be more common in better drained and more base-rich habitats, and the latter is found in more acid soils. (1582)

Cichorium intybus L.   Chicory
Along roadsides and in pastures on sandy or base-rich soils. Local, mostly scattered around the coast or a little way inland, especially in the south. Perhaps sometimes a relic of cultivation. (58)

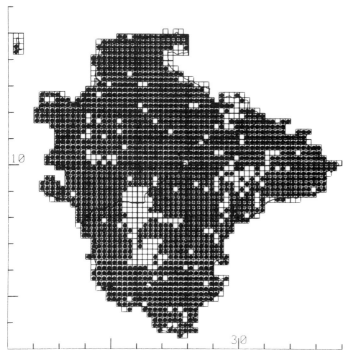

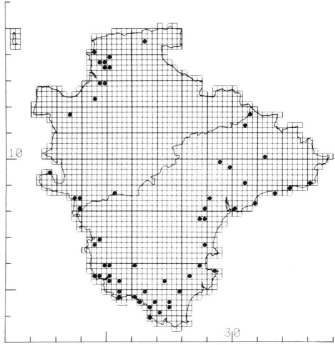

Cichorium endivia L., the Endive, is sometimes cultivated and may escape, but does not persist.

Hypochaeris glabra L.   Smooth Cat's-ear
In dry heathland, sand-dunes and other sandy places. Rare, with very scattered localities, but an inconspicuous plant and rather easily overlooked. (16)

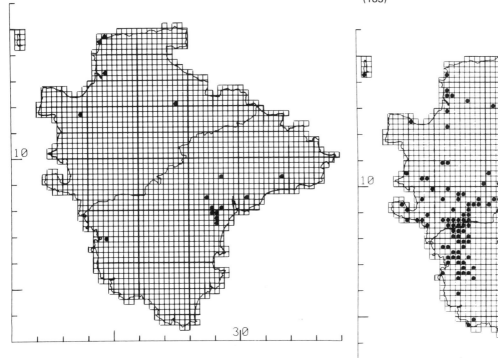

Leontodon hispidus L.   Rough Hawkbit
In fields and rough grassland, especially on calcareous or base-rich soils. Common in E. Devon and also found north of Plymouth on roadsides, where it may benefit from the use of calcareous grit, and in churchyards; rare and local elsewhere. (183)

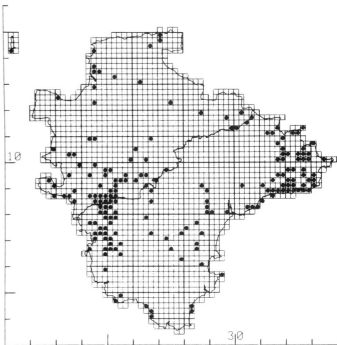

Hypochaeris radicata L.   Cat's-ear
In grassland, sand-dunes and hedgebanks. Very common and generally distributed. (1672)

Leontodon autumnalis L.   Autumnal Hawkbit
In meadows, pastures and along roadsides. Common and fairly generally distributed. (817)

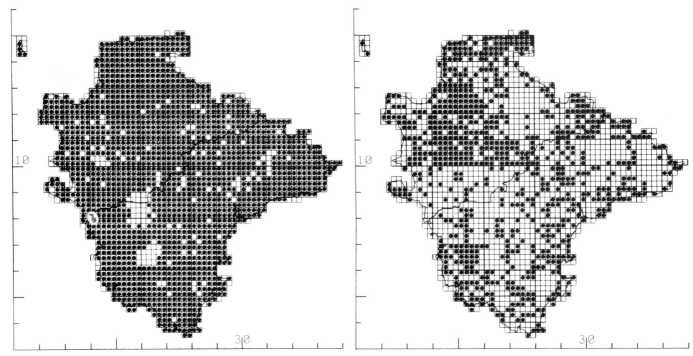

Leontodon taraxacoides (Vill.) Mérat   Hawkbit
(*L. leysseri* (Wallr.) Beck)
In dry grassland and on roadsides and dunes, especially on calcareous soils. Fairly common and generally distributed. (342)

Picris hieracioides L.   Hawkweed Ox-tongue
On dry banks and in hedges and waste places, usually on calcareous soils. Rather rare, mostly around Torbay and on the chalk in E. Devon, with scattered records elsewhere. (61)

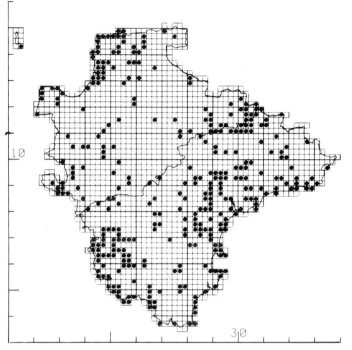

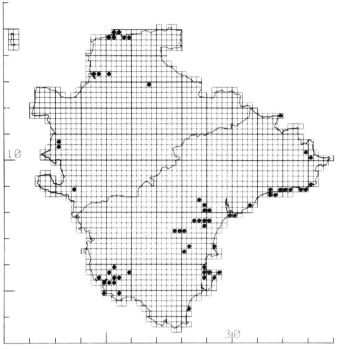

Tragopogon porrifolius L.   Salsify
Introduced; a native of the Mediterranean region. Grown as a vegetable for its edible roots and sometimes established in waste places, but scarcely naturalised. (5)

Tragopogon pratensis L.   Goat's-beard
On roadsides and in pastures and waste places. Not uncommon in parts of the south and east of the county, local or rare elsewhere. (309)

Picris echioides L.   Bristly Ox-tongue
Along roadsides, and in hedges and waste places, especially on calcareous or clayey soils near the sea. Fairly common around the south coast and on Braunton Burrows; rare inland. (207)

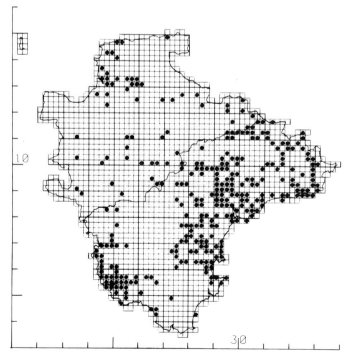

Ssp. **pratensis** which includes forms in which the ligules about equalling the involucral bracts, probably does not occur in Devon.
Ssp. **minor** (Mill.) Wahlenb., (*T. minor* Mill.), includes plants in which the ligules are decidedly shorter than the bracts.

Sonchus asper (L.) Hill   Rough Sow-thistle
In fields, hedges and waste places. Common and generally distributed, though rather less frequent than *S. oleraceus*. (1525)

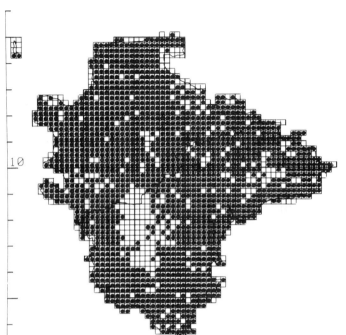

Sonchus arvensis L.   Corn Sow-thistle
In arable fields, hedges and waste places, usually in rather damper situations than the preceding species. Fairly common and generally distributed in the lowlands. Rather characteristic of 'weedy' habitats near the sea, and especially along the strand-line of brackish marshes. (810)

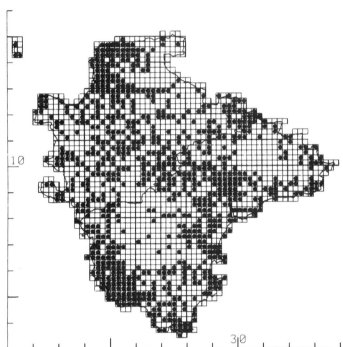

Sonchus oleraceus L.   Sow-thistle
In cultivated and waste ground, and on sea cliffs. Common and generally distributed, but confined to the lowlands. (1361)

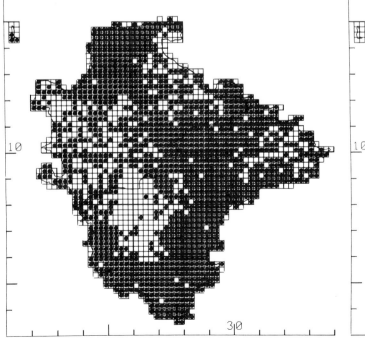

Lactuca serriola L.   Prickly Lettuce
Introduced; a native of Europe. In waste places and on walls. Rather frequent around Exeter and Newton Abbot, and perhaps spreading, rare elsewhere. (27)

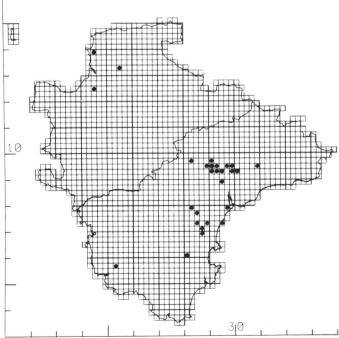

Lactuca virosa L.   Wild Lettuce
Introduced; a native of Europe. On walls and waste ground. Scattered over the county and of uncertain origin, perhaps an escape from cultivation. (10)

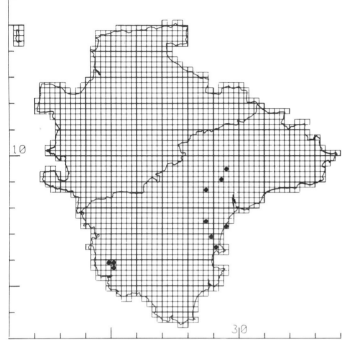

Cicerbita macrophylla (Willd.) Wallr.   Blue Sow-thistle
Introduced; a native of E. Europe. Scattered over the county, probably originally as an escape from cultivation, but now becoming established in several places. A spectacular plant with it conspicuous blue flowers. (12)
Our plants are ssp. **uralensis** (Rouy) P.D.Sell.

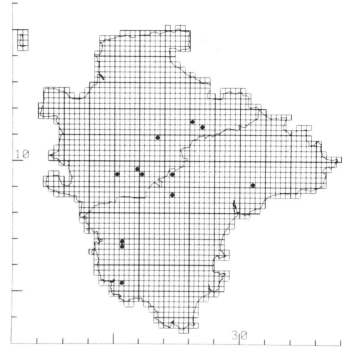

Mycelis muralis (L.) Dum.   Wall Lettuce
On walls, rocky banks, sea cliffs and in waste ground, especially on limestone, and sometimes in woods and other shaded habitats. Rather rare and probably less frequent than formerly. (28)

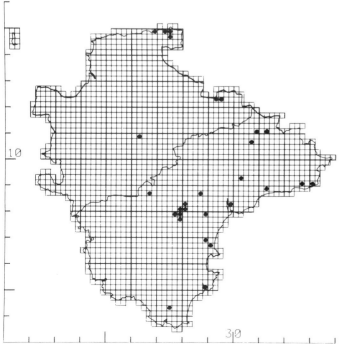

Taraxacum officinale L.   Dandelion
In grassland, on roadsides and in waste places. Very common and generally distributed. (1723)

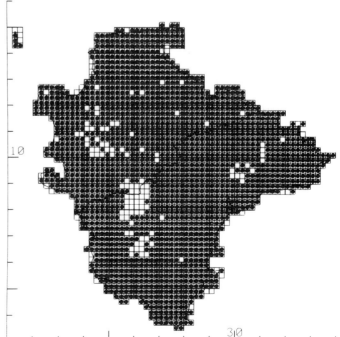

Many workers still treat *T. officinale* as an aggregate species, or at best, raise the various sections to the level of species and recognise these. Richards (1972) made the first serious attempt to sort out which species could be recognised in the British flora. The following account is based on his work, though subsequent investigations have necessitated some modifications. Very little information is available on the distribution of the species in Devon and the habitat information is that for the plants as they occur in Britain. It is hoped that this may stimulate enquiry into the occurrence of the various species in the county, as many of them are undoubtedly quite frequent.

Section ERYTHROSPERMA Dahlst. em. H.Lindb.f.
Usually in dry rocky and sandy places, or short grassland in full sun. The following species have been recorded from Devon, and have often been referred to *T. erythrosperma* agg.; almost all are from the south:

T. brachyglossum (Dahlst.) Dahlst., often in sand-dunes, and found in Dawlish in 1929.
T. lacistophyllum (Dahlst.) Raunk., which seems to be quite frequent in dunes and dry rocky places.
T. rubicundum (Dahlst.) Dahlst., which is usually in calcareous grassland.
T. hispanicum H.Lindb.f., usually in dry rocky places in partial shade; it seems rather rare.
T. laetum (Dahlst.) Dahlst., in sand-dunes and sandy grassland.
T. fulviforme Dahlst., which is found in dunes, grassland and on sea cliffs.
T. oxoniense Dahlst. which occurs commonly in grassland and dunes, and which has been recorded from Churston Cove and Brixham.
T. pseudolacistophyllum van Soest, which occurs in dry grassland and sand-dunes.

Section OBLIQUA Dahlst.
Despite the suggestion in Fl. Dev., there are no records of **T. obliquum** currently accepted for Devon.

Section PALUSTRIA Dahlst.
No plants in this section are known to occur in Devon, despite the records listed under **T. palustre** (Lyons) Symons in Fl. Dev., though it would be worth looking for them in suitable habitats.

Section SPECTABILIA Dahlst.
The members of this and the three subsequent Sections all usually occur in wet places especially in upland habitats. Most of the records are from South Devon.
T. faeroense (Dahlst.) Dahlst. occurs in wet places and seems to be a common and widespread British species.

Section NAEVOSA M.P.Chr.
Members of this Section generally have spotted leaves and a rather northerly distribution in Europe.
T. unguilobum Dahlst. occurs on wet paths, roadsides and flushes in hilly regions, and seems to be quite common.
T. fulvicarpum Dahlst. is found in wet grassland, the edges of woods and in dune-slacks.
T. euryphyllum (Dahlst.) M.P.Chr. is found in sheltered, wet base-rich habitats, and has been recorded from Tavistock.
T. maculosum A.J.Richards is found in wet wood margins and on cliff-faces, and has been recorded from Tavistock.

Section CELTICA C.-I.Sahlin
These species all seem to have a western distribution in Britain.
T. praestans H.Lindb.f. occurs in wet places by paths and roads and has also been reported from the Tavistock area.
T. laetifrons Dahlst. occurs in wood margins and open woodland.
T. nordstedtii Dahlst. is common in wet places, usually below about 450 m. (1400 ft.), on walls, banks and in waste ground, and has been recorded from both vice-counties, and occurs on Dartmoor.
T. adamii Claire occurs in wet meadows, on walls and in gardens, and is thought to have been found at Teignbridge, but it has been confused with **T. gelertii** in the past.
T. raunkiaerii Wiinst occurs commonly in grassy places in base-rich soils and also on sand-dunes.

Section HAMATA H.Øllgaard
T. bracteatum Dahlst. occurs in grassy places and on roadsides.
T. hamatum Raunk. occurs in grassy and waste places, among scrub and in gardens.
T. hamatiforme Dahlst. is found in hedges, on roadsides and in grassy places.

T. subhamatum M.P.Chr. occurs in grassy places, roadsides and poor pastures.
T. pseudohamatum Dahlst. is a common and widespread species which has been recorded from S. Devon.

Section TARAXACUM (Vulgaria Dahlst.)
Generally common plants, occurring in grassland, waste places and on roadsides, usually in some way associated with man. The plants are often referred to *T. officinale* s.s. agg.
T. pannucium Dahlst. in herb-rich meadows and on banks. Has been found between Exminster and Powderham, and also at Dunchideock.
T. ekmanii Dahlst. occurs in grassy places and on roadsides.
T. dahlstedtii H.Lindb.f. also occurs in grassy places and on roadsides.
T. ostenfeldii Dahlst. is found in waste places, gardens and on paths.
T. oblongatum Dahlst. is found in good quality pastures and has been recorded from near Exeter.
T. polyodon Dahlst. occurs in grassy places and on roadsides.

Lapsana communis L. Nipplewort
By roadsides and in hedges and waste places. Common and generally distributed. (1594)

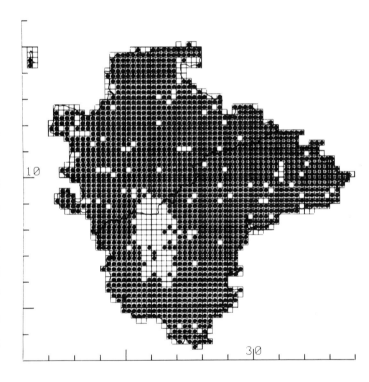

Crepis biennis L.   Rough Hawk's-beard
On roadsides and in pastures, hedges and waste places.
Scattered over the county, mostly in the south, and rather local.
(34)

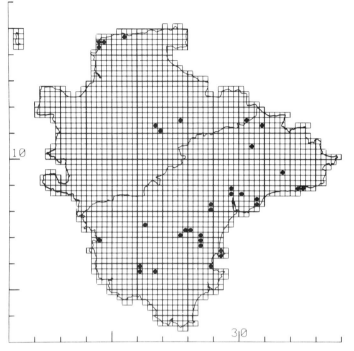

Crepis capillaris (L.) Wallr.   Smooth Hawk's-beard
In grassland, hedges, dry heaths and waste places. Common
and generally distributed. (981)

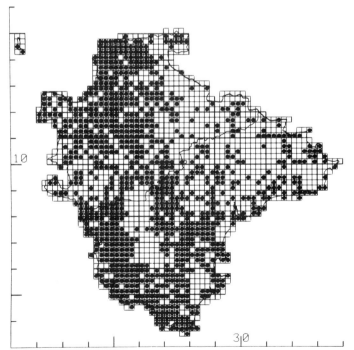

Crepis vesicaria L.   Beaked Hawk's-beard
(*C. taraxacifolia* Thuill.)
In rough grass by roadsides and in hedges and dry waste places,
often on base-rich soils. Locally plentiful, especially in the
southern half of the county and around Barnstaple. (484)
Our plant is ssp. **haenseleri** (Boiss. ex DC.) P.D.Sell.

Crepis vesicaria L.   Beaked Hawk's-beard

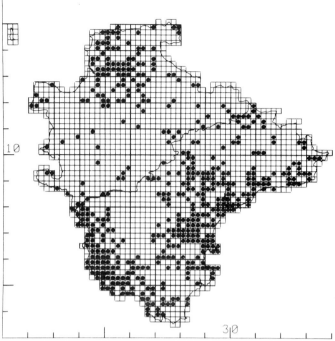

Crepis setosa Haller f. has been recorded on one occasion as a
weed of cultivated ground. There are no recent records of **C.
nicaeensis** Bab.

Hieracium   Hawkweed
A very difficult genus. In sub-genus *Hieracium* little or no pollen
is viable and seeds are normally produced without fertilization.
This results in numerous true-breeding lines, modified occasionally by mutations or the rare hybrid. In sub-genus *Pilosella*
sexual reproduction is more usual, but apomixis and vegetative
propagation also occur frequently. The numbers of species
records probably only give a very rough idea of the true
occurrence of the species. It has not been possible to relate in
any satisfactory way the information given in Fl. Dev. to modern
treatments of the genus.

Sub-genus HIERACIUM
1. *Section UMBELLATA*
Hieracium umbellatum L.
On roadsides and the edges of heaths. Probably fairly common.
(63)

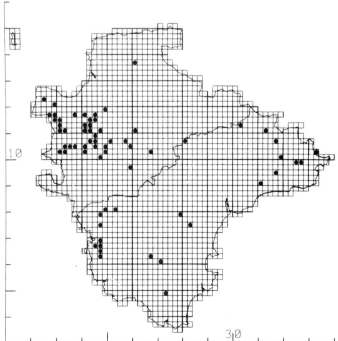

Ssp. **bichlorophyllum** (Druce & Zahn) Sell & West is sometimes recognised and has been recorded quite frequently, but can only be separated from the type with difficulty. (113)

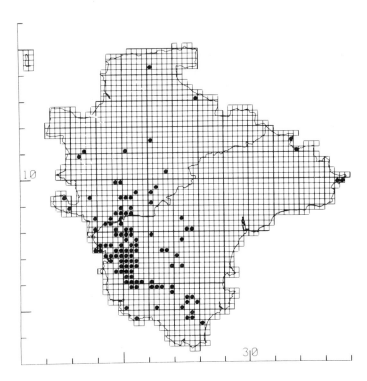

2. *Section SABAUDA*
Hieracium sabaudum L.
(inc. *H. perpropinquum* (Zahn) Druce)
In hedges, scrub and the margins of woods; probably not uncommon, and recorded from Chudleigh Knighton heath. (7)

3. *Section VULGATA*
Hieracium grandidens Dahlst.
(*H. exotericum* auct. p.p., *H. murorum* agg.)
Usually by roadsides and on railway banks; probably quite frequent in lowland areas, e.g. around Plymouth and Ashburton (Perring & Sell, 1968) (13)

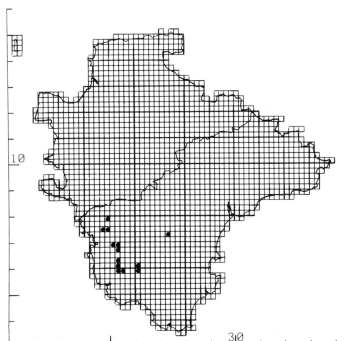

H. sublepistoides (Zahn) Druce, (*H. lepistoides* K.Joh.), is another member of this group reported as locally common in Fl. Dev., though some records may be of **H. torticeps** Dahlst.

Hieracium maculatum Sm.
Introduced; a native of Europe. Found occasionally in waste ground, on walls and in quarries, and frequent at the old station at Halwill Junction. (6)

Hieracium diaphanum Fries
(inc. *H. anglorum* A.Ley, *H. scanicum* Dahlst. var. *anglorum* (A.Ley) Pugsl.)
Recorded from the Lynton area.

Hieracium strumosum (Linton) A.Ley
(*H. lachenalii* auct.)
This has been reported from Lynton and the south-western slopes of Exmoor, especially around E. Anstey.
The closely related **H. cheriense** Jord. ex Bor. has been recorded from Lynton and Plymouth, and **H. subamplifolium** (Zahn) Roffey from Lynton.

Hieracium lepidulum (Stens.) Omang
On roadsides, railway banks and in grassland; known from Lynton and Plymouth.

4. *Section OREADEA*
Hieracium schmidtii Tausch
Recorded from the Lynton and Tavistock areas (Perring & Sell, 1968).

Hieracium stenopholidium (Dahlst.) Omang
Recorded from the Ashburton area (Perring & Sell, 1968).

Hieracium eustomon (E.F.Linton) Roffey
Recorded from the N. Devon coast, between Mortehoe and Lynton (Perring & Sell, 1968).

Sub-genus *PILOSELLA*
1. *Section PILOSELLA*
Hieracium pilosella L.   Mouse-ear Hawkweed
In grassy pastures, on heaths and banks and in sand-dunes. Locally quite common, but rather scattered. (593)

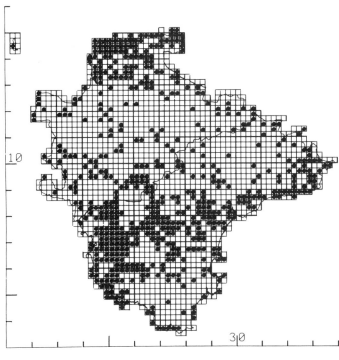

Hieracium peleteranum Mérat ssp. **tenuiscapa** (Pugsl.) Sell has been recorded from Torquay (Perring & Sell, 1968).

2. Section PRATENSINA
Hieracium aurantiacum L.
Introduced; a native of Europe. On roadsides, railway banks and in grassy and waste places. Rather rare. (14)

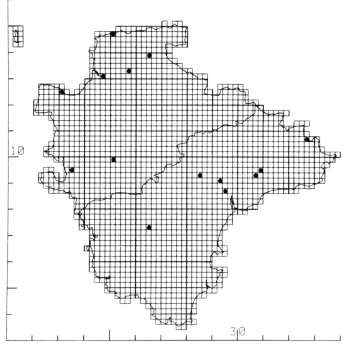

Ssp. **carpathicola** Naegli & Peter, (*H. brunneocroceum* Pugsl.), occurs in similar habitats, but is more frequent as a garden escape. (31)

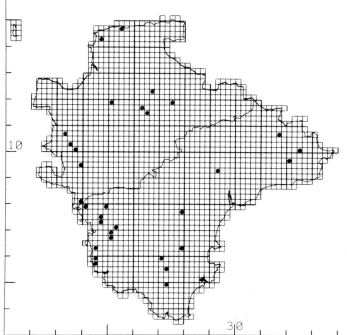

3. Section PRAEALTINA
Hieracium praealtum Vill. ex Gochnet
Introduced; a native of Europe. Mainly on railway banks; there are a number of records from Plymouth and Newton Abbot (Perring & Sell, 1968), and also from Chudleigh Knighton heath. (1)

ALISMATACEAE

Sagittaria sagittifolia L.   Arrow-head
Beside canals and rivers, usually in shallow water. Confined to the Tiverton and Exeter canals and their vicinity, where it is local. (8)

Sagittaria rigida Pursh   Canadian Arrow-head
Introduced; a native of N. America. Known only from two localities in the Exeter canal. (2)

Baldellia ranunculoides (L.) Parl.   Lesser Water-plantain
By pools and in ditches and dune-slacks. Local on Braunton Burrows; elsewhere recorded only from Thurlestone. (2)

Alisma plantago-aquatica L.   Water-plantain
In ponds and ditches and beside rivers and canals. Not uncommon in suitable habitats, but local. (129)

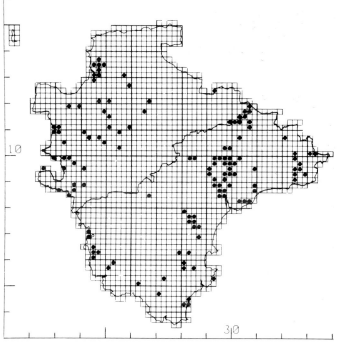

Alisma lanceolatum With.   Narrow-leaved Water-plantain
Confined to the Exeter and Tiverton canals, where it is rather rare. (7)

BUTOMACEAE

Butomus umbellatus L.   Flowering Rush
In canals, rivers and pools. Rare, confined to Slapton Ley and the Exeter canal, but it is sometimes cultivated and may be found as an escape. (5)

HYDROCHARITACEAE

Hydrocharis morsus-ranae L.   Frog-bit
In ponds and ditches and similar wet habitats. Confined to the Tiverton Canal, where it is rather rare, and to the Exminster Marshes near Exeter, where it is now very rare. (8)

Elodea canadensis Michx   Canadian Pondweed
Introduced; a native of N. America. In ponds, ditches, canals and slow-flowing streams. Scattered over the county, and locally frequent. (61)

Triglochin palustris L.   Marsh Arrow-grass
In wet muddy or marshy places, sometimes in salt-marshes with the previous species. Rather rare. (17)

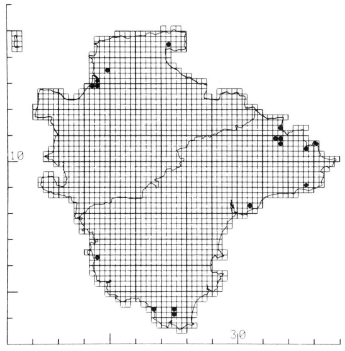

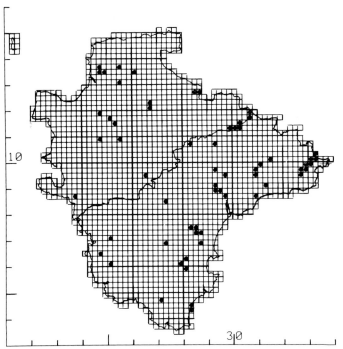

Elodea nuttallii (Planch.) St. John
Introduced; a native of N. America. Known only from one locality in the Exeter Canal. (1)

JUNCAGINACEAE

Triglochin maritima L.   Sea Arrow-grass
In salt-marshes, often extending some way inland along estuaries, where it may be locally frequent. Rarely further inland. (70)

POTAMOGETONACEAE

Potamogeton
Species of *Potamogeton* are very variable in their vegetative morphology and care must be taken in assigning specimens to several of the following species.

Potamogeton natans L.   Broad-leaved Pondweed
In lakes, ponds and ditches; usually lowland and in organic-rich water which is relatively shallow. Scattered over the county, fairly frequent around Exeter, but rather rare elsewhere. (84)

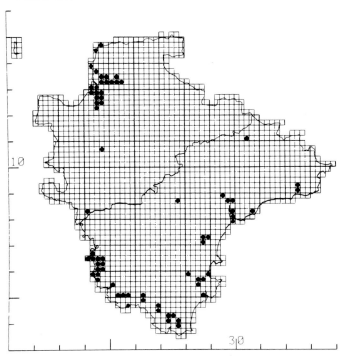

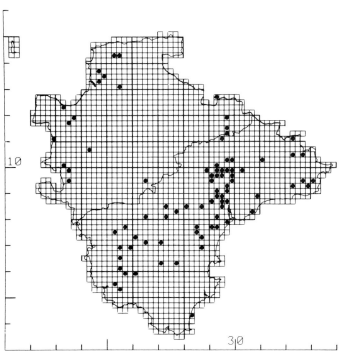

Potamogeton polygonifolius Pourr. Bog Pondweed
In pools and streams, and on boggy ground, usually with acid
and shallow or slow-flowing water. The commonest species on
the moors and also frequent in boggy patches on heaths. (251)

Potamogeton x nitens Weber
(*P. perfoliatus* x *gramineus*)
This hybrid has been recorded on one occasion near Beaford.

Potamogeton pusillus L. Lesser Pondweed
In ponds and ditches. Very rare, and only recorded from
Braunton Marshes, Slapton Ley and near Totnes. (4)

Potamogeton obtusifolius Mert. & Koch
Blunt-leaved Pondweed, Obtuse-leaved Pondweed,
Grassy Pondweed
In lakes, ponds and streams; rare, and confined to a few
localities in S. Devon, where it is very local. (13)

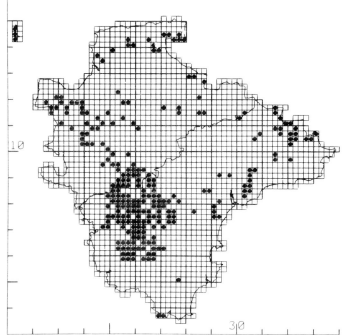

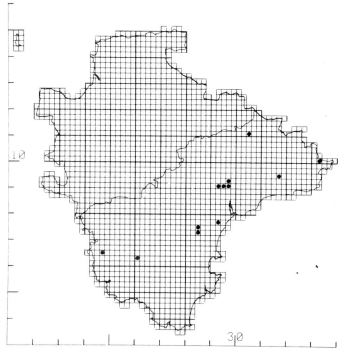

Potamogeton coloratus Hornem. Fen Pondweed
In shallow pools in base-rich peat. Only recorded with certainty
from Braunton Burrows, where it has been known for many
years. (1)

Potamogeton lucens L. Shining Pondweed
In lakes and ponds with base-rich and slow-flowing water. Very
rare, and only known from the Exeter Canal. (1)

Potamogeton perfoliatus L. Perfoliate Pondweed
In streams, rivers and canals; usually found in water with large
amounts of organic matter, but quite rare. (13)

Potamogeton berchtoldii Fieb. Small Pondweed
In ponds and ditches. Scattered over the county and apparently
rare, though perhaps overlooked. (12)

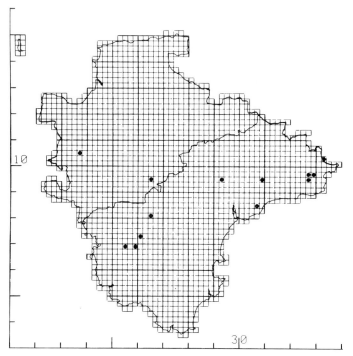

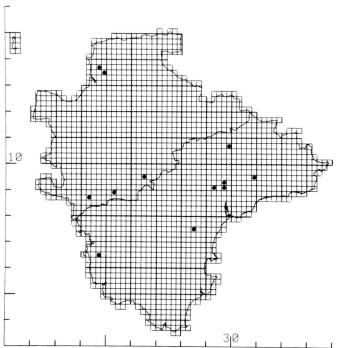

Potamogeton crispus L.   Curled Pondweed
In lakes, ponds and streams; thinly distributed over the county, mostly in the north and east, but nowhere more than locally frequent. (42)

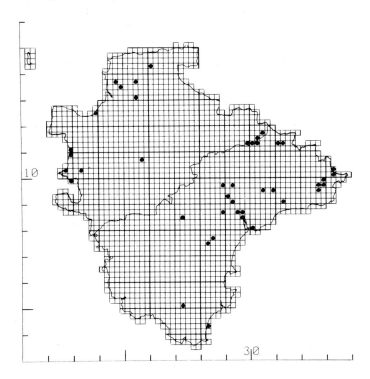

Potamogeton pectinatus L.   Fennel-leaved Pondweed
In streams and ditches, usually in base-rich and sometimes in brackish water. Local and rather rare, largely confined to the region around Exminster and along the R. Axe, but also occurring in Braunton Marshes. (11)

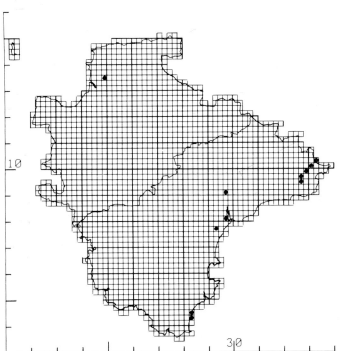

Groenlandia densa (L.) Fourr., the Opposite-leaved Pondweed, has been reported from the vicinity of Dartmouth, Exeter and Seaton, but there are no recent records.

RUPPIACEAE

Ruppia maritima L.   Beaked Tasselweed
In brackish pools and the edges of salt-marshes and estuaries. Locally fairly frequent, but only known from Braunton and Instow Marshes and the lower reaches and estuaries of the rivers Otter, Avon and Tavy. (8)

ZANNICHELLIACEAE

Zannichellia palustris L.   Horned Pondweed
(inc. *Z. pedicellata* Fr.)
In streams and ditches of fresh or brackish water. Scattered around the county, usually in the vicinity of rivers, and also found at Slapton Ley. (8)

ZOSTERACEAE

Zostera marina L.   Eel-grass
On fine gravel, sand or mud, at or below low-water mark for spring tides. Only known from Salcombe and Tor Abbey sands, though possibly occurring elsewhere along the south coast. (2)

Zostera angustifolia (Hornem.) Reichb.
                                   Narrow-leaved Eel-grass
(*Z. hornemanniana* Tutin)
On mud in estuaries, usually between high-water and low-water of neap tides. Locally common in the Exe estuary, and also found in the Kingsbridge estuary, and perhaps in other estuaries further west. (5)

Zostera noltii Hornem.   Dwarf Eel-grass
(*Z. nana* auct.)
On soft mud in estuaries, usually between high-water and low-water of neap tides. Rather rare, and confined to the estuaries of the rivers Exe, where it is locally abundant, Avon and Tavy. (4)

LILIACEAE

Narthecium ossifragum (L.) Huds.   Bog Asphodel
In peat bogs and boggy places on heaths. Common and locally abundant on Dartmoor, and frequent elsewhere in suitable habitats. (274)

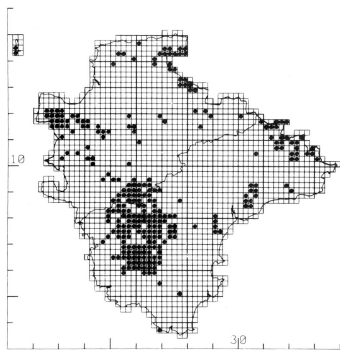

Asphodelus fistulosus L., (*A. tenuifolius* Cav.), has been reported as a casual from time to time, but there are no recent records.

Colchicum autumnale L.   Meadow Saffron, Autumn Crocus
In damp meadows and woods. Very rare, perhaps extinct as a native plant. It has been reported from Braunton Burrows, but the record from Ashburton is probably a garden escape. (1)

Tulipa sylvestris L., the Tulip, and **Fritillaria meleagris** L., the Snake's-head Lily, may both occur occasionally as garden escapes, but seldom persist.

Lilium pyrenaicum Gouan   Pyrenean Lily
Introduced; a native of the Pyrenees. Naturalised in grassy roadsides, mostly in northern parts of the county and around S. Molton. (10)

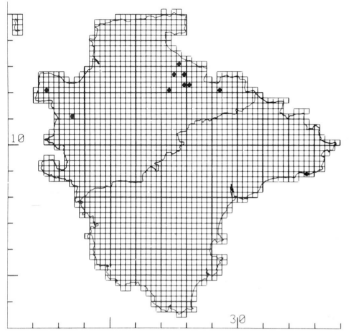

Lilium martagon L., the Martagon Lily, is recorded occasionally as a garden escape. (1)

Ornithogalum umbellatum L.   Star of Bethlehem
Introduced in Devon. In open woods, meadows and on waste ground; probably always an escape from cultivation. Scattered over the county, but quite rare. (38)

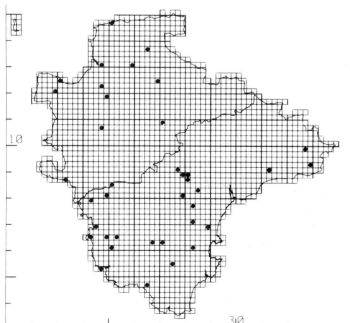

Ornithogalum nutans L., the Drooping Star of Bethlehem, and **O. pyrenaicum** L., the Bath Asparagus, have both been reported as escapes in the past, but there are no recent records.

Scilla verna Huds.   Spring Squill
In dry grassy and heathy places near the coast. Scattered around both coasts, especially near Hartland and between Prawle Point and Plymouth. (19)

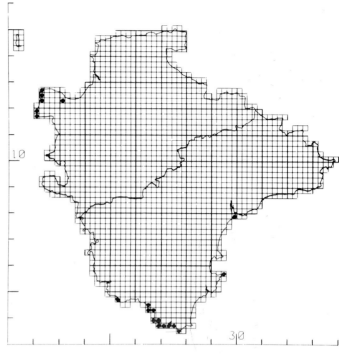

Scilla autumnalis L.   Autumnal Squill
In dry grassland near the coast; chiefly along the south coast between Torquay and Plymouth, where it is local, and it also occurs near Saunton and at Baggy Point. (22)

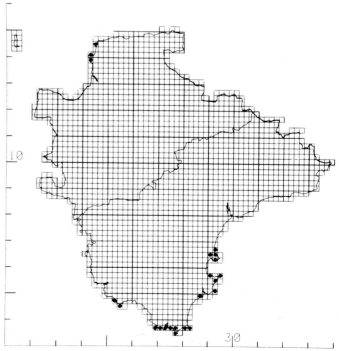

Hyacinthoides non-scripta (L.) Chouard ex Rothm.   Bluebell
(*Scilla non-scripta* (L.) Hoffmanns. & Link, *Endymion non-scriptus* (L.) Dum.)
In woods, shaded pastures, often under bracken, and in grassy hedgebanks. A woodland plant which is sometimes found on tors and may be locally abundant on sea cliffs. Common and generally distributed. (1476)

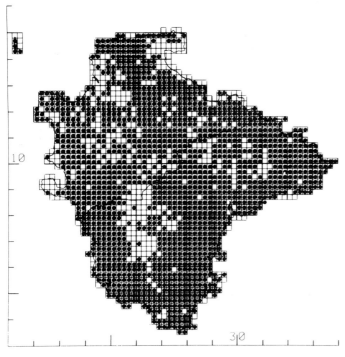

Muscari neglectum Guss. ex Ten.   Grape Hyacinth
(*Muscari racemosum* auct., *M. atlanticum* Boiss. & Reut.)
Introduced; a native of Europe. Frequently grown in gardens and sometimes escaping or thrown out with rubbish, but scarcely naturalised. (3)

Allium roseum L.
Introduced; a native of the Mediterranean region. Naturalised at Frithelstock, where it has been known for many years, and also in the vicinity of Torrington and Instow. (9)

Allium paradoxum (Bieb.) G.Don
Introduced; a native of the Mediterranean region. Occasionally grown in gardens, and sometimes naturalised. Recorded from Plymouth and Weare Giffard. (3)

Allium triquetrum L.   Triquetrous Garlic
Introduced; a native of the Mediterranean region. In hedges and waste places, and apparently spreading quite rapidly, mostly fairly near the coast, in base-rich habitats. (62)

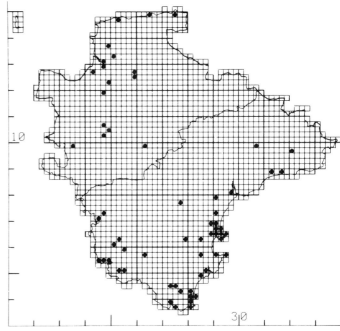

Hyacinthoides hispanica (Mill.) Rothm.   Garden Bluebell
(*Scilla hispanica* Mill., *Endymion patulus* Dum.)
Introduced; a native of the Iberian peninsula. Fairly frequently cultivated in gardens and sometimes escaping or thrown out with rubbish, but scarcely naturalised. (20)

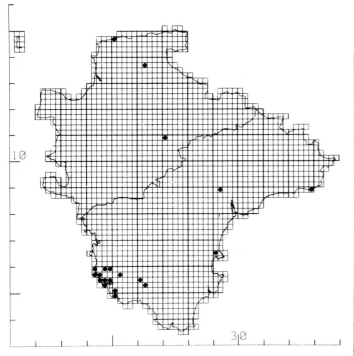

Hybrids are known between this species and *H. non-scripta*.

Allium ursinum L.   Ramsons
In damp woods, scrub and hedges. Common and locally abundant in base-rich habitats, but absent from the most acid soils. (629)

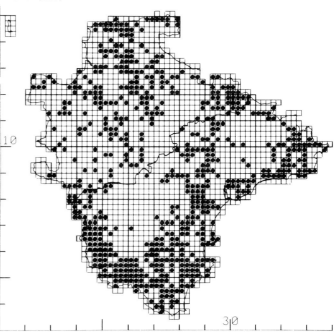

198

Allium oleraceum L.   Field Garlic
In scrub and grassy places. Now apparently very rare, with a
single record from Chudleigh Knighton heath. (1)

Allium carinatum L.   Keeled Garlic
Introduced; a native of W. Europe. Recorded from two localities,
near Plymouth and Sourton, probably as a garden escape. (2)

Allium vineale L.   Crow Garlic
In dry grassland, on cliffs and banks. Often fairly plentiful,
especially near the sea, and mostly in the south and east of the
county. (181)

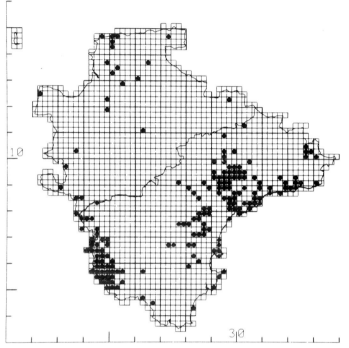

Allium schoenoprasum L., Chives, **A. ampeloprasum** L., Wild
Leek, and **A. scorodoprasum** L., Sand Leek, have all been
reported as garden escapes; only the last has been recorded
recently, on one occasion.

Convallaria majalis L.   Lily of the Valley
Introduced in Devon. In woods and scrub on base-rich soils.
Very rare, and perhaps only as a garden escape, but occasion-
ally naturalised. (3)

Polygonatum multiflorum L.   Solomon's Seal
Introduced in Devon. In woods and scrub, scattered over N.
Devon, but probably always as a garden escape or from rubbish
tips. (39)

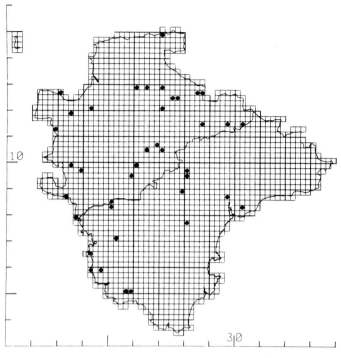

Asparagus officinalis L.   Asparagus
Introduced; a native of Europe. All records refer to the cultivated
plant, which belongs to ssp. **officinalis**; this is locally common
near the sea from Torbay, eastwards, and extending some
distance inland. (13)

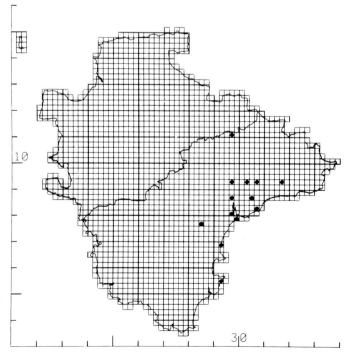

There are no records of the native taxon, ssp. **prostratus** (Dum.)
E.F.Warb.

Ruscus aculeatus L.   Butcher's Broom
In woods, scrub and hedges. Thinly scattered on base-rich soils,
and most frequent fairly near the sea. (92)

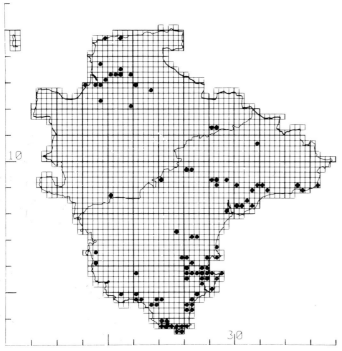

Narcissus pseudonarcissus L.   Daffodil, Lent Lily
In woods, scrub and pastures, often by rivers or where it is in
sunlight; still quite common as an native plant over much of the
county, and locally very abundant. Some records undoubtedly
refer to garden escapes. (271)

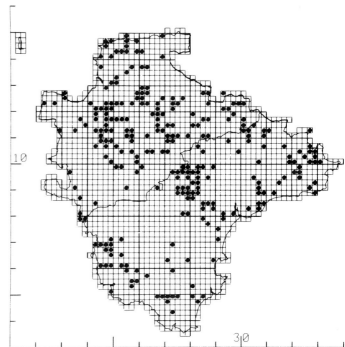

Ssp. **major** Curtis, (*N. hispanicus* Gouan), has been recorded
once and a number of other species and hybrids are grown in
gardens and may escape, including *N. obvallaris* Salisb., which
was reported from Umberleigh in 1913.
Narcissus x intermedius Loisel., (*N. jonquilla* x *tazetta, N. x
biflorus* Curtis), has also been reported, but is probably a garden
escape. (1)

DIOSCOREACEAE

Leucojum aestivum L.   Loddon Lily, Summer Snowflake
Most records are probably of garden escapes, but it has been
reported as being native at Littlehempston, near Totnes, and still
persists there and in the vicinity. (6)

Galanthus nivalis L.   Snowdrop
Commonly grown in gardens and widely naturalised by roadsides and streams and in grassy waste places; perhaps native in
some damp woods. (155)

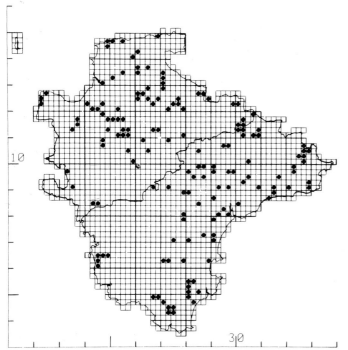

Tamus communis L.   Black Bryony
In scrub, hedges and waste places, especially on base-rich soils.
Generally distributed, though absent from the moors and much
of the central region of W. Devon. (1118)

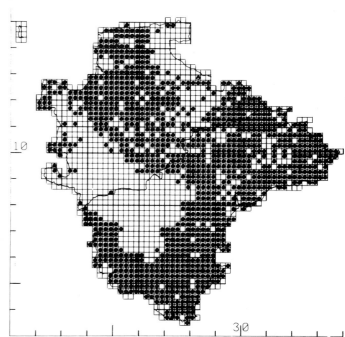

IRIDACEAE

Hermodactylus tuberosus L.   Snake's-head Iris
Introduced; a native of Europe. Naturalised locally in hedges at
Kingsbridge, and on sandhills at Woolacombe. (2)

Iris foetidissima L.   Gladdon, Stinking Iris
In dry hedges, waste ground and sea cliffs, usually on base-rich
or calcareous soils. Quite common in the south and south-east
of the county, and also on Braunton Burrows, but rare
elsewhere. (332)

Tritonia x crocosmiflora (Lem.) Nicholson   Montbretia
(*Crocosmia x crocosmiflora* (Lem.) N.E.Br.)
Introduced; of garden origin, the parents are native in S. Africa.
Commonly naturalised in hedges, scrub, woodland and in waste
places; fairly generally distributed. (359)

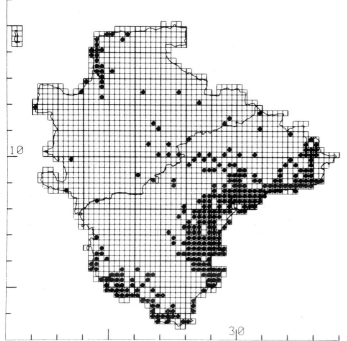

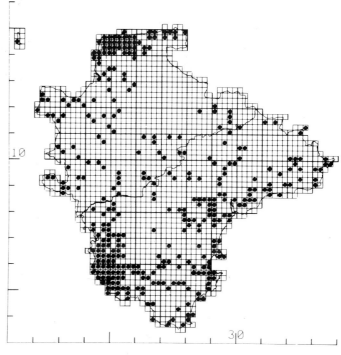

Iris pseudacorus L.   Yellow Flag
In wet meadows and the margins of ponds and streams. Fairly
common in suitable habitats, and quite generally distributed.
(651)

JUNCACEAE

Juncus maritimus Lam.   Sea Rush
In salt-marshes and muddy places along estuaries and near the
sea. Not very common except in the estuaries of the Exe, Taw
and Torridge. (34)

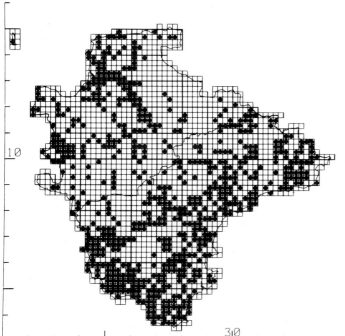

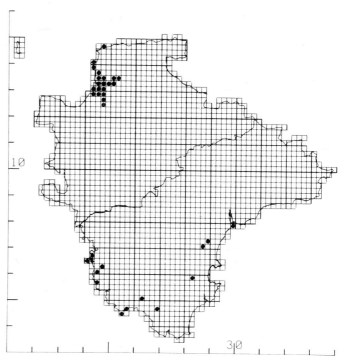

Romulaea columnae Seb. & Mauri
                    Sand Crocus, Jersey Crocus
Only known from short, well-drained grassy sward at Dawlish
Warren, where it is locally frequent. (1)

Juncus acutus L.   Sharp Sea Rush
On sandy sea shores and in dune-slacks, more rarely in salt-marshes. Quite common at Instow, and on Northam and Braunton Burrows, but probably nowhere else. (13)

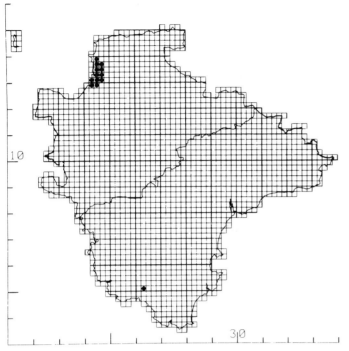

Juncus effusus L.   Soft Rush
In wet pastures, damp woods and bogs, especially on acid soils. Common and locally abundant on the moors and in wet heathland. (1541)

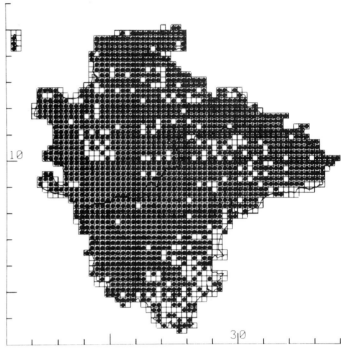

Juncus x diffusus Hoppe, (*J. effusus* x *inflexus*), has not been recorded recently in Devon; although it is likely to occur, in view of the comments made by Stace (1975), care should be taken with its identification.

Juncus inflexus L.   Hard Rush
In damp pastures, usually on base-rich or clayey soils. Fairly common around Exeter, Torbay and in E. Devon, very scattered elsewhere, though locally frequent. (332)

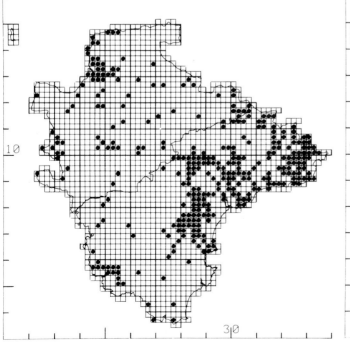

Juncus conglomeratus L.   Common Rush
In similar situations to *J. effusus*, but more local and perhaps restricted to more base-rich habitats. Common and quite generally distributed, though not frequent on the moors. Many earlier records are the result of confusion with *J. effusus* var. *compactus*. (789)

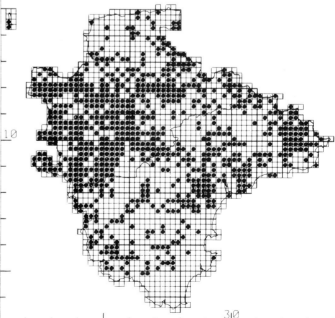

Juncus squarrosus L.   Heath Rush
On moors and wet heaths, especially in blanket bog. Locally
common on Dartmoor and Exmoor, less frequent elsewhere in
heathland. (246)

Juncus gerardi Loisel.   Mud Rush
In salt-marshes and muddy estuaries, and confined to the
immediate vicinity of the coast, where it is locally abundant. (56)

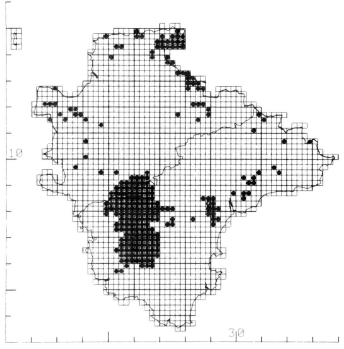

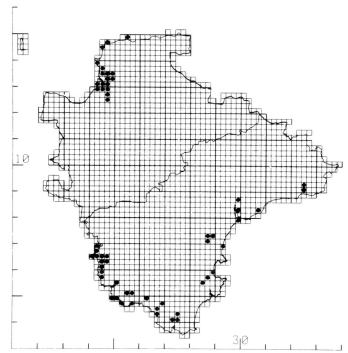

Juncus compressus Jacq.   Round-fruited Rush
In marshes and damp grassland, especially on alluvial and
reasonably base-rich soils. Very scattered over the county and
rather rare. (21)

Juncus tenuis Willd.   Slender Rush
(*J. macer* S.F.Gray)
Introduced; a native of N. America. On roadsides, tracks and
waste ground, and perhaps spread by vehicles. Fairly uncommon in the south-west of the county, rather rare and local
elsewhere. (69)

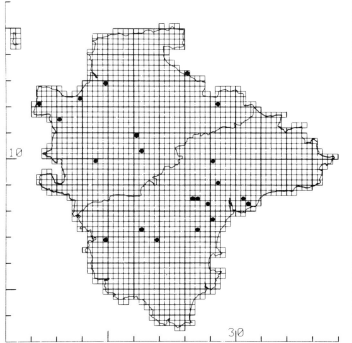

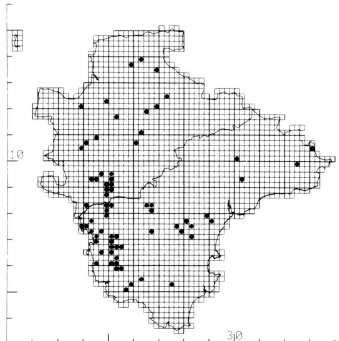

Juncus bufonius L.   Toad Rush
In the margins of ponds, streams and ditches, in marshes, at the muddy edges of roads and in bare patches in acid and seasonally wet pastures. Common and generally distributed. (1076)

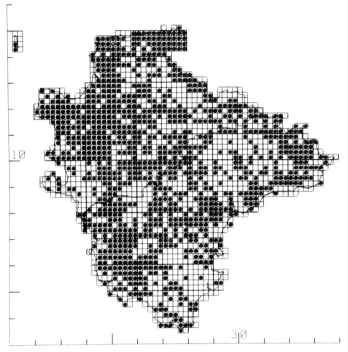

Juncus bulbosus L.   Bulbous Rush
(inc. *J. kochii* Schultz, *J. bulbosus* var. *kochii* (Schultz) Druce)
In heaths and wet gravelly or sandy places, usually on acid soils. Often abundant on Dartmoor and in the north-west of the county, frequent in suitable habitats elsewhere. (595)

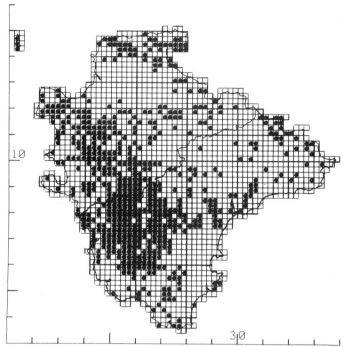

Juncus subnodulosus Schrank   Blunt-flowered Rush
In marshes, dune-slacks and occasionally in base-rich habitats in wet heathland. Scattered over the county, and rather local. (26)

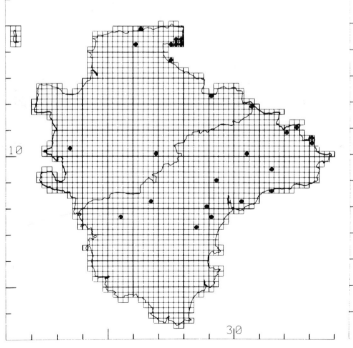

Juncus acutiflorus Ehrh. ex Hoffm.   Sharp-flowered Rush
In wet meadows, moorland and woods, usually on acid soils. Rather common on deep peat on and around Dartmoor, and in E. Devon, and sometimes abundant in acid habitats in lowland marshes; rather uncommon elsewhere. (517)

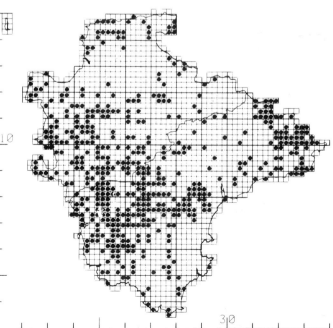

Juncus articulatus L.   Jointed Rush
In wet grassland, by tracks and in roadside ditches, less
frequently on heaths and moors. Fairly common and generally
distributed, often in trampled and disturbed habitats. (784)

Luzula multiflora (Retz.) Lej.   Many-headed Woodrush
In heaths and moorland, usually in fairly dry acid soils over
shallow peat. Locally common and generally distributed,
though tending to avoid coastal districts. (707)

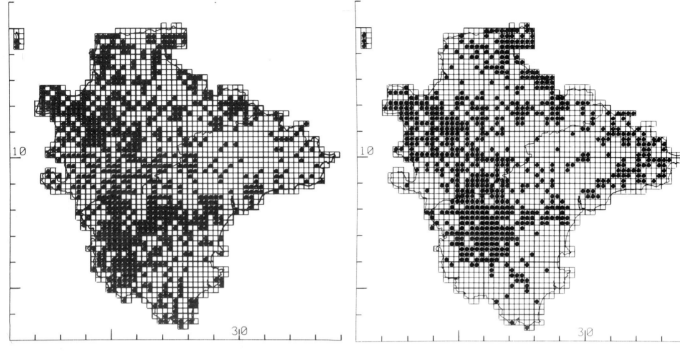

Juncus x surrejanus Druce, (*J. acutiflorus* x *articulatus*), has
been recorded from both vice-counties without locality (Stace,
in Stace, 1975).

Luzula sylvatica (Huds.) Gaud.   Greater Woodrush
In damp woods on acid soils, among rocks on open moorland
and in partial shade on tors. Locally dominant in some woods
but with a rather patchy distribution, and quite rare in E. Devon.
(417)

Luzula campestris (L.) DC.   Field Woodrush
In meadows and pastures, and on dry heaths and grassy banks.
Common and generally distributed. (882)

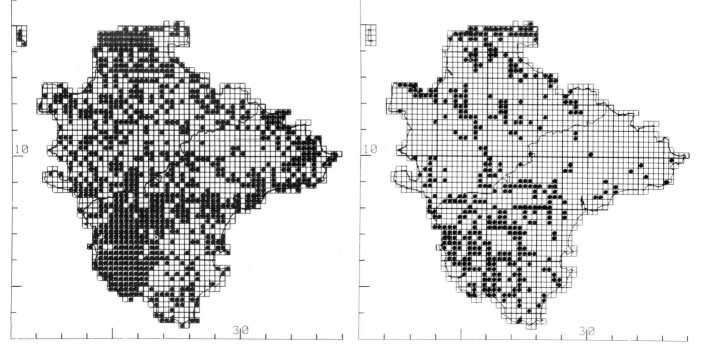

Luzula pilosa (L.) Willd.   Hairy Woodrush
In woods and shaded places on moderately base-rich soils. Fairly common in the lowlands, and quite generally distributed. (455)

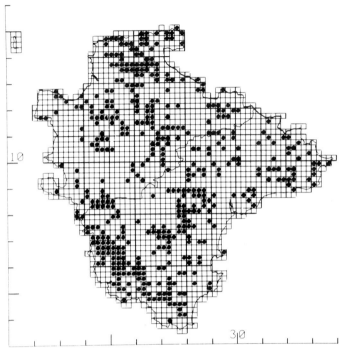

Luzula forsteri (Sm.) DC.   Forster's Woodrush
In woods and shaded hedgebanks, perhaps in more base-rich soils than *L. pilosa.* Local in the southern half of the county, largely absent from the north. (155)

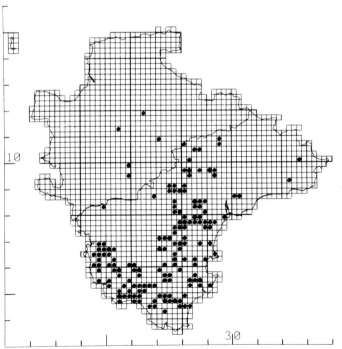

Luzula x borreri Bromf. ex Bab., (*L. forsteri* x *pilosa*), Is usually common where the populations overlap. It has only been recorded on one occasion, near Chagford, but is probably much more frequent than this. There are several old records from various parts of S. Devon.

Luzula luzuloides (Lam.) Dandy & Wilmott has been reported from Shaugh Bridge and Filleigh, but is not known to persist.

Festuca gigantea (L.) Vill.   Tall Brome
In woods, scrub and shaded hedges. Fairly common and generally distributed. (450)

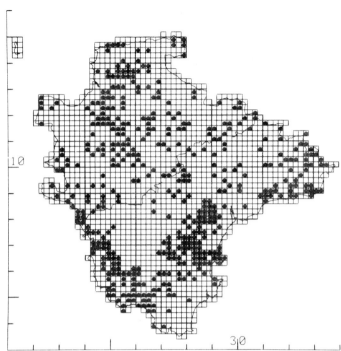

Festuca pratensis Huds.   Meadow Fescue
(*F. elatior* ssp. *pratensis* (Huds.) Hack.)
In meadows, pastures and grassy hedges. Fairly common in some parts of the county, and perhaps planted on some road verges, but rather scattered and avoiding heaths and moors. (222)

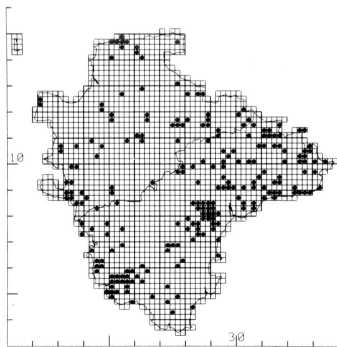

Festuca arundinacea Schreb.   Tall Fescue
(*F. elatior* ssp. *arundinacea* (Schreb.) Hack.)
In rough grassland, hedge banks and sea cliffs. Locally abundant around the coast in base-rich or clayey soils; rare and scattered inland. (282)

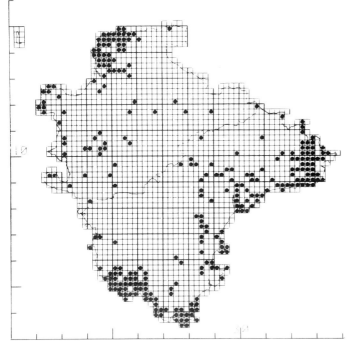

Festuca heterophylla Lam.   Various-leaved Fescue
In scrubby waste ground. It has been recorded twice in the past, from Topsham and Bovey Tracey; there is a single recent record from Moretonhampstead. (1)

The distribution patterns of the various forms of the *Festuca rubra* and *Festuca ovina* complexes are not well represented here, as some recorders have failed to distinguish clearly between them.

Festuca rubra L.   Red Fescue
In meadows, pastures, hedges and waste places. Generally distributed, but usually more common near the coast, and often very abundant on sea cliffs and in maritime grasslands. (1195)

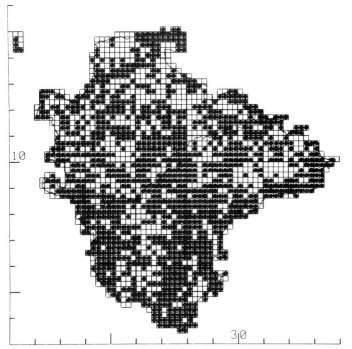

Festuca juncifolia St.-Amans   Rush-leaved Fescue
Only known from sandy habitats at the mouth of the R. Exe at Dawlish, but it also used to occur at Exmouth. Probably not always separated from sand-dune forms of *F. rubra*. (1)

Festuca guestfalica Boenn. ex Reichb.
(*F. longifolia* auct. non Thuill.)
Introduced; a native of Europe. In open grassland on base-rich chalky soils. Very rare, and only known from S.E. Devon. (4)

Festuca ovina L.   Sheep's Fescue
In hilly pastures and on roadside banks. Very abundant in short grassland over shallow acid peaty or mineral soils on the moors; scattered elsewhere, but fairly common. (668)

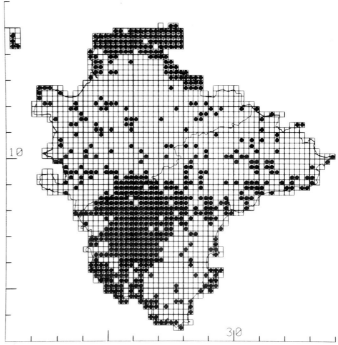

Var. *glauca* (Lam.) Hack., (*F. glauca* Lam.), occurs occasionally.

Festuca tenuifolia Sibth.   Fine-leaved Sheep's Fescue
On peaty moors and pastures. Apparently rare, with only a few records from the periphery of Dartmoor. (11)

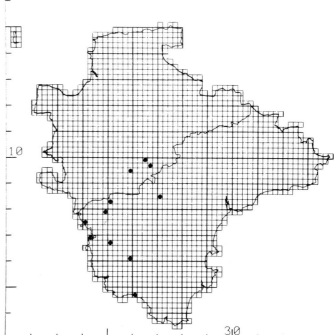

X Festulolium loliaceum (Huds.) P.Fourn.　　　Spiked Fescue
(*Festuca pratensis* x *Lolium perenne*)
In meadows. Said to be quite common, but rarely recorded and
only from scattered localities, mostly in S. Devon. (5)

Lolium perenne L.　　　Rye-grass
In meadows, pastures and waste places. Widely cultivated for
fodder. Common and generally distributed.
Ssp. **perenne** is common as a native plant, and is also frequently
sown. (1636)

Lolium temulentum L.　　　Darnel
Introduced; a native of Europe. Scattered over the county in
fields and rubbish tips; probably not long-persistent. (49)

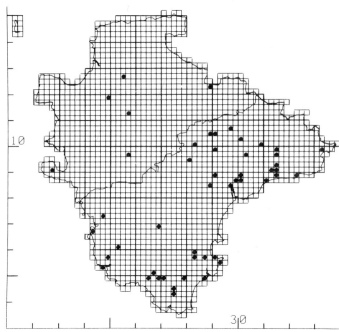

Lolium remotum Schrank has been reported from near Exeter,
but not seen recently.

Vulpia fasciculata (Forsk.) Samp.　　　Dune Fescue
(*V. membranacea* auct.)
In dry sandy places along the coast. Very local, only known from
Northam and Braunton Burrows, and Dawlish Warren. (6)

Vulpia bromoides (L.) S.F.Gray　　　Barren Fescue
On dry banks, wall tops and in sandy waste places. Fairly
common in the south, less frequent in the north of the county.
(247)

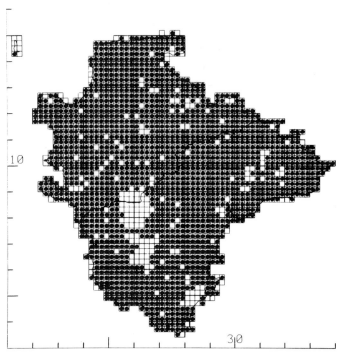

Ssp. **multiflorum** (Lam.) Husnot, (*L. multiflorum* Lam.), the
Italian Rye-grass, is introduced, widely cultivated and quite
frequently naturalised. (113)

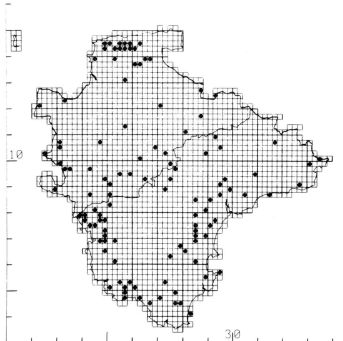

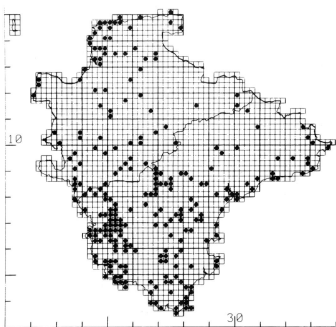

Vulpia myuros (L.) G.C.Gmelin
　　　　　　　　　Rat's-tail Fescue, Wall Fescue
In similar habitats to *V. bromoides*, but much rarer, though
records are scattered over much of the county. It frequently
occurs in railway sidings and has become much less common
following the closure of railway lines. (33)

Vulpia myuros (L.) G.C.Gmelin

Rat's-tail Fescue, Wall Fescue

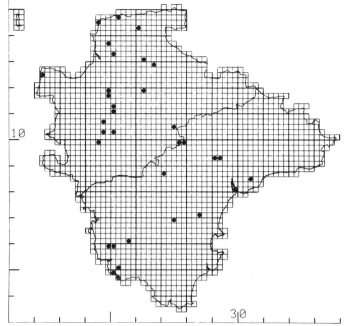

Vulpia ciliata Dum.   Bearded Fescue

This was reported from Mortehoe in 1931, and recorded from a railway siding at Totnes in 1968. It is still quite plentiful on the dunes at Woolacombe and was recorded at Dawlish Warren in 1953. (3)

Our plant belongs to ssp. **ambigua** (Le Gall) Stace & Auguier (*V. ambigua* (Le Gall) More).

Vulpia unilateralis (L.) Stace, (*Nardurus maritimus* (L.) Murb.), was reported as a casual at Torbryan in 1936, but has not been seen since.

X Festulpia hubbardii Stace & Cotton, (*Festuca rubra* x *Vulpia membranacea*), has been reported from coastal sand-dunes on Braunton Burrows (Stace & Cotton, 1974), and also from S. Devon (Willis in Stace, 1975).

Desmazeria marina (L.) Druce   Darnel Poa

(*Catapodium loliaceum* (Huds.) Link, *C. marinum* (L.) C.E.Hubb.)

On sand, shingle, rocks and walls by the sea. Not uncommon around both coasts. (49)

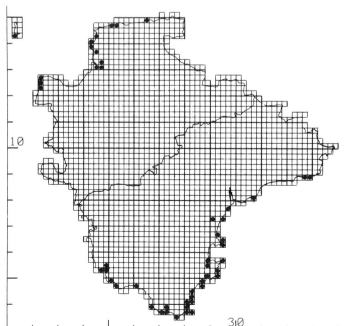

Desmazeria rigida (L.) Tutin   Hard Poa

(*Catapodium rigidum* (L.) C.E.Hubb., *Scleropoa rigida* (L.) Griseb.)

On walls, in rock crevices and dry, often sandy, places. Not uncommon in the south of the county, and around Braunton and Ilfracombe, but generally rare away from the coast and in agricultural districts. (229)

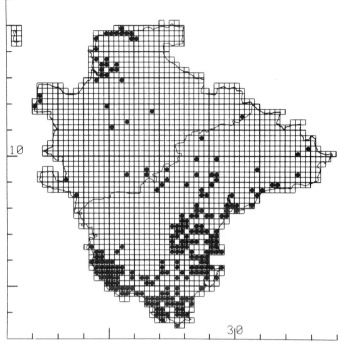

Ssp. **majus** (C.Presl) Perring & Sell, which has been referred to as *C. rigidum,* is reported from Torbay and Braunton (Perring & Sell, 1968).

Poa annua L   Annual Poa, Annual Meadow-grass

In waste places, grassland and as a garden weed. Very common and generally distributed. (1697)

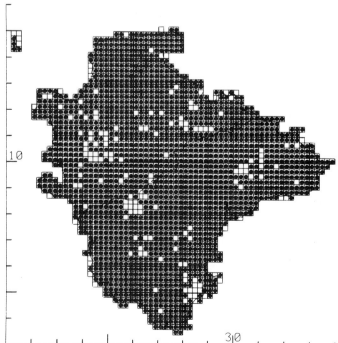

209

Poa trivialis L.   Rough-stalked Meadow-grass
In meadows, pastures and disturbed ground. Absent from the moors, but otherwise common and generally distributed. (1312)

Poa angustifolia L.   Narrow-leaved Meadow-grass
In dry habitats in fields, and on walls; less common on walls than *P. pratensis*. Scattered over the county, and perhaps not as uncommon as the rather few records suggest. Recorded from Dawlish, Exeter and Slapton in Perring & Sell (1968). (25)

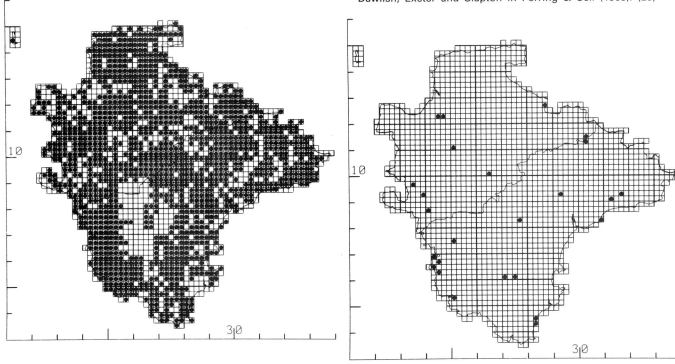

Poa subcaerulea Sm.   Spreading Meadow-grass
In damp, base-rich grassland. Recorded from Braunton and scattered localities elsewhere. Perhaps rather rare, but probably not always distinguished from *P. pratensis*. (8)

Poa pratensis L.   Smooth-stalked Meadow-grass
In dry, usually base-rich grassland, and on the tops of walls. Common and generally distributed. (1254)

Poa compressa L.   Flat-stalked Meadow-grass
On walls and dry waste places. Local, but scattered over the county, and often only in small amounts. (84)

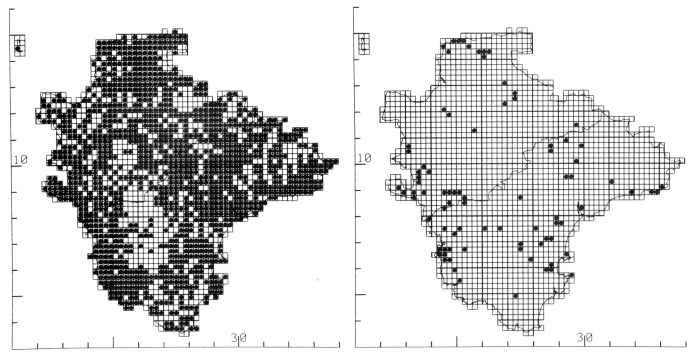

Poa chaixii Vill.   Broad-leaved Meadow-grass
Occasionally introduced with grass-seed, but it does not persist.
There is a single record from Tavistock. (1)

Poa nemoralis L.   Wood Poa, Wood Meadow-grass
In woods, scrub and shaded hedges. Locally quite common, but
rather scattered over the county. (396)

Puccinellia maritima (Huds.) Parl.   Sea Poa
In salt-marshes and muddy estuaries. Locally abundant in
suitable habitats. (41)

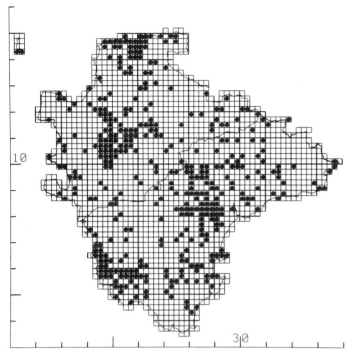

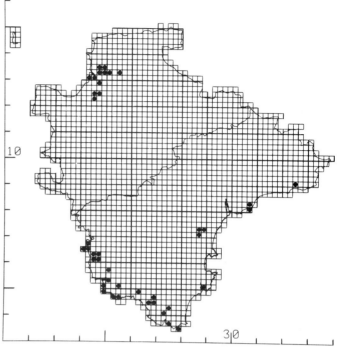

Poa bulbosa L.   Bulbous Meadow-grass
In dry sandy places near the sea. Only known from the vicinity of
Torbay, and on the Maer at Exmouth, where it is rather rare.
There is a single record from Plymouth Hoe, and it has recently
been found on Dawlish Warren. (6)

Puccinellia rupestris (With.) Fern. & Weath.
                    Procumbent Sea Meadow-grass
On occasionally inundated wet mud or sand in estuaries and
salt- or brackish marshes, and it can often be found some
distance inland. Rare, with few recent records. (4)

Puccinellia fasciculata (Torr.) Bicknell has been reported from
the Teign estuary and from a number of similar sites along the
south coast in the past, but there are no recent records.

Puccinellia distans (L.) Parl.   Reflexed Poa
In salt-marshes and on mud in estuaries, rarely on sandy ground
inland. (27)

Dactylis glomerata L.   Cock's-foot
In meadows, roadsides and waste places. Very common and
generally distributed. (1706)

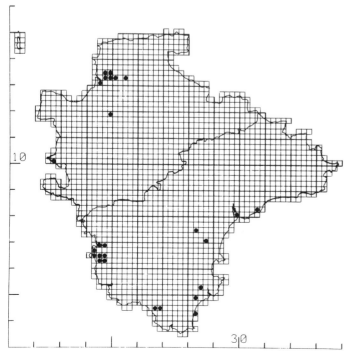

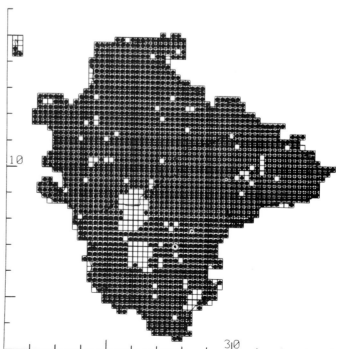

Cynosurus cristatus L.   Crested Dog's-tail
In dry pastures, along roadsides and in fields at the edges of moorland. Common and generally distributed, though locally rather sparse. (1453)

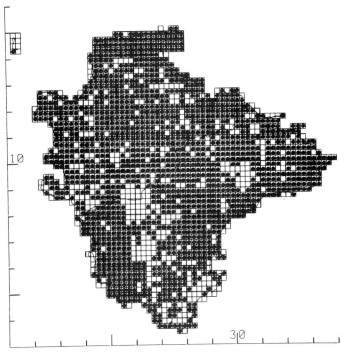

Briza media L.   Quaking-grass
In dry and often coastal pastures, usually on base-rich or calcareous soils, rarely on damp, base-rich peat. Most common in the south and east of the county, rare and very scattered elsewhere. (102)

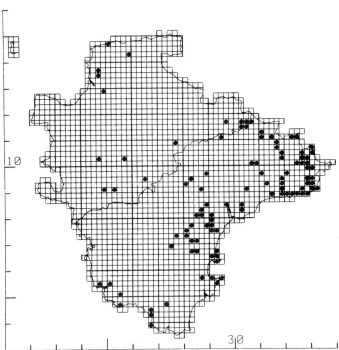

Briza maxima L.   Great Quaking-grass
Introduced; a native of the Mediterranean region. Sometimes cultivated, as it is much used by flower-arrangers, and found occasionally as an escape, usually near habitations. Naturalised on Dawlish Warren. (3)

Briza minor L.   Lesser Quaking-grass
Introduced; a native of the Mediterranean region. Very rare as an alien in dry fields and waste places; probably introduced with grass-seed. (3)

Melica uniflora Retz.   Wood Melick
On shaded banks and in woods, often on base-rich soils. Locally abundant and fairly generally distributed. (322)

Catabrosa aquatica (L.) Beauv.   Water Whorl-grass
By shallow streams, ponds and ditches. Rare, and with very scattered records, mostly in the north of the county. (16)

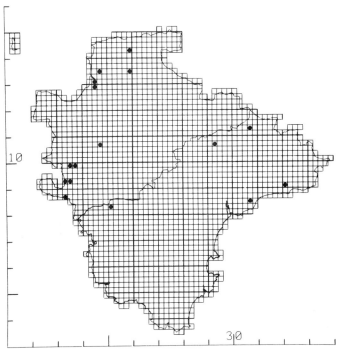

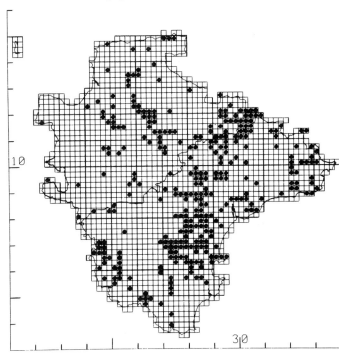

Apera spica-venti (L.) Beauv., the Silky Bent-grass, has been reported as a very rare alien from S. Devon, but there are no recent records and it is undoubtedly extinct.

Melica nutans, the Mountain Melick, no longer occurs in Devon.

212

Glyceria maxima (Hartm.) Holmb.   Reed Sweet-grass
Along river and stream banks, and in wet waste places. Rare,
and with very scattered records. (25)

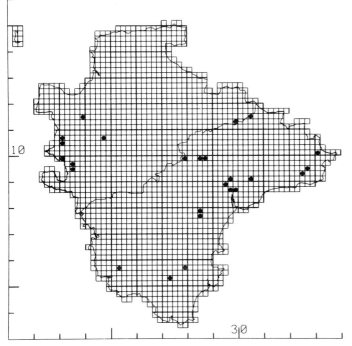

Glyceria fluitans (L.) R.Br.   Floating Sweet-grass, Flote-grass
In ponds, streams and ditches with slow-flowing water, usually
in the lowlands. Locally common and generally distributed in
suitable habitats. (908)

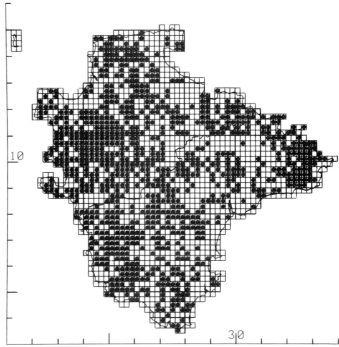

Glyceria declinata Bréb.   Small Sweet-grass
By the margins of ponds, usually in trampled and muddy places,
including those on the moors. Rather local, though sometimes
abundant, and widely scattered over the county. (206)

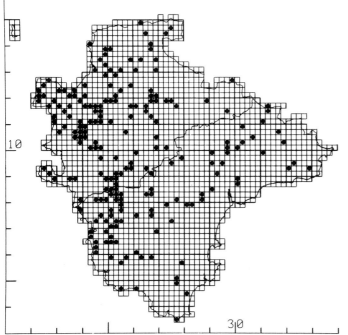

Glyceria plicata (Fries) Fries   Plicate Sweet-grass
In ponds, ditches and streams. Much less common than *G.
fluitans,* but scattered over much of the county. (89)

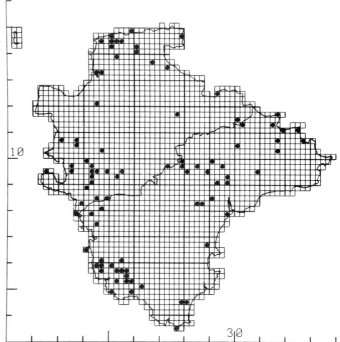

213

Glyceria x pedicellata Towns.
(*G. fluitans* x *plicata*)
In slow-flowing water in ditches and streams. Mostly in the southern half of the county, and rather rare, though probably under-recorded. (22)

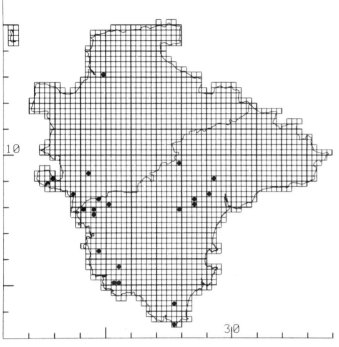

Bromus pseudosecalinus P.M.Sm. was recorded from clover fields at Cove and Cobbacombe, near Tiverton in 1943, and from a hay-field at Woolfardisworthy in 1945 (Smith, 1973), but does not seem to persist.

Bromus madritensis L.
Introduced; a native of S. Europe. In waste places and on walls. Recorded from Exeter and a few scattered localities elsewhere, but rare and not seen since 1959. (3)

Bromus ramosus Huds.   Hairy Brome
(*Zerna ramosa* (Huds.) Lindm.)
In woods and hedges, usually on base-rich soils. Locally frequent throughout the county, though absent from moorland and heathy areas. (397)

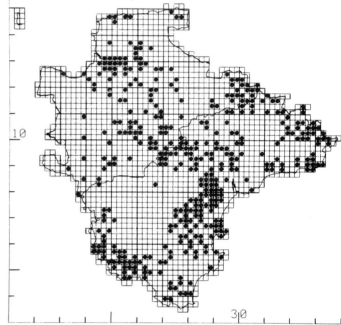

Bromus erectus Huds.   Upright Brome
In dry grassland, usually in base-rich or calcareous habitats. Rare, with very scattered records, and only frequent on the Axmouth-Lyme Regis landslip. (8)

Bromus secalinus L.   Rye Brome
Introduced; a native of Europe. Formerly in cultivated fields, especially of cereals, and on roadsides, but now very rare. (1)

Bromus commutatus Schrad.   Meadow Brome
In pastures, fields and waste places. Scattered over the county, especially in the west, where it is locally frequent, but rare elsewhere. (44)

Bromus sterilis L.   Barren Brome
(*Anisantha sterilis* (L.) Nevski)
On hedgebanks, in waste places and along roads. Common, often abundant and fairly generally distributed, though scarce in some districts. (883)

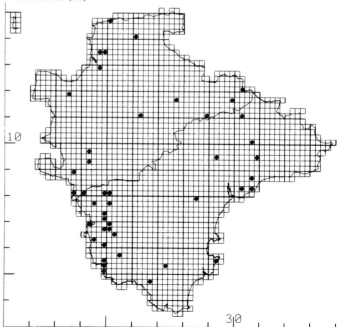

Bromus racemosus L.   Smooth Brome
In waste places, pastures and arable fields. Rare, and with very
scattered records. (30)

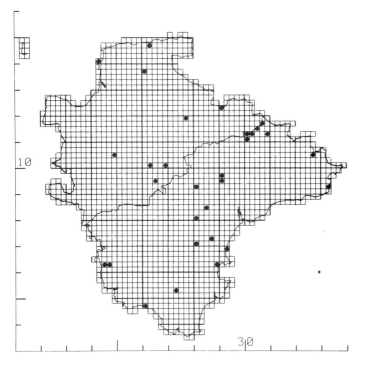

The common form is ssp. **hordeaceus.**
Ssp. **ferronii** (Mabille) P.M.Sm., (*B. ferronii* Mabille), is found on
cliff-tops near the sea, and has been recorded from both coasts;
it is probably more frequent than the records suggest. (4)

Bromus x pseudothominii P.M.Sm.
(*B. thominii* auct. non Hard., *B. hordaceus* ssp. *hordaceus* x
lepidus)
This hybrid has been recorded from three sites along the south
coast but its distribution pattern is not clear and is probably
incomplete. (3)

Bromus lepidus Holmb.   Slender Soft Brome
Introduced; a native of Europe. At the edges of fields and
pastures, and probably always accidentally introduced with
other grass seed. Rare, and widely scattered over the county. (9)

Bromus arvensis L., the Field Brome, is an introduced species
which has been reported from various sites in S. Devon, but
there is only a single recent record, from Torbay. **Bromus
diandrus** Roth is also introduced from S. & W. Europe, and has a
single recent record.

Bromus rigidus Roth was recorded on one occasion as a casual
from Dawlish Warren and Torbay, but has not been seen since
1960.

Bromus willdenowii Kunth, (*B. unioloides* (Willd.) H.B.K.), a
native of S. America, has been reported from Exmouth Docks,
but only recorded recently from Newton Abbot.

Brachypodium sylvaticum (Huds.) Beauv.
                              Slender False-brome
In woods, scrub and hedgebanks, and often considered to be a
relict from old woodland. Common and generally distributed,
except on the moors and in heathland. (1341)

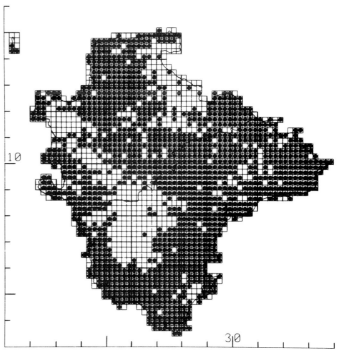

Brachypodium pinnatum (L.) Beauv.   Heath False-brome
In calcareous or base-rich grassland. Rare, and largely confined
to the chalk and limestone around Branscombe and Torbay,
though also occurring on Braunton Burrows. (8)

Bromus hordeaceus L.   Lop-grass, Soft Brome
(*B. mollis* L.)
In meadows, sandy places near the sea and along roads. Rather
common and generally distributed. (921)

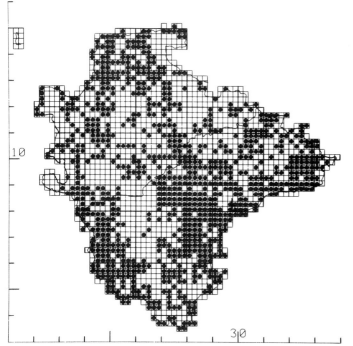

Leymus arenarius (L.) Hochst.   Lyme Grass
(*Elymus arenarius* L.)
In dunes and sandy waste ground. Recorded from Dawlish
Warren and Exmouth, but very rare and only a few plants
remain; it could disappear at any time. (3)

Elymus caninus (L.) L. Bearded Couch-grass
(*Agropyron caninum* (L.) Beauv.)
In hedges, fields and scrub. Thinly scattered over the county and rather uncommon. (116)

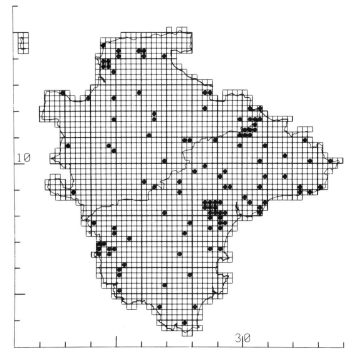

Elymus repens (L.) Gould Couch-grass, Twitch
(*Agropyron repens* (L.) Beauv.)
In fields, hedges, gardens and waste places. Very common and generally distributed, and in places a persistent weed, though absent from heath and moorland. (902)

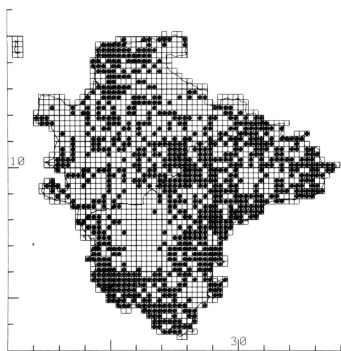

Elymus pycnanthus (Godron) Meld. Sea Couch-grass
(*Agropyron pungens* auct., non Roem. & Schult.)
On sea shores, sand-dunes and in the drier parts of salt-marshes. Locally abundant in sand-dunes, and forming a fringe around many estuaries; scattered in other habitats. (66)

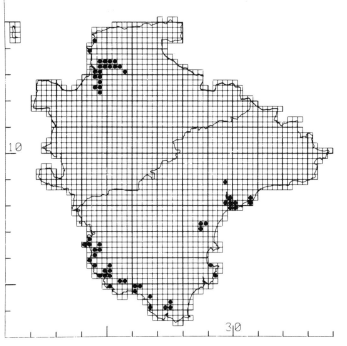

Elymus farctus (Viv.) Runem. ex Meld. Sand Couch-grass
(*Agropyron junceiforme* (A. & D.Löve) A. & D.Löve)
On young (yellow) sand-dunes. Very common on the fore-shore of Braunton Burrows and also in scattered localities along the south coast, especially at Dawlish Warren. (20)

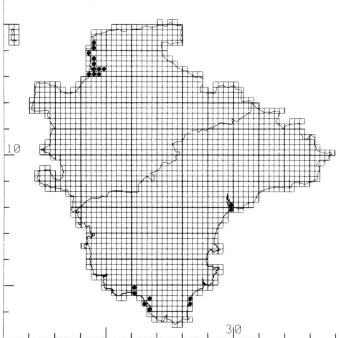

Our plant is ssp. **boreali-atlanticus** (Simmet & Guin.) Meld.

Elymus x obtusiusculus (Lange) nom. prov. (*E. farctus* ssp. *boreali-atlanticus* x *pycnanthus, Agropyron x acutum* auct.), has been reported as occurring not infrequently with its parents, but there are no specific records.

Various races of **Triticum aestivum** L., the Wheat, are cultivated as Winter or Spring Wheats. They may be found quite frequently around the margins or in the vicinity of fields, but do not persist and are not naturalised.

Hordeum murinum L.   Wall Barley
In waste places, usually by roadsides, and often near the sea. Locally common in E. Devon, on Braunton Burrows and around Torbay and Plymouth, but rather rare elsewhere. (243)

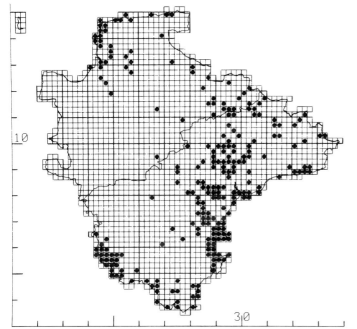

Hordeum marinum Huds.   Sea Barley
In waste places near the sea. Very rare, with only a single recent record, from Exmouth. (1)

Hordeum secalinum Schreb.   Meadow Barley
(*H. nodosum* L.)
In meadows and pastures, often in rather damp habitats. Now apparently quite rare, and most frequent in the vicinity of the Taw and Torridge estuaries. (12)

There are no recent records for **Hordeum jubatum** L. **Hordeum distichum** L. and **H. vulgare** L. are the cultivated barleys and may be found occasionally around fields, but they are not naturalised.

Avena fatua L.   Wild Oat
Introduced; a native of Europe. A weed of arable land and also found along roads. Not uncommon around Plymouth, and from Exeter eastwards, but rare elsewhere. (172)

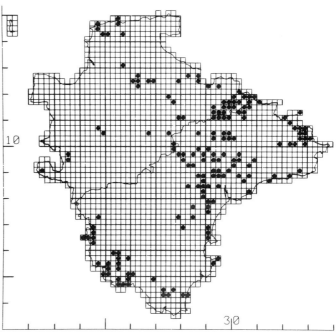

Avena strigosa Schreb., the Black Oat, is reported from time to time, probably sown with cultivated oats. There are no recent records. The cultivated oat, **Avena sativa** L., is found occasionally, but does not persist. Some records for *A. fatua* could be of this species.

Avena x marquandii Druce, (*A. fatua* x *sativa*), has been reported from N. Devon, and can sometimes be found around the periphery of fields in which oats have been sown.

Avenula pubescens (Huds.) Dum.   Hairy Oat
(*Avena pubescens* Huds., *Helictotrichon pubescens* (Huds.) Pilger)
In meadows and rough grassland on chalk and limestone, occasionally on base-rich soils elsewhere. Local, though often rather frequent where it occurs. (32)

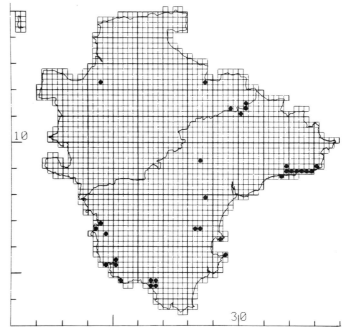

217

Avenula pratensis (L.) Dum.　　　　　　Meadow Oat
(*Avena pratensis* L., *Helictotrichon pratensis* (L.) Pilger)
In rough grassland, usually over chalk or limestone. Rare, though locally frequent. (8)

Arrhenatherum elatius (L.) Beauv. ex J. & C.Presl
　　　　　　　　　　　　　　　　　Oat-grass, False Oat
In rough grassland, hedges, roadsides and in waste ground. Very common and generally distributed. (1559)

Trisetum flavescens (L.) Beauv.　　　　　　Yellow Oat
In meadows, grassland and dry hedges, most commonly over chalk or limestone, but also found in base-rich habitats in much of the county. Local. (89)

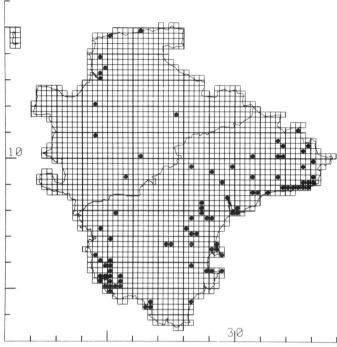

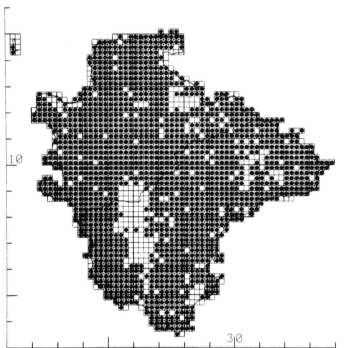

Ssp. **bulbosum** (Willd.) Schübler & Martens, (*A. tuberosum* (Gilib.) Schultz), which is reported from various localities in Fl. Dev., cannot be easily separated as a distinct taxon. Forms with tuberous stem-bases are quite common in the county.

Lagurus ovatus L.　　　　　　　　　　Hare's-tail
Introduced; a native of Europe. Recorded on Dawlish Warren in 1950, but it is scarce and sporadic, though was seen there in 1981. There is a recent record from Tavistock, but the habitat has been destroyed. (2)

Koeleria macrantha (Ledeb.) Schultes　　Crested Hair-grass
(*K. cristata* (L.) Pers. p.p., *K. gracilis* Pers.)
In calcareous grassland on downs and dunes, especially on the Chalk and the Torbay limestone. Very local, though frequent where it occurs. (24)

Deschampsia caespitosa (L.) Beauv.　　Tufted Hair-grass
In meadows, grassy heaths, marshes and wet woods, often in rather poorly drained soils. Common and generally distributed. (1014)

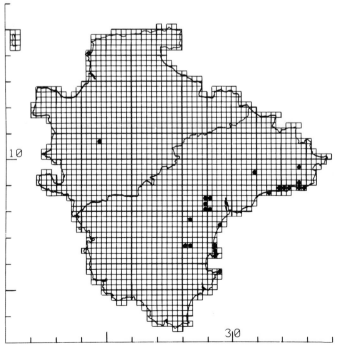

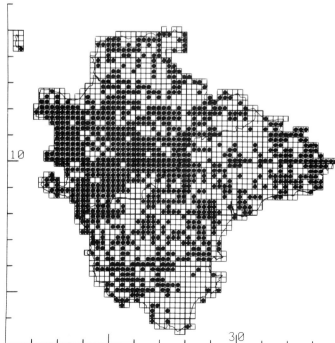

Deschampsia flexuosa (L.) Trin.   Wavy Hair-grass
On heaths and moors, in hedgebanks and acid woodland, often under bracken, on fairly dry, acid soils. Sometimes very abundant, especially around Dartmoor and Exmoor. (490)

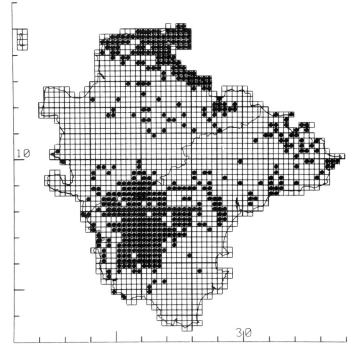

Aira caryophyllea L.   Silver Hair-grass
In dry heaths, and on sand-dunes, banks and walls. Quite common around Dartmoor and Exmoor, fairly frequent elsewhere. (395)

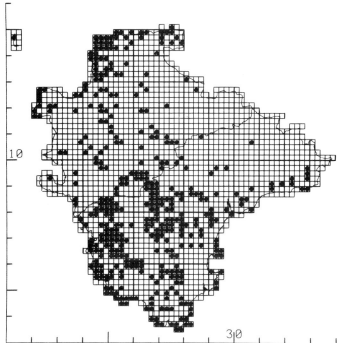

Aira praecox L.   Early Hair-grass
On dry rocky slopes, dry heaths and walls, always in exposed sandy or well-drained soils. Quite common around Dartmoor and Exmoor, rather local elsewhere. (285)

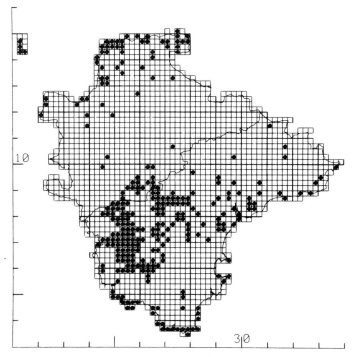

Anthoxanthum odoratum L.   Sweet Vernal-grass
In pastures, roadsides and in dry, grassy heathland. Common and often abundant, and generally distributed. (1643)

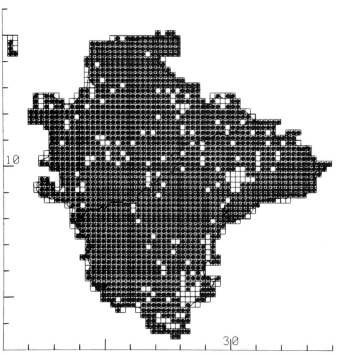

Anthoxanthum aristatum Boiss., (*A. puelii* Lec. & Lam.), has been reported as an introduction in various localities, but there are no recent records.

Holcus lanatus L.   Yorkshire Fog
In waste places, fields, woods and along roadsides. Very common and generally distributed. (1712)

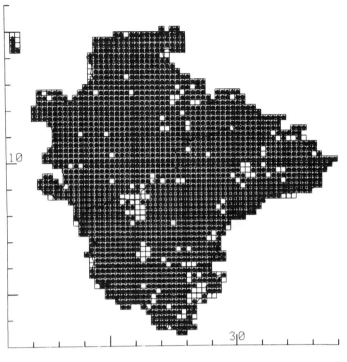

Agrostis canina L.   Brown Bent-grass
In damp grassland and boggy moorland, usually on acid soils, and sometimes in or near ditches. The closely related species **A. vinealis** Schreb., (*A. canina* ssp. *montana* (Hartm.) Hartm.), is confined to dry acid grassland; the two have not been separated, but the latter is probably the more common form. (574)

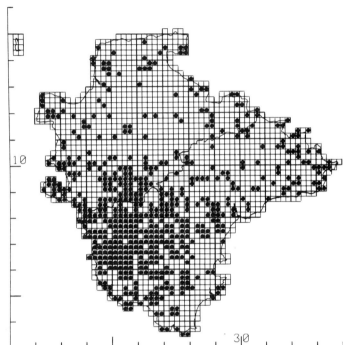

Holcus mollis L.   Creeping Soft-grass
In acid woods, fields and dry grassy heaths. Common and sometimes abundant, though rather less common than *H. lanatus*. (1127)

Agrostis curtisii Kerguélen   Heath Bent-grass
(*A. setacea* Curt. non Vill.)
In dry heaths and acid grassland. Often very abundant and a dominant species after heath fires, but in time giving way to the ericaceous shrubs. (376)

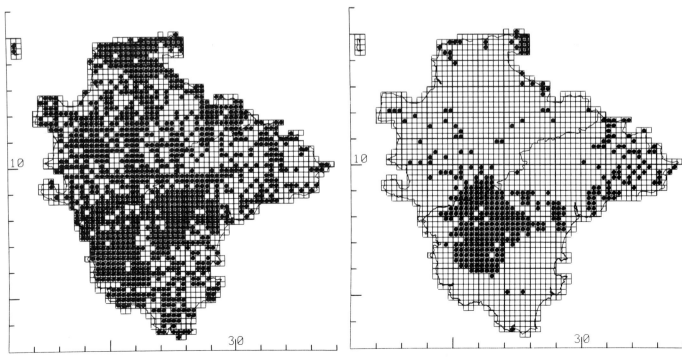

Agrostis capillaris L.   Common Bent-grass
(*A. tenuis* Sibth.)
In acid grassland on brown earth soils over acid rocks. Very common and generally distributed. (1349)

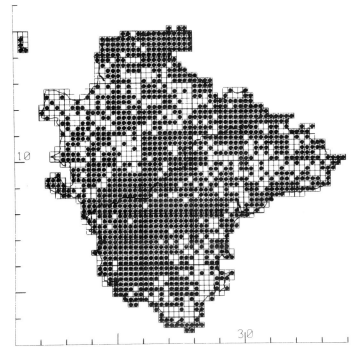

Agrostis stolonifera L.   Creeping Bent-grass, Fiorin
In damp grassland and waste places, usually on base-rich soils, and also in the drier parts of salt-marshes and in the vicinity of the coast. Quite common and generally distributed. (970)

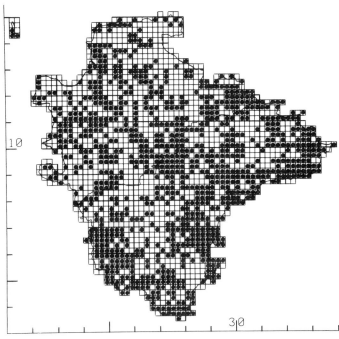

Gastridium ventricosum (Gouan) Schinz & Thell.   Nit-grass
This has been reported from various maritime habitats, but the only recent record is of a number of plants on Berry Head. (1)

Polypogon monspeliensis (L.) Desf.   Annual Beard-grass
Introduced; a native of the Mediterranean region. In waste places and grassland, usually near the sea. It has been found on one occasion on a wall near Tavistock and is also reported from Newton Abbot. (2)

Polypogon viridis (Gouan) Breistr.   Beardless Beard-grass
(*Agrostis semiverticillata* (Forsk.) Christ.)
Introduced; a native of the Mediterranean region. Occurs very rarely in waste places, usually near the sea; only known from Newton Abbot. (1)

Ammophila arenaria (L.) Link   Marram Grass
In yellow and grey sand-dunes, where it is often dominant. Very common on Braunton Burrows, and also found in smaller dune systems elsewhere around the coast. (21)

Agrostis gigantea Roth   Black Bent-grass
In arable land, damp grassland and scrub, usually in disturbed soil. Rather rare, though quite widely distributed. (234)

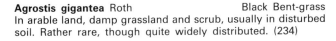

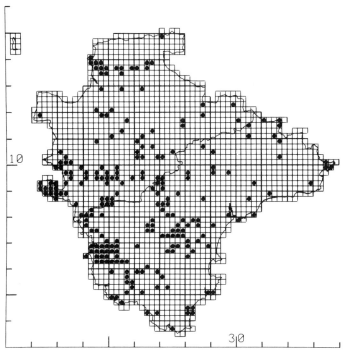

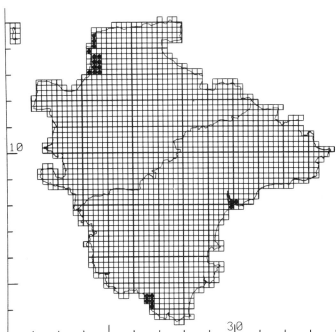

Calamagrostis epigejos (L.) Roth   Bush-grass
In woods, damp grassland and on sea cliffs. Mostly scattered around the coast, where it is local; rare inland. (30)

Ssp. bertolonii (DC.) Serb. & E.I.Nyárády, (*P. nodosum* L., *P. bertolonii* DC.), is quite frequent in drier grassy habitats, but has not always been distinguished from the aggregate. (102)

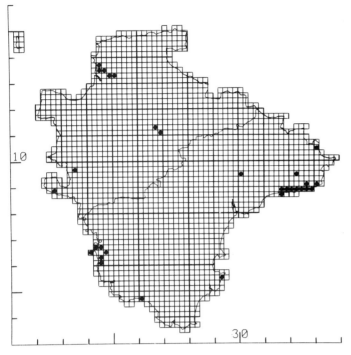

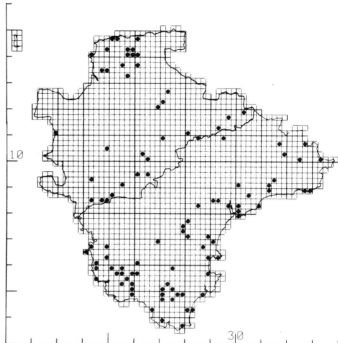

Phleum pratense L.   Timothy, Cat's-tail
In meadows, pastures and rough dry grassland. Common and generally distributed in the lowlands. (1165)

Phleum arenarium L.   Sand Cat's-tail
On dunes and in sandy places near the sea. Local on Braunton Burrows, rather rare elsewhere. (20)

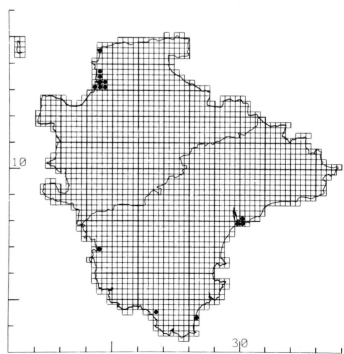

Ssp. **pratense**, (*P. nodosum* auct., non L.), is commonly cultivated and frequently naturalised.

222

Alopecurus pratensis L. Meadow Fox-tail
In meadows and pastures, along roadsides and in waste places.
Common and generally distributed. (976)

Alopecurus myosuroides Huds. Black Twitch, Field Fox-tail
Probably introduced in Devon. A weed of arable fields and
waste places. Local, mostly in E. Devon; rare elsewhere. (39)

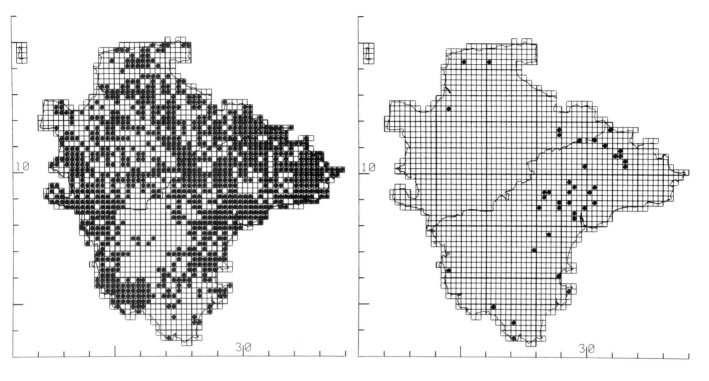

Alopecurus bulbosus Gouan Tuberous Fox-tail
In grassy places in salt-marshes. Very local around the coast in
suitable habitats. (4)

Alopecurus geniculatus L. Marsh Fox-tail
In wet meadows, the margins of ponds and ditches and in
gate-ways on clayey soils. Fairly common, especially in the
north-west of the county, but generally distributed in suitable
habitats. (575)

Parapholis strigosa (Dum.) C.E.Hubb. Sea Hard-grass
(*Pholiurus filiformis* (Roth) Schinz & Thell.)
In salt-marshes and sandy or gravelly places on or near the
coast. Rare, scattered around the south coast, and also in the
vicinity of the Taw and Torridge estuaries. (12)

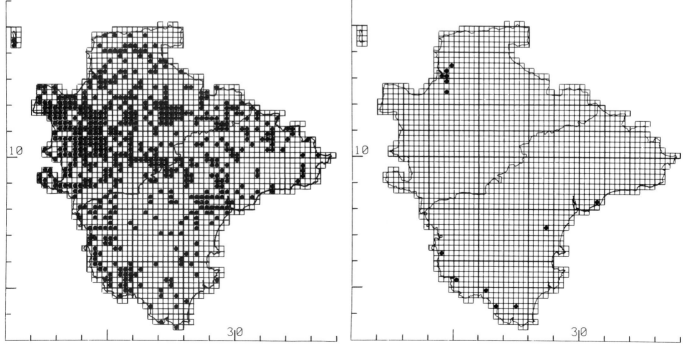

Phalaris arundinacea L.   Reed-grass
In wet meadows, ditches and the edges of streams. Common
and often abundant in lowland habitats, and generally distributed. (590)

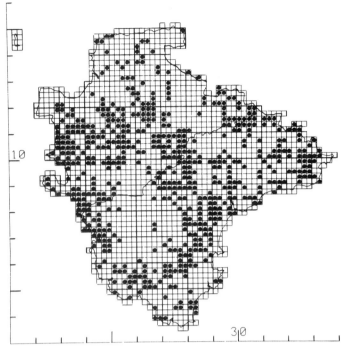

Milium effusum L.   Wood Millet
In damp shaded woodland, usually on base-rich soils. Widely
but thinly scattered over the county, occasionally locally
plentiful. (143)

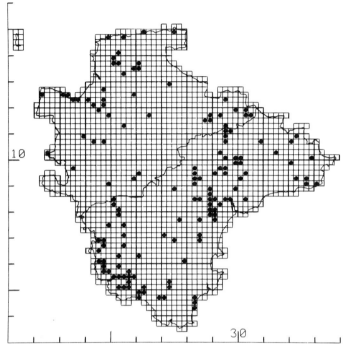

Phalaris canariensis L.   Canary Grass
Introduced; a native of the Canary Islands. In waste places and
around rubbish tips. A frequent component of bird-seed, and
sometimes establishing itself for a few years, but scarcely
naturalised. (22)

Phragmites australis (Cav.) Trin. ex Steudel   Reed
(*P. communis* Trin.)
In swamps and shallow water, beside ditches and streams and
in wet flushes on cliffs; often around salt-marshes and able to
withstand occasional inundation by the sea. Locally abundant,
scattered over lowland parts of the county, most frequent near
the coast. (225)

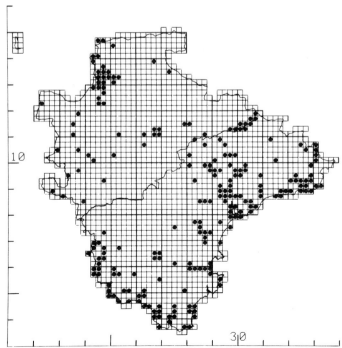

Phalaris minor Retz
Introduced; a native of the Mediterranean region. In similar
situations to *P. canariensis,* but much less common. (1)

224

Cortaderia selloana (Schultes & Schultes f.) Asch. & Graeb.
Pampas Grass
Introduced; a native of S. America. In muddy cliff-faces, mostly along the south coast from Dawlish Warren eastwards, and in the Axmouth-Lyme Regis Undercliffs NNR, where it is naturalised. (4)

Danthonia decumbens (L.) DC. Heath Grass
(*Sieglingia decumbens* (L.) Bernh.)
In moderately acid grassland, often in heaths over base-rich substrata or affected by calcareous water. Locally frequent in suitable habitats. (454)

Nardus stricta L. Mat-grass
In acid grassland on heaths and moors. Dominant over large tracts of poor pasture on Dartmoor and Exmoor, and frequent on heaths elsewhere. (312)

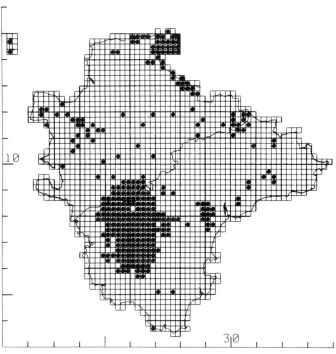

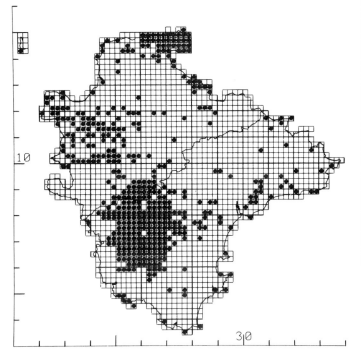

Molinia caerulea (L.) Moench Purple Moor-grass
On heaths and moors, especially in wetter habitats. Very abundant on Dartmoor and Exmoor, and in suitable habitats elsewhere. Tends to become dominant after repeated swaling fires. A harsh, wiry grass, of which only the youngest growth is readily grazed. (556)

Cynodon dactylon (L.) Pers. Bermuda Grass
Introduced; a native of Europe. Occasionally recorded from roadsides and waste places, e.g. from Staverton, near Totnes. (3)

Spartina x townsendii H. & J. Groves Cord-grass
(*S. alterniflora* x *maritima*)
On tidal mud-flats. Originally planted on Dawlish Warren in 1935 and now locally abundant in the major estuaries around the south coast, and also in the Taw-Torridge estuary. (48)

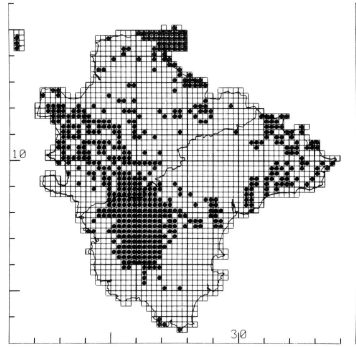

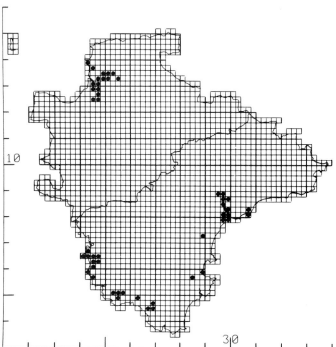

The distribution of the amphidiploid and fertile species **S. anglica** C.E. Hubb. in Devon is not known, but there are no records of it. **Spartina maritima** (Curt.) Fernald, (*S. stricta* (Ait.) Roth), was, at one time, not uncommon on mud-flats to the north of Dawlish Warren, but it has not been found recently and it is probably extinct.

Panicum miliaceum L.   Millet
Introduced from sub-tropical regions. Found around rubbish tips and in waste places, usually derived from bird-seed; not naturalised. (4)

Echinochloa crus-galli L.   Cockspur
Introduced; a native of warm temperate regions. Occurs around rubbish tips and also probably introduced with bird-seed. Not naturalised. (4)

Digitaria ischaemum (Schreb.) Muhl. is an introduced species found occasionally in waste places, and recorded from the Braunton bulb farm. (1)

Digitaria sanguinalis (L.) Scop., (*Panicum sanguinale* L.), the Finger Grass, has been reported as an alien from Torquay, but there are no recent records. **Setaria verticillata** (L.) Beauv., the Whorled Bristle-grass, **S. viridis** (L.) Beauv., the Green Bristle-grass and **S. pumila** (Poir.) Schultes, (*S. lutescens* F.T.Hubbard, *S. glauca* auct.), have all been recorded on occasion from waste places, but nowhere are they naturalised.

Arum italicum Mill.
(inc. *A. neglectum* (Towns.) Ridl.)
In hedges, waste places and disturbed ground. Largely confined to the vicinity of the south coast, where it is locally frequent, and it has also been recorded from Dawlish. The status of the records from around Exeter must be suspect. (17)

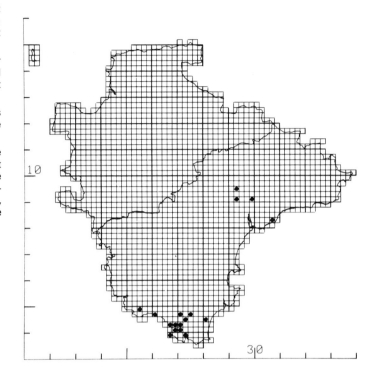

ARACEAE

Acorus calamus L.   Sweet Flag
Introduced; a native of S. Asia and N. America. It has been established along the banks of the Exeter canal for many years. (4)

Arum maculatum L.   Lords-and-Ladies, Cuckoo-pint
In base-rich woods, shaded hedgebanks and waste places. Common and generally distributed, except in peaty habitats. (1248)

LEMNACEAE

Lemna trisulca L.   Ivy-leaved Duckweed
In ditches, ponds and sluggish streams. Rare, mostly in the vicinity of Exeter and in the Tiverton canal. (23)

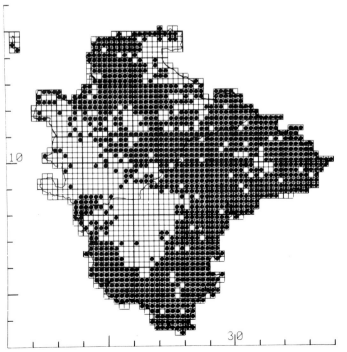

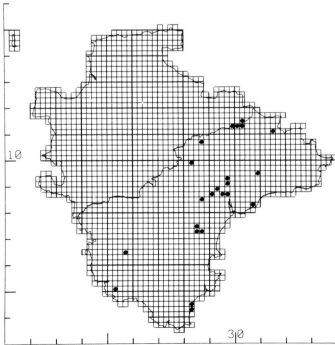

Lemna gibba L.   Gibbous Duckweed
In stagnant water in ponds and ditches. Rare, mostly scattered localities in the vicinity of Exeter. (26)

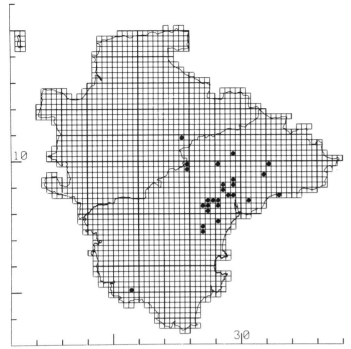

Lemna minor L.   Duckweed
In ponds, ditches and slow-flowing streams. Common and locally abundant in suitable habitats. (309)

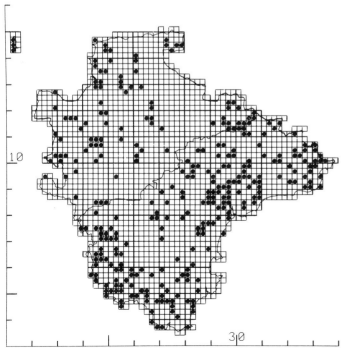

Lemna polyrhiza L.   Great Duckweed
(*Spirodela polyrhiza* (L.) Schleid.)
In ponds and ditches with stagnant water. Very rare, and only known from the Exminster marshes and the Exeter and Tiverton canals. (5)

SPARGANIACEAE

Sparganium erectum L.   Bur-reed
(*S. ramosum* Huds.)
Along the edges of rivers and streams, sometimes around ponds. Fairly common and locally abundant, over much of the county. (231)

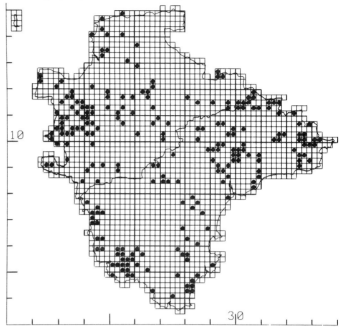

Four subspecies have been recognised, and three probably occur in Devon, though their distribution patterns are not known; the following is taken from Perring & Sell (1968):
Ssp. **erectum** probably does not occur in the county;
Ssp. **microcarpum** (Neuman) Domin has been reported from near S. Molton; the precise locality is unclear;
Ssp. **neglectum** (Beeby) Schinz & Thell. has been recorded from Exmouth;
Ssp. **oocarpum** (Čelak.) Domin has been recorded from near Teignmouth. Fl. Dev. gives a rather wider distribution pattern for subspecies *microcarpum* and *neglectum,* and these are probably the most generally distributed.

Sparganium emersum Rehmann   Unbranched Bur-reed
(*S. simplex* Huds.)
In pools, streams, ditches and canals. Rather uncommon, but can be found in the vicinity of the R. Exe and the Tiverton canal, as well as scattered in the north-west of the county, including Braunton Marshes. (45)

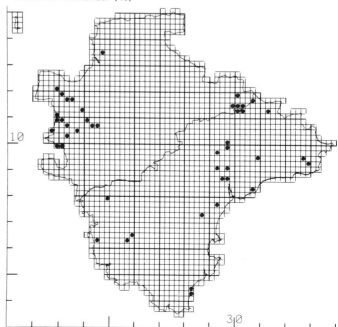

TYPHACEAE

Typha angustifolia L.　　　　　　　　Lesser Reed-mace
At the edges of ponds, canals and leys. Rare, though locally
abundant, with often only a few plants in any one locality,
though it forms a substantial component of the reed-swamp
around Slapton Ley. (23)

CYPERACEAE

Scirpus sylvaticus L.　　　　　　　　Wood Club-rush
In marshes and sheltered wet places, especially in scrub and
woodland, and also beside rivers. Very local, but quite widely
scattered over the county. (66)

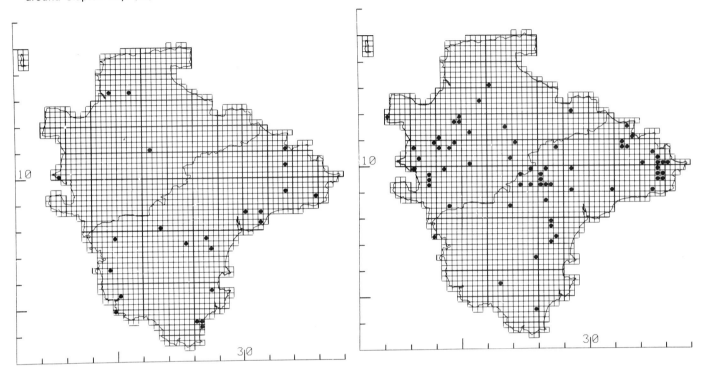

Typha latifolia L.　　　　　　　　Great Reed-mace
In pools, canals, rivers and streams. Locally common and
sometimes quite abundant, especially in rivers flowing south.
(145)

Scirpus maritimus L.　　　　　　　　Sea Club-rush
In salt-marshes, shallow water in estuaries and brackish ditches.
Locally abundant around the south coast and also in the
Taw-Torridge estuary. (61)

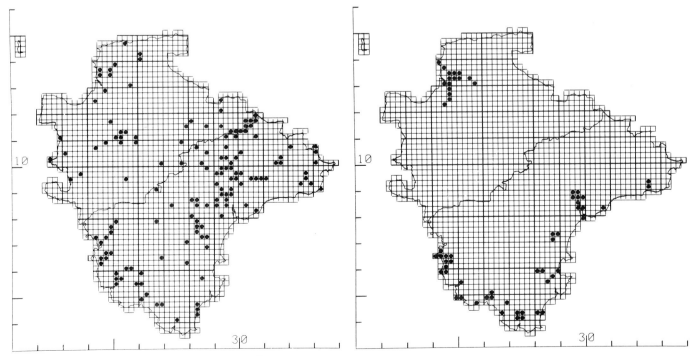

228

Schoenoplectus lacustris (L.) Palla   Bulrush
(*Scirpus lacustris* L., inc. *Scirpus tabernaemontani* C.C.Gmel.)
Ssp. **lacustris** occurs in ponds and slow-flowing streams. Very local and rather rare, in few localities. (19)

Schoenoplectus triqueter (L.) Palla   Triangular Club-rush
Restricted to the Tamar estuary, where it occurs on muddy tidal banks, and is very rare. (2)

Schoenoplectus x carinatus (Sm.) Palla, (*S. lacustris* x *triqueter*), has been reported from the banks of the R. Tamar (Lousley, in Stace (1975)).

Schoenoplectus x scheuchzeri (Brügg.) Palla, (*S.* x *keukenthalianus* Junge, *S. lacustris* ssp. *tabernaemontanus* x *triqueter*), has been reported from the Cornish bank of the R. Tamar, with one locality on the Devon side. (1)

Holoschoenus vulgaris Link   Round-headed Club-rush
(*Scirpus holoschoenus* L.)
Confined to dune-slacks on Braunton Burrows, where it has been known for many years and is locally abundant. (6)

Isolepis setacea (L.) R.Br.   Bristle Club-rush
(*Scirpus setaceus* L.)
In wet sandy or gravelly places on tracks and foot-paths, and at the edges of pools. Locally frequent in western parts of the county, very scattered and rare elsewhere. (254)

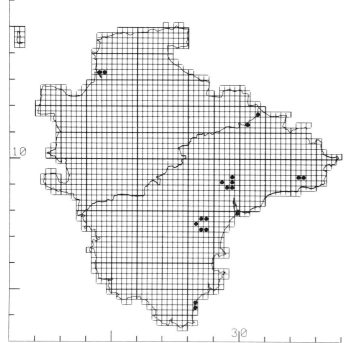

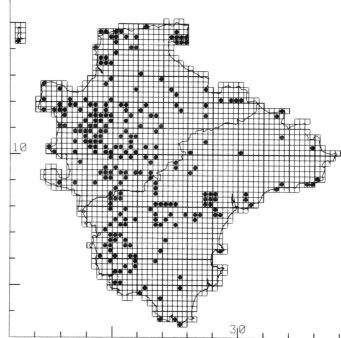

Ssp. **tabernaemontani** (C.C.Gmel.) Syme occurs in salt-marshes, estuaries and brackish ditches. It is locally frequent around the south coast and in the Taw-Torridge estuary. (32)

Isolepis cernua (Vahl) Roem. & Schultz.   Slender Club-rush
(*Scirpus cernuus* Vahl, *S. pygmaeus* (Vahl) A.Gray)
In wet places, mostly near the sea, usually in rather acid peaty or
sandy habitats. Rare, and most frequent in the north-west of the
county. (18)

Trichophorum cespitosum (L.) Hartm.   Deer-grass
(*Scirpus cespitosus* L.)
On heaths and moors. Abundant on the higher parts of
Dartmoor and Exmoor, and frequent elsewhere in rather damp
heathland. (225)

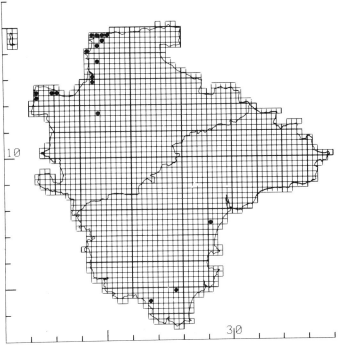

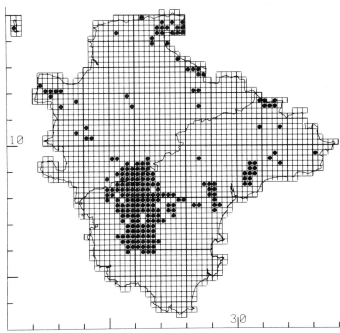

Most records refer to ssp. **cespitosum**.
Ssp. **germanicum** (Palla) Hegi has been reported from N. Molton
and probably occurs elsewhere.

Blysmus compressus (L.) Panzer ex Link has been reported from
Lynmouth and Sidmouth, but there are no recent records and it
is probably extinct.

Eleogiton fluitans (L.) Link   Floating Club-rush
(*Scirpus fluitans* L.)
In ponds and slow-flowing moorland streams; especially common in streams around the periphery of Dartmoor, but scattered
elsewhere in similar habitats. (48)

Eriophorum angustifolium Honck.   Common Cotton-grass
In wet peat and bogs on the moors. Common on Dartmoor and
Exmoor, and also in wet heaths and marshes elsewhere. (273)

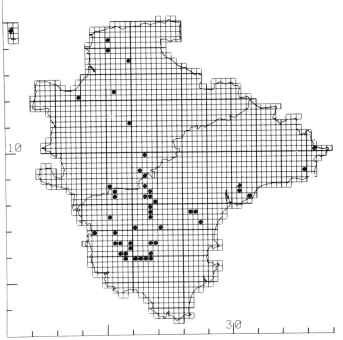

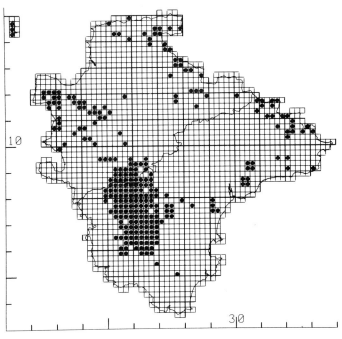

Eriophorum latifolium Hoppe   Broad-leaved Cotton-grass
In wet heaths and bogs on base-rich soil. Rare, with a few
records scattered around the Haldon Hills near Exeter, and on
the Greensand in E. Devon. (7)

Eriophorum vaginatum L.   Hare's-tail, Cotton-grass
In damp acid peat on the moors. Common on Dartmoor, where it is not restricted by altitude; local elsewhere, and not as frequent on Exmoor as formerly, probably due to agriculture and drainage. (116)

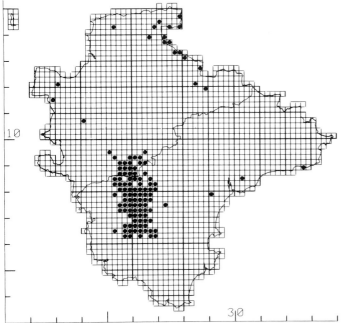

Eleocharis quinqueflora (F.X.Hartm.) O. Schwartz
                Few-flowered Spike-rush
(*Scirpus pauciflorus* Lightf.)
In damp peaty places, usually on base-rich soils. Frequent on Braunton Burrows, and with 2 localities in S. Devon, but not recorded from Dartmoor. (5)

Eleocharis parvula (Roem. & Schult.) Link ex Bluff, Nees & Schauer.   Dwarf Spike-rush
Only known from a muddy creek at Aveton Gifford, where it is now very rare. (1)

Eleocharis acicularis (L.) Roem. & Schult.
                Slender Spike-rush
In wet gravel and beside lakes and ponds, usually on acid soils. Apparently very rare, but easily overlooked. (4)

Eleocharis palustris (L.) Roem. & Schult.
         Common Spike-rush, Marsh Spike-rush
In marshes, wet places around pools and in ditches. Rather uncommon, but generally distributed. (113)

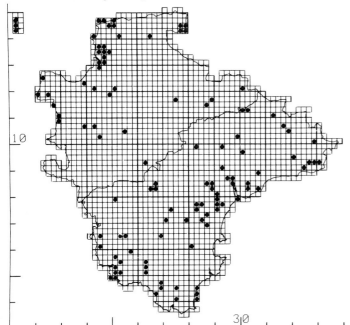

Eleocharis uniglumis (Link) Schult.   Slender Spike-rush
Around ponds and in marshes. Only recorded from Braunton Burrows, where it is locally frequent. (1)

Eleocharis multicaulis (Sm.) Desv. Many-stemmed Spike-rush
In marshes, wet heaths and seepages on acid soils. Quite frequent on the E. Devon commons and on Dartmoor, rare and local elsewhere. (105)

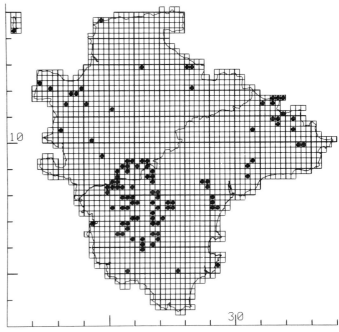

Cyperus longus L.   Galingale
In ponds and marshes. Only known from the vicinity of Braunton Burrows, where it is local. (2)

Cladium mariscus (L.) Pohl, the Saw Sedge, occurs in marshes and ditches on base-rich soils. It was known from the vicinity of Braunton Burrows, but the site has been obliterated by tipping, and it also occurred on the banks of the Tamar at Morwellham, but the habitat has again been destroyed. It is probably now extinct in Devon.

Rhynchospora alba (L.) Vahl   White Beak-sedge
In moorland bogs on wet acid peat. Scattered over Dartmoor, and in a few wet heaths elsewhere, but local and often in only small quantities. (43)

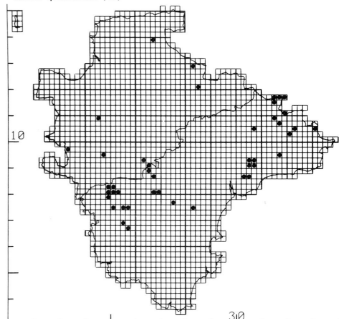

231

Rhynchospora fusca (L.) Ait.f.   Brown Beak-sedge
This may still occur in a bog at Burlescombe, but there are no
recent records. It was recorded from Bicton Common in 1954. (1)

Schoenus nigricans L.   Black Bog-rush
In wet heaths, bogs, marshes and coastal land-slips, usually on
peat in base-rich habitats. Scattered over the county, and often
locally abundant. (29)

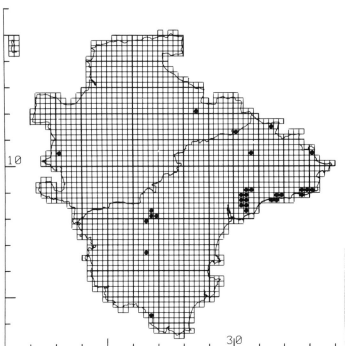

Carex otrubae Podp.   False Fox-sedge
In damp grassland, ditches, wet hedgerows and the upper
fringes of brackish marshes. Quite common around the south
coast and in the vicinity of Braunton, but rare elsewhere. This
species is listed in Fl. Dev. under *C. vulpina* L. (116)

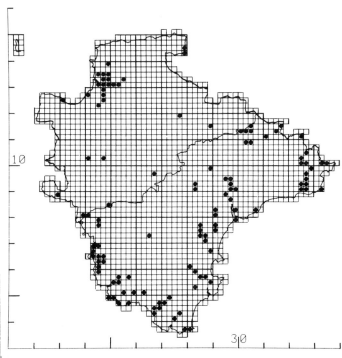

Carex paniculata L.   Tussock Sedge
In marshes, wet woodlands and scrub around the margins of
ponds and ditches. Local, though fairly generally distributed,
though much less common than formerly due to drainage and
agricultural "improvement". (218)

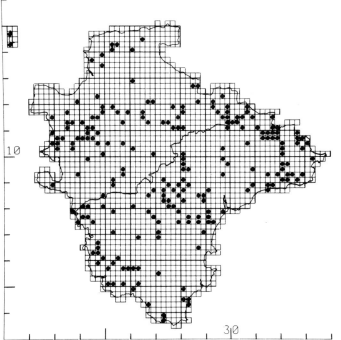

Carex spicata Huds.   Spiked Sedge
In fairly damp and base-rich soils, in scrub and hedgerows.
Rare, though in several scattered localities. (16)

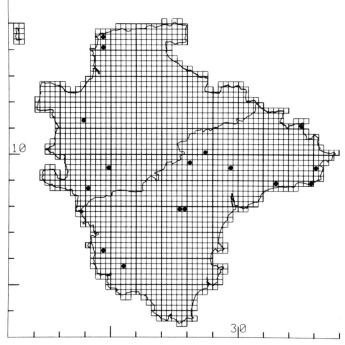

Carex muricata L.   Prickly Sedge
In dry grassland.

Ssp. **muricata** is calcicole; its distribution is not known with certainty, but it is probably very rare. It is thought to occur on the chalk in the vicinity of Branscombe, and has also been recorded from Bideford. (1)

Ssp. **lamprocarpa** Čelak. (*C. pairaei* F.W. Schultz), is calcifuge and all records around Dartmoor and probably most elsewhere belong here. (56)

Ssp. **divulsa** is moderately common in more shaded habitats and seems to be scattered over much of the county.
Ssp. **leersii** (Kneuck.) W. Koch, (*C. pairaei* var. *leersii* (Kneuck.) Kük, *C. polyphylla* Kar. & Kir., *C. leersii* F.W. Schultz), occurs in more base-rich habitats and seems to be rather rare.

Carex arenaria L.   Sand Sedge
In sandy places by the sea, especially in semi-fixed dunes and at the edges of dune-slacks. Locally abundant in suitable habitats. (31)

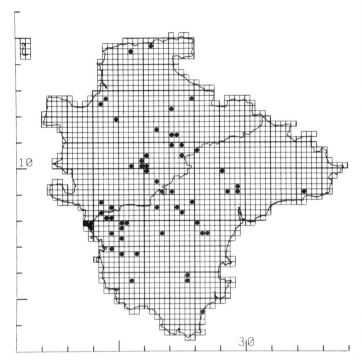

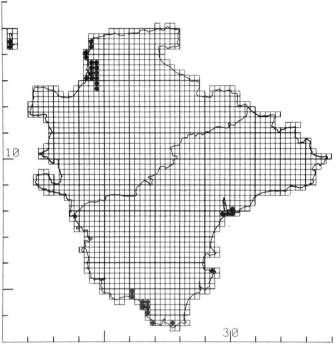

Carex disticha Huds.   Brown Sedge, Soft Sedge
In marshes and wet meadows. Rare, and widely scattered over the county. (4)

Carex divisa Huds.   Divided Sedge
In grassy places at the edge of salt-marshes. Very rare, and only known from the mouths of the rivers Otter and Avon. (2)

Carex remota L.   Remote Sedge
In damp hedges, lane-side ditches and shaded grassy or woodland habitats. Quite common and generally distributed, in moderately base-rich habitats. (741)

Carex divulsa Stokes   Grey Sedge
In banks, hedges and rough grassland. (266)

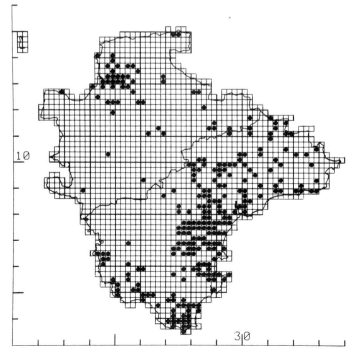

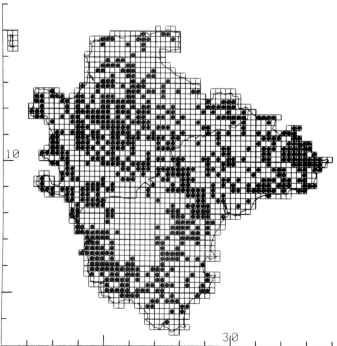

233

Carex ovalis Good.   Oval Sedge
In rough wet grassland, often with rushes, on acid soils. Fairly frequent in the north-west of the county and around Dartmoor and Exmoor, but rare elsewhere. (313)

Carex dioica L.   Dioecious Sedge
In wet heathland on moderately base-rich soils. Very rare, with only a single record from Haldon. (1)

Carex curta Good.   White Sedge
In bogs and marshes on acid soils. Very rare, occurring only on Dartmoor with some records from the north-west. (4)

Carex hirta L.   Hairy Sedge, Hammer Sedge
In damp grassy and marshy places. Local, and found only in those parts of the county where the soil is moderately base-rich. (105)

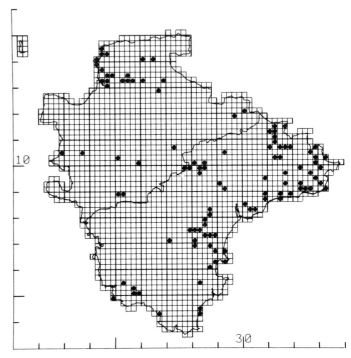

Carex echinata Murr.   Star Sedge
In wet acid grassland, wet heaths and bogs. Common on Dartmoor, rather less frequent in suitable habitats elsewhere. (407)

Carex lasiocarpa Ehrh.   Slender Sedge
In marshes and ditches on base-rich soils. Only known from Braunton Marshes where it is now very rare. (1)

Carex acutiformis Ehrh.   Lesser Pond Sedge
Beside ponds and ditches and along river banks, in wet woods and on sea cliffs. Fairly common in the Exe valley, rather local elsewhere. (36)

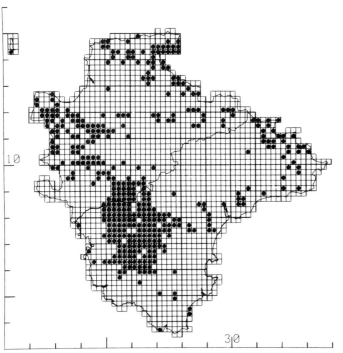

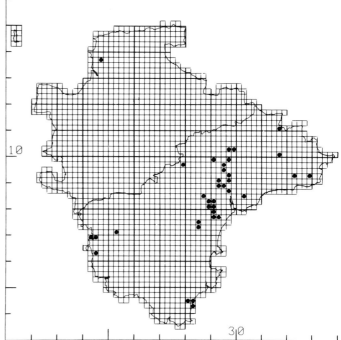

Carex riparia Curt.   Great Pond Sedge
By rivers and ponds, and in wet woodland. Local, though often quite common where it occurs, and rare in much of the county. (32)

Carex vesicaria L.   Bladder Sedge
At the margins of ponds and ditches, and in wet woods. A lowland plant, thinly scattered over the county, and now becoming quite rare. (14)

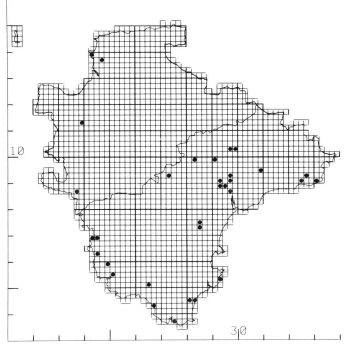

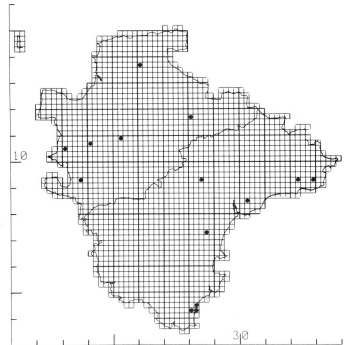

Carex pseudocyperus L.   Cyperus Sedge
At the margins of ponds and ditches, and in wet woodland. Very rare, and only known from a few localities in the Exe valley, with a single record from near Torrington. (7)

Carex rostrata Stokes   Bottle Sedge
In bogs, marshes and ditches, usually over peaty substrata. Local on Dartmoor and in the marshes in the north-west of the county; rare elsewhere. (54)

Carex pendula Huds.   Pendulous Sedge
In damp woods and hedges, especially on heavy clayey soils. A lowland plant, scattered over the county and locally common. (267)

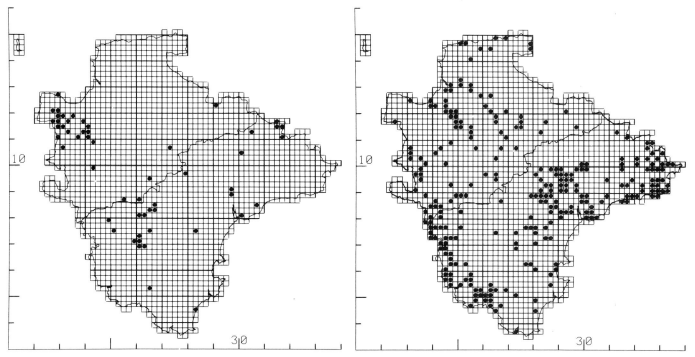

Carex sylvatica Huds.   Wood Sedge
In woods and on shaded banks, often on damp, base-rich soils.
Quite common and generally distributed, though absent from
many apparently suitable habitats. (496)

Carex panicea L.   Carnation-grass
In wet grassland, heaths and bogs. Very common in suitable
habitats. (512)

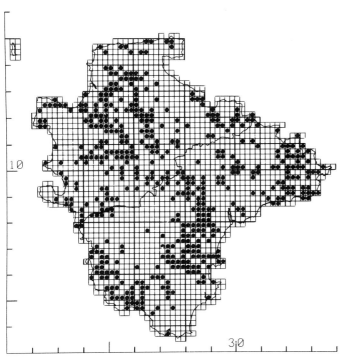

Carex strigosa Huds.
In damp woodland. Only known from a few localities in the
vicinity of Haldon, where it is very rare. (4)

Carex flacca Schreb.   Carnation Sedge, Carnation-grass
In wet pastures and marshes on clayey soils, and in calcareous,
grassland. Fairly common and generally distributed. (424)
Our plants belong to ssp. **flacca**.

Carex laevigata Sm.   Smooth Sedge
In damp woods and scrub, and on heaths. Scattered over the
county, and only locally common. Mostly lowland, but also
found around the periphery of Dartmoor. (182)

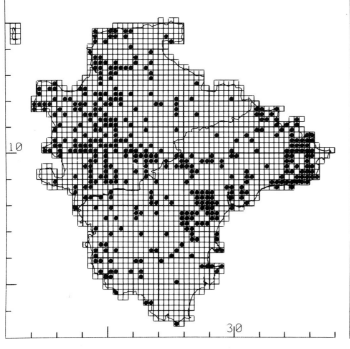

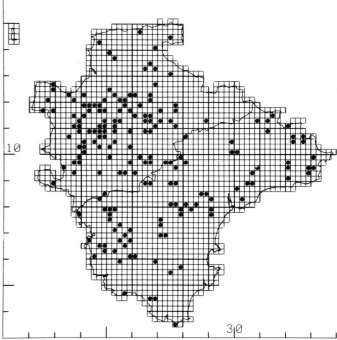

Carex binervis Sm.   Ribbed Sedge
On heaths and moors, usually in drier habitats. Rather common and locally abundant. (405)

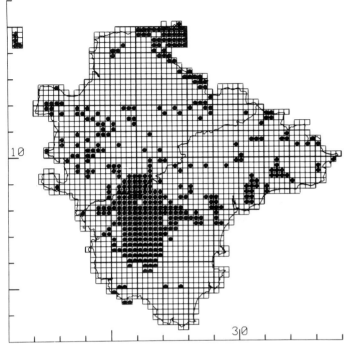

Carex extensa Good.   Long-bracted Sedge
At the edges of salt-marshes, on sea cliffs and in grassland near the sea. Locally quite common in suitable habitats. (37)

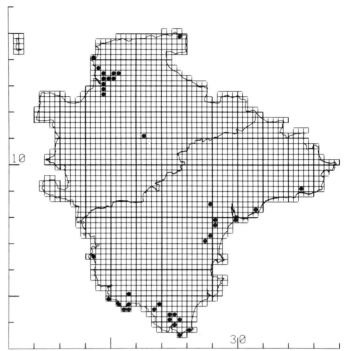

Carex distans L.   Distant Sedge
In marshy fields and at the edges of salt-marshes and estuaries, usually near the coast, where it is fairly frequent; Rare inland. (38)

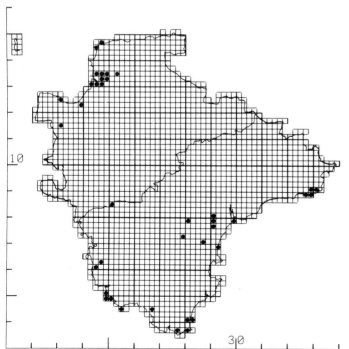

Carex punctata Gaud.
Only known from near Wadham Rocks (David, 1981), where it occurs locally on sheltered sea-cliffs with a supply of fresh water. It was collected from Torquay a long while ago, but it is doubtful if it survives there. (1)

Carex hostiana DC.   Tawny Sedge
(*C. hornschuchiana* Hoppe)
In marshes, damp pastures and in base-rich damp heathland. Quite common in the north-west of the county, scattered elsewhere, though locally frequent. (105)

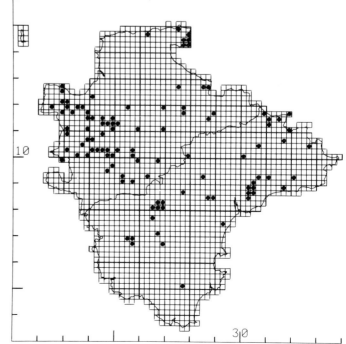

Carex lepidocarpa Tausch   Long-stalked Yellow-sedge
In damp, base-rich habitats on heaths and in dune-slacks. Rare, though probably somewhat under-recorded. Only known from the Branscombe and Axmouth-Lyme Regis landslips. (3)

Carex demissa Hornem.   Common Yellow-sedge
In damp habitats in acid grassland, wet heaths and bogs. Frequent on Dartmoor, in the marshes in the north-west of the county and in wet heaths elsewhere. (448)

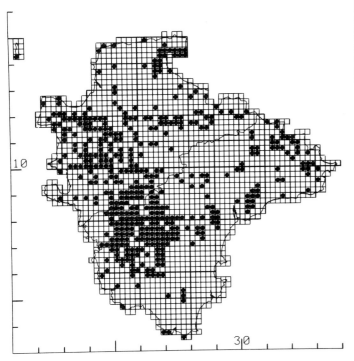

This was probably the plant recorded as *C. flava* in Fl. Dev.

Carex serotina Mérat   Small-fruited Yellow-sedge
(*C. oederi* auct. non Retz)
In damp habitats, usually on rather base-rich soils in heaths, grassland and dune-slacks. Rare, and widely scattered over the county, perhaps under-recorded, but not a common plant. (4)

Carex pallescens L.   Pale Sedge
In damp woods and meadows. Scattered over the county and rather rare, though locally frequent where it occurs. (50)

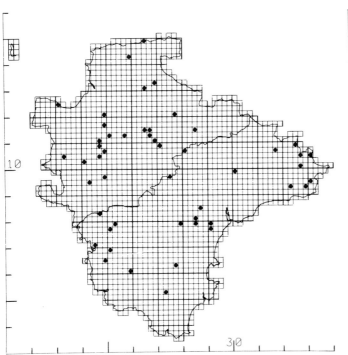

Carex caryophyllea Latour.   Spring Sedge
In dry grassland, usually on base-rich soils. Quite common in calcareous habitats, rather rare and scattered elsewhere. (102)

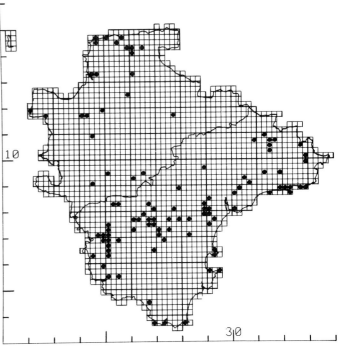

Carex montana L.
Confined to heathy grassland on Roborough Down, where it is now local and scarce. (1)

Carex pilulifera L.   Pill-headed Sedge
On heaths and moors and in acid grassland, usually in rather dry habitats. Locally common, though a rather insignificant plant. (279)

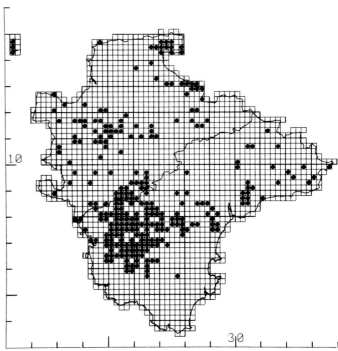

Carex nigra (L.) Reich.   Common Sedge
(*C. goodenowii* Gay)
In damp, usually acid grassland, wet heaths and on the moors. Locally common on Dartmoor, and fairly frequent in suitable habitats elsewhere. (281)

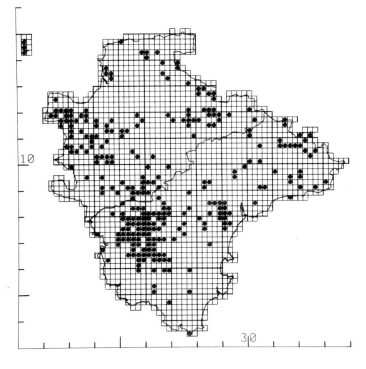

Carex *Hybrids*
Many hybrids between *Carex* species have been reported from time to time, although many of them are incorrect identifications. Hybrids generally form only between fairly closely related species, though certain aggregate species (*C. flava* agg., *C. nigra* agg.) may form hybrid swarms. The following hybrids are known to occur in the county, though others could probably be found:
C. x boenninghausiana Weihe, (*C. paniculata* x *remota*), occurs in wooded swamps, often with *C. paniculata,* and is recorded from the R. Erme, and near Tiverton.
C. x pseudoaxillaris K.Richt., (*C. otrubae* x *remota, C. x axillaris* auct.), is fairly frequent in ditches and along roadsides; there have been a number of records from the vicinity of Braunton, Torbay and Plymouth. Records in Fl. Dev. for *C. x pseudo-axillaris* auct. non K.Richt., (*C. remota* x *spicata*), must, in view of the scarcity of *C. spicata,* be treated with great reserve.
Quite a number of other species of *Carex* have been reported as occurring in Devon. The majority are probably errors of identification; *C. limosa* is unlikely to have been correctly identified from Sidmouth.

Carex pulicaris L.   Flea Sedge
On heaths and moors, usually in fairly damp but not boggy habitats. Fairly common, but rather easily overlooked. (131)

ORCHIDACEAE

Epipactis palustris (L.) Crantz   Marsh Helleborine
In base-rich marshes, moist grassland, and dune-slacks where it may be locally abundant. Very local, but scattered over the county in suitable habitats. (19)

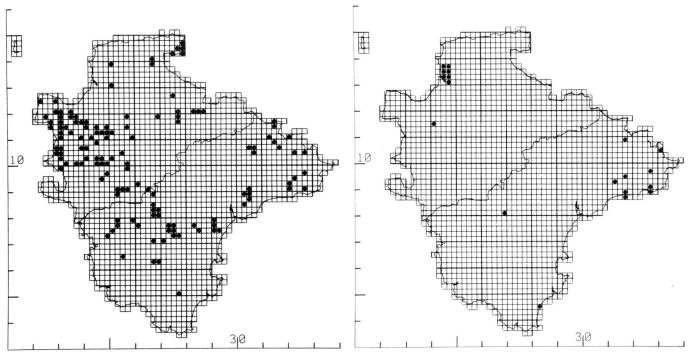

239

Epipactis helleborine (L.) Crantz   Helleborine
(*E. latifolia* (L.) All.)
In woods, hedgebanks and scrub, usually on base-rich soils.
Rather rare, but with scattered records from all over the county.
(103)

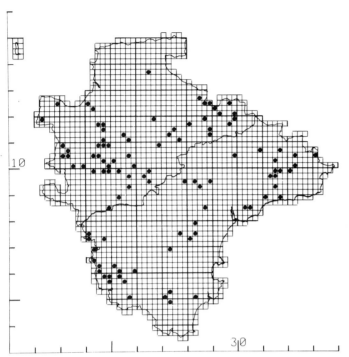

Listera ovata (L.) R.Br.   Twayblade
In woods, scrub, damp grassland and dune-slacks. Locally
frequent and widely scattered over the county. (124)

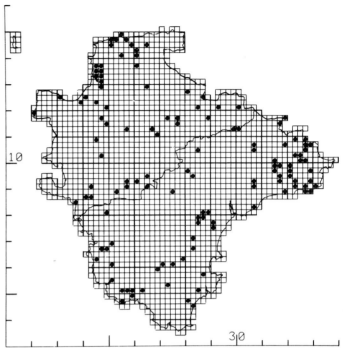

Epipactis leptochila (Godfery) Godfery
          Narrow-lipped Helleborine
In shaded woods and verges. There is a single, but rather
doubtful, record from near Farway, in E. Devon. (1)

There is no evidence that **Epipactis purpurata** Sm., the Violet
Helleborine, occurs in Devon.

Cephalanthera damasonium (Mill.) Druce   White Helleborine
In a beech wood on Stockland Hill. A solitary plant in 1956. (1)

Neottia nidus-avis (L.) Rich.   Bird's-nest Orchid
In woods, often of beech, in fairly deep shade and usually on
base-rich soils. Rare, scattered over the county, and often with
only a few specimens when it occurs. (18)

Listera cordata (L.) R.Br.   Lesser Twayblade
This species still occurs in open acid grassland on Brendon
Common, where it has been known for many years. (2)

Spiranthes spiralis (L.) Chevall.   Autumn Lady's Tresses
In closely grazed turf, lawns and dune-slacks, usually on
base-rich soils. Not uncommon over chalk or limestone, otherwise local. The flower spikes frequently do not appear every
year. (41)

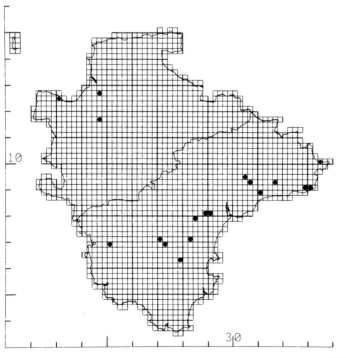

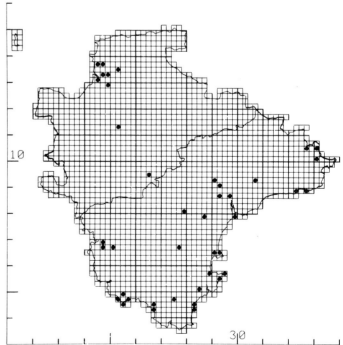

Spiranthes romanzoffiana Cham.   Drooping Lady's Tresses
In open boggy grassland on acid soils. Very rare, and only
known from one locality to the west of Dartmoor, where it
flowers very infrequently due to heavy grazing. (1)

Platanthera bifolia (L.) Rich.   Lesser Butterfly Orchid
In grassland, damp heaths, woods and scrub. Rather sparsely
distributed and rare, though it can be locally frequent. (60)

Gymnadenia conopsea (L.) R.Br.   Fragrant Orchid
In grassland, especially over chalk or limestone, occasionally at
the margins of heaths. Rare, and only found in the south of the
county. (11)

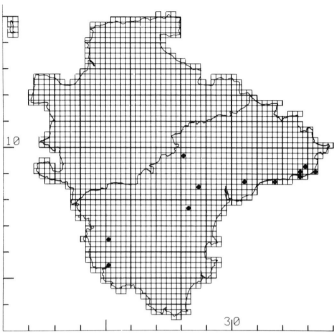

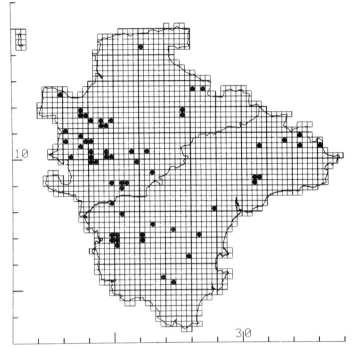

Plants in wet, fenny areas are often extremely robust, and have
been named var. *densiflora* (Wahl.) Lindl., (*G. densiflora* Wahl.),
and plants conforming to this description have been found at
Axmouth and in the Axmouth-Lyme Regis Undercliffs N.N.R.,
but their taxonomic status is unclear.

Coeloglossum viride (L.) Hartm., the Frog Orchid, has not been
seen on Braunton Burrows recently, and it is probably extinct in
Devon.

Dactylorhiza incarnata (L.) Soó   Early Marsh Orchid
(*O. latifolia* L. p.p.)
In wet meadows and dune-slacks. Fairly common in eastern
parts of the county, though perhaps confused in part with *D.
praetermissa.* (39)

Platanthera chlorantha (Curt.) Reichenb.
     Greater Butterfly Orchid
In woods, scrub and moist pastures, less tolerant of acid
habitats than *P. bifolia.* Rare, in several scattered localities,
mostly in S. Devon. (26)

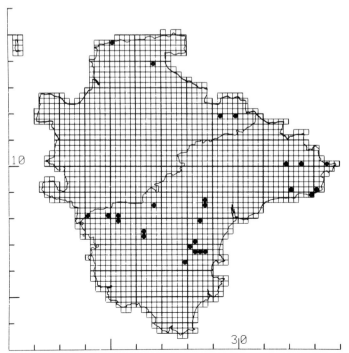

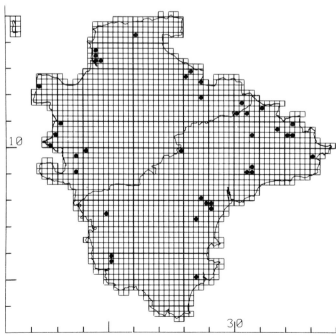

Ssp. **coccinea** (Pugsl.) Soó is characteristic of dune-slacks on
Braunton Burrows, where it is rather frequent.

Dactylorhiza praetermissa (Druce) Soó
Southern Marsh Orchid, Fen Orchid
(*Orchis praetermissa* Druce, *D. majalis* ssp. *praetermissa* (Druce) Moore & Soó)
In wet meadows, often in base-rich habitats and abundant in dune-slacks on Braunton Burrows. (276)

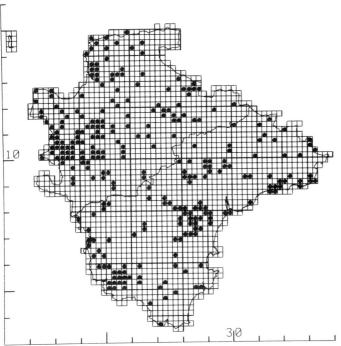

The status of the Fl. Dev. records under *D. pardalina* is not clear. They are probably all referable to *D. praetermissa*.

Dactylorhiza maculata (L.) Soó
Heath Spotted Orchid
(*Orchis maculata* L., *O. ericetorum* (Linton) Marsh.)
In damp heaths, grassland and woods on acid soils. Generally distributed and locally common or abundant in suitable habitats. (324)
Our plant is ssp. **ericetorum** (Linton) Hunt & Summerhayes.

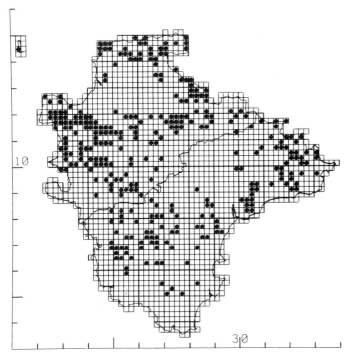

Dactylorhiza fuchsii (Druce) Soó   Common Spotted Orchid
(*Orchis maculata* L. p.p.)
In damp grassland, scrub and woods on calcareous or base-rich soils. Largely confined to chalk and limestone areas, where it is quite common, but also found on Braunton Burrows and along the coast nearby. (131)

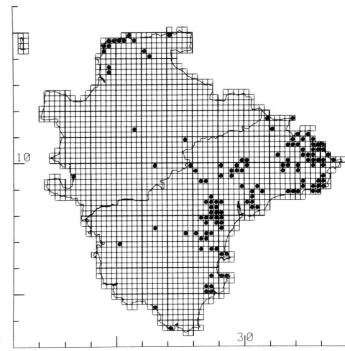

Several **Dactylorhiza** hybrids have been reported; the following are probably not uncommon, but their detailed distribution and current status is not known:

Dactylorhiza x grandis (Druce) P.F. Hunt, (*D. fuchsii x praetermissa*, *Orchis x mortonii* Druce), has been reported from several localities in S. Devon;

Dactylorhiza x hallii (Druce) Soó, (*D. praetermissa x maculata*), has been reported from Woodbury Common, Bovey Heathfield and Bridford;

Dactylorhiza x wintoni (A. Camus) P.F. Hunt, (*D. incarnata x praetermissa*), is recorded from Hartland, Axmouth and Bovey Heathfield;

Dactylorhiza x transiens (Druce) Soó, (*D. maculata x fuchsii*), has been reported from Torquay.

Orchis morio L.   Green-winged Orchid
In meadows, pastures and along roadsides, mainly on calcareous soils. Largely confined to the south and east of the
county, where it is local. (36)

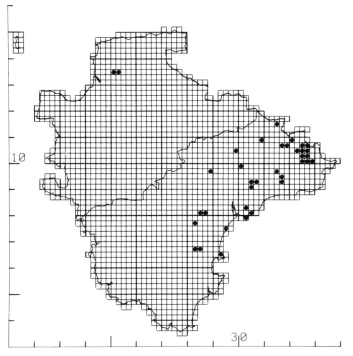

Orchis mascula L.   Early Purple Orchid
On hedgebanks and road verges, less commonly in woods,
scrub and pastures, usually on base-rich soils. Fairly common
and rather generally distributed. (569)

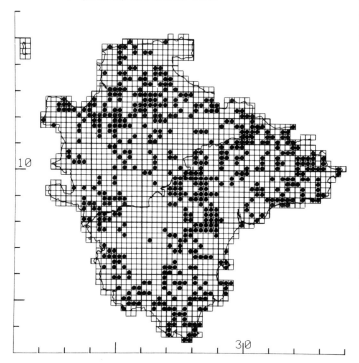

There is no evidence for the continued existence of **Orchis
ustulata** L., the Burnt Orchid, in Devon.

Himantoglossum hircinum (L.) Spreng.   Lizard Orchid
In scrub and at the edges of fields. Only known from near
Croyde, in N. Devon, but the site has now been destroyed. It last
flowered in 1969. (1)

Anacamptis pyramidalis (L.) Rich.   Pyramidal Orchid
In rough grassland, usually on calcareous soils. Not uncommon,
and locally abundant, on the chalk in E. Devon, on the Torbay
limestone and on Braunton Burrows. (46)

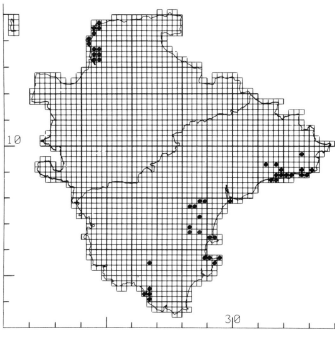

Ophrys apifera Huds.   Bee Orchid
In grassland, on banks and in open scrub, on calcareous soils.
Local in E. Devon, rare around Torquay and on Braunton
Burrows. (16)

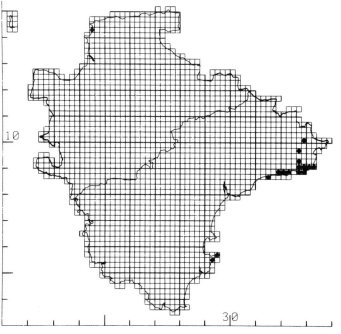

Ophrys insectifera L.   Fly Orchid
(*O. muscifera* Huds.)
This occurs in dry, base-rich grassland and has been recorded
from the vicinity of Plymouth, but can only be found spasmodi-
cally. (1)

Hammarbya paludosa (L.) O.Kuntze   Bog Orchid
This has been reported from several sites in the county,
including once at Widecombe in 1940, but appears now to be
established on Dartmoor, at the foot of Meldon Reservoir. (1)

Liparis loeselii (L.) Rich.   Fen Orchid
First found on Braunton Burrows in 1966; the population has
fluctuated since, but it still persists. (1)

English names in **bold** type, Latin names in ordinary type, synonyms in *italics*.

249

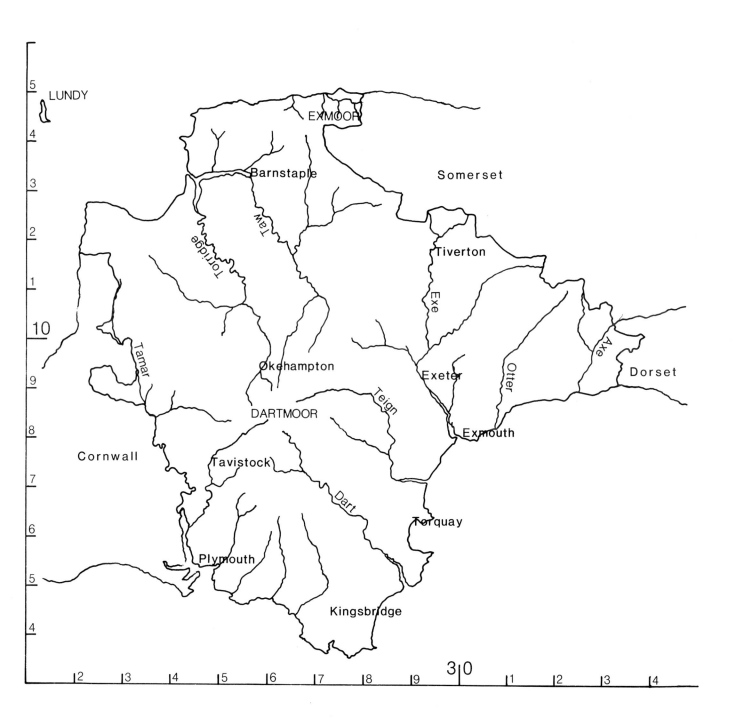